OCEANOGRAPHY

FOR

GEOGRAPHERS

*

OCEANOGRAPHY

FOR

GEOGRAPHERS

By

CUCHLAINE A. M. KING, M.A., Ph.D.

Reader in Geography
University of Nottingham

LONDON

EDWARD ARNOLD (PUBLISHERS) LTD.

First published 1962

551,46
K58o
c1

Printed in Great Britain
by W. & J. Mackay & Co Ltd, Chatham

PREFACE

Oceanography is a rapidly growing science, which becomes more and more complex as detailed theoretical analyses of the different oceanic phenomena are carried out and as more observations become available to check and direct them. The oceans cover over two-thirds of the Earth's surface and play a vital part in life on Earth, quite apart from their own intrinsic interest. There are several volumes which deal in detail, and at an advanced level, with different aspects of the physical and biological aspects of oceanography, but the aim of the present book is to gather together those aspects of the subject which are relevant to geographers and others, who do not wish to enter deeply into the physics, mathematics and biology of the oceans, but who need to know something of modern trends and discoveries in this very extensive field of knowledge. Much information of importance which is hidden beneath and within the ocean waters is relevant to a study of the character of the Earth. For example, the deep-sea sediments provide valuable data on climatic change, and the great variety of life within the ocean will become increasingly important to feed the growing population. From many points of view, both practical and academic, the study of the oceans leads to a better understanding of the character of the Earth.

I am greatly indebted to Dr. G. E. R. Deacon, F.R.S., Director of the National Institute of Oceanography, and to Dr. J. Crease for reading chapters 3 and 4, and for their helpful advice concerning them. I am also very grateful to Dr. M. N. Hill, F.R.S., of the Department of Geodesy and Geophysics in the University of Cambridge for reading and making helpful comments on chapters 1 and 2. Nevertheless all errors in these and other chapters are my responsibility. I would also like to acknowledge gratefully all other help received and to thank those authors whose figures I have been given permission to reproduce for their kindness.

Permission kindly given by Publishers to use illustrations from the following books, is gratefully acknowledged.

Gebrüder Borntraeger—*Allgemeine Meereskunde*, by Dietrich and Kalle, 1957.

Edward Arnold—*Sea Fisheries*, by Graham, 1956.

Edward Arnold—*The Plaice*, by Wimpenny, 1953.

Cambridge University Press—*Physical Geography*, 4th Edition, by Lake, edited by Steers, 1958.

v

Collins—*The Open Sea*, I and II, by Sir Alister Hardy, 1956 and 1959.

Geological Society of America—*Special Paper 62*, 1955, and *Special Paper 65*, 1959.

Her Majesty's Stationery Office—*Admiralty Manual of Tides*, by Doodson and Warburg, Hydrographic Department of the Admiralty, 1941.

Hutchinson and Co—*Waves and Tides*, by Russell and Macmillan, 1952.

Marine Biological Association of the United Kingdom.

Pergamon Press Ltd—*Physics and Chemistry of the Earth*, Ed. Ahrens, Vol. 4, 1961.

Prentice-Hall Inc., U.S.A.—*The Oceans: Their Physics, Chemistry and General Biology*, by H. U. Sverdrup, M. W. Johnson, and R. H. Fleming, © 1942.

Charles E. Turtle Company. Modern Asia Edition of *The Oceans; Their Physics, Chemistry and General Biology*.

Routledge and Kegan Paul—*The Herring and its Fishery*, by Hodgson, 1957.

University of California Press—*The Gulf Stream*, by Stommel, 1958.

University of Chicago Press, Department of Geography—for Fig. 4–2 from *Goode Base Map Series*, C.

Wiley and Sons, Inc.—*The Sea off southern California*, by Emery, 1960.

The Geography Department,
The University,
Nottingham.
December 1961.

CONTENTS

CHAPTER 3. THE WATER OF THE OCEANS

CHAPTER 4. THE CIRCULATION OF THE OCEANS

Chapter 7. SEDIMENT IN THE OCEAN

Chapter 8. SOME ASPECTS OF LIFE IN THE OCEAN

CHAPTER 9. THE GEOGRAPHICAL SIGNIFICANCE OF THE OCEANS

INTRODUCTION

OCCASIONALLY the oceans make themselves felt in a dramatic and often disastrous way; great waves resulting from a submarine earthquake may sweep across a low coastal area, laying it waste, or storm waves may break down sea defences and flood low-lying land, or a ship may be lost at sea. At other times the great ocean streams pass almost unnoticed on their way, the tide ebbs and flows unobserved, and little thought is given to the vital part the ocean plays in life on earth. It is not only because the oceans are vast in area, covering over 70 per cent of all the earth's surface, but because of their own intrinsic interest that they are worthy of closer study.

Enormous quantities of water are moved by some ocean currents; the Gulf Stream, for example, transports more than one thousand times the greatest Mississippi flood from southern latitudes northwards. Modern oceanographical work suggests that its influence on the climate of north-west Europe is very complex; it has been suggested by Iselin that the warming of the climate of this part of Europe may be greater during periods of smaller transport by the Gulf Stream. There are some facts which support this view, although it is no more than an interesting suggestion at the moment.

The oceans pose many fascinating problems to geographers and others. The origin of the ocean basins and the water which fills them is of fundamental importance to an understanding of the global pattern of land and sea, and is a basic geographical fact. The fluctuations of the level of the oceans has far-reaching effects on land and is at present closely linked to glacier fluctuations and through this to climatic change. Sea-level is also the base level to which subaerial erosion is working, in areas drained by rivers which reach the sea. It is one of the tasks of modern geomorphology to establish the denudation chronology of areas in terms of changes in base level. The response of the rivers to negative changes in base level is clearly dependent on the gradient of the sea floor exposed by the fall in sea-level. Thus the nature of the sea floor close to the land and the oscillations of sea-level are important to geomorphological analysis.

The connexion between the oceans and the climate is an intimate one, the two interacting in many different ways to influence each other. Through the climate, the general character of the land areas is related to the nature of the ocean water and its circulation. Recently new techniques have been devised for the study of the oceans; one of the very interesting and useful ones is a new method of measuring directly the movement of the deep ocean waters. These new techniques have already given results of great value, which help to clarify the picture of the general circulation of the water and to support theoretical reasoning concerning the cause of the movements. New methods of measuring waves in the open ocean have also yielded very valuable results. In this branch of oceanography there is also a close connexion between meteorology and the formation of waves, which are directly generated by the winds which blow over the oceans. The waves, moving out from the storm areas in the oceans, play their part in modifying the edge of the land, helping to create the great variety of coastal forms.

The rhythmic flow of the tides is one of the most reliable of oceanic phenomena, and it alone, at the moment, permits long-term forecasting, such as waves will probably never allow. Even the tides, however, are liable to a certain amount of modification, by meteorological conditions, as the generation of storm surges indicates. Thus the connexion between air and water is again manifest, and in extreme cases the effect is felt with disastrous results on coasts where surges can form, such as the North Sea. The tides are also responsible for one of the most impressive phenomena of nature, the tidal bores which move up some rivers.

The oceans were the original home of life on Earth, and long before creatures moved out of the sea and plants grew on dry land a complex marine fauna and flora had evolved. Some of the creatures and plants which now live in the sea are very small—they are nevertheless very important; only the marine flora can create growing organisms from the chemical elements which are found in sea water, with the aid of sunshine which penetrates into the upper layers of water. The smallest of these creations, the phytoplankton, form the broad base of the vast triangle of marine life, which leads up to the higher forms of fish, which are of great economic importance. These smaller organisms are also important in their own right; their dead bodies sink down to cover great areas of the ocean floor, where they have settled in sheltered ground for long periods of time. They can, then, tell a story of the changing conditions in which they lived, which is revealed to the scientist who obtains cores of these deep sea oozes. From these data changes in climate over the past geological period can be assessed.

It is, however, the living creatures of the oceans which are materially more important; the oceans house a vast store of food, which may well be needed to feed the growing world population. Despite great advances in the techniques of fishing, the collecting of this food from the sea is still in the stage of primitive hunting; whether sea farming will ever be evolved to help feed the growing numbers is an interesting question. The open sea, however, belongs to all nations; this kind of development, therefore, depends on international co-operation, as the fish are not bound by territorial waters. In this field and in that of marine research, there is much scope for international work; in the latter field in particular much progress has been made.

At a meeting of the Special Committee on Oceanographical Research three long-term problems, which may be critical to the welfare of man in the future, were discussed. The first concerned the disposal in the deep ocean basins of the radioactive waste, which will increase in amount as atomic power is used more for industry. This cannot be done safely until more is known of the deep-water circulation and the effect of these waste materials on the life in the sea. The second problem is concerned with the use of the resources of the sea for the growing population of the world; its proper and full use depends on a clear knowledge of the conditions in which marine life can flourish best, and that involves a special study of the most fertile areas of the sea and their ecology. These zones depend for their fertility on the upward transport of nutrients towards the surface. This again requires an understanding of the circulation of the ocean.

The other vital problem, which is the most complex and probably the most difficult to solve, is the role which the ocean plays in the processes of meteorology and climatic change. At the moment the north Atlantic area is warming up markedly; whether this trend will continue or be reversed is of very great importance in many ways. Not only does it affect the potentiality of the land to grow crops and feed stock, but it also influences the use of the sea for transport in those areas where winter freezing reduces the time during which some northern routes can be used. It is also associated with the changes of sea-level which are now in progress.

It can be seen that a study of the oceans is by no means of academic interest only; they play a vital role in life on earth, as a result of the interrelation between them and the atmosphere, through which their influence is transmitted to the land. They also influence many other aspects of geography, both physical and human.

CHAPTER I

THE ORIGIN AND STRUCTURE OF THE OCEAN BASINS AND THEIR WATER

INTRODUCTION

THE oceans form one of the fundamental divisions of the Earth's surface and their volume is considerably greater than that of the land above sea-level. Indeed, if all the inequalities of the Earth were levelled off there would be enough water in the oceans to cover the whole surface of the Earth to a depth of about 8,600 ft. Most of the land lies fairly close to sea-level, the mean height of the continents being 2,300 ft. above sea-level, while the oceans, on the other hand, have their greatest area between 12,000 and 18,000 ft. below sea-level. In fact, 41 per cent of the whole surface of the Earth lies between the last two depths. It is worth noting that in terms of the diameter of the globe, which is nearly 8,000 miles, the relief features of the continents and oceans are relatively insignificant. The highest mountains and greatest deeps are only just over 65,000 ft. apart vertically; this is about 12·3 miles or 1/330 of the radius. Nevertheless there are very important differences between the structure and relief of the ocean basins and the continental areas.

Of all the major units of the Earth's surface the Pacific Ocean is the greatest, covering about half of the whole globe. It also contains the largest single unit of truly oceanic structure, although this is considerably smaller than the aerial extent of the whole of the Pacific. Recent work has given a much clearer picture of the nature and extent of the major structural types within the oceans (Gaskell, Hill, and Swallow, 1958). On the basis of this and other recent work, the character of the major ocean basins can be described and the speculative, but interesting, views of their permanency or otherwise can be discussed.

1. THE CHARACTER OF THE MAJOR STRUCTURAL UNITS OF THE EARTH

There is a fundamental difference in structure between the continents and the truly oceanic sections of the Earth's crust. This is seen most clearly in the thickness of the crust, which is much thinner beneath the oceans. The thickness of the crust is directly related to the depth of the Mohorovičić discontinuity, which separates it from the mantle beneath;

this discontinuity is usually called the Moho, or M discontinuity, for convenience. It can be recognized by seismic surveys, as it is associated with a sudden change in the speed of seismic waves, which increase from 6·7 km./sec. to 8·1 km./sec. below it.

The Moho lies at a depth of 10 to 12 km. below the sea surface or about 6 km. below the ocean floor in the oceanic sectors of the crust; on the other hand, in the continental areas it is found at a depth varying between 30 and 50 km. below the surface. Above the Moho the crust in the continental areas is much more complex than it is in the true oceans; there are layers of different density in the continental areas, but these do not always show an orderly arrangement. The main distinguishing characteristic is the existence of a thick layer of rocks of fairly low density and associated with seismic waves travelling relatively slowly; these rocks contain much granitic type of material, which is entirely lacking from the true ocean areas.

The generalized picture of the true oceanic structure, as put forward by Hess (1954), shows that under about 6 km. of water there is a layer of about 6 km. of basaltic-type rock; the Moho separates this basaltic crust from the ultra-basic rocks of the mantle beneath. These ultra-basic rocks are thought to be peridotite, but this has not yet been proved directly. The rather generalized picture, shown in fig. 1–1, does illustrate the fundamental difference between the oceanic structure and that

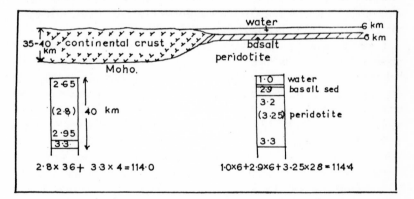

FIG. 1–1. Diagram to show the general characteristics of the oceanic and continental crustal types and their approximate isostatic balance. (After Hess.)

of the continents, and a consideration of the density of the layers in each environment shows how isostasy almost maintains equilibrium in these very different structural units.

The detailed seismic survey carried out by the Challenger expedition from 1950 to 1952 and many surveys made by Scripps, Woods Hole,

O.–B

and the Lamont institutes in America, have filled in the details of this generalized structural pattern and have enabled a more precise description of the oceanic structure to be given. Seismic observation has shown a remarkable uniformity of oceanic structure (Hill, 1957); four layers have been recorded as follows:

Average structure in oceans more than 4 km. deep

	Thickness km.	Velocity of wave travel in km./sec.
Sea water	4·5	1·5
Layer 1 (Unconsolidated sediments)	0·45	2·0
Layer 2 (Volcanics or consolidated sediments)	1·75	4–6
Layer 3 (Basaltic rocks)	4·7	6·71
Layer 4 (Ultrabasic rocks)	—	8·09

These figures apply only to those regions for which observations are available, which are mainly in low and middle latitudes. Layer 1 consists of unconsolidated sediments and is slightly thinner in the Pacific than the Atlantic; for depths over 4 km., which cover much of the ocean, the mean thickness of layer 1 is about 0·3 km. This is much thinner than is suggested by extrapolating present rates of sedimentation back in time. The greater thickness suggested by this method could be explained if layer 2 consists of consolidated sediments. Layer 2 is difficult to interpret and could be either consolidated sediments or volcanic rocks; it probably varies from place to place and both types may be combined in some areas. It seems that this layer is present in most areas, although in some the data are doubtful.

Layer 3 certainly exists very widely and is probably composed of massive basic igneous rocks. It is found at a mean depth of 6·91 km. below sea-level where the sea is 4–5 km. deep and at 7·54 km. where the depth exceeds 5 km. Layer 4 is probably also uniform wherever observations have been made, and may be associated with the ultra-basic rocks below the Moho, although the close similarity of wave velocity at 11 km. below the ocean and 35 km. below the continents may be misleading, in view of the very different conditions in the two zones. The suggestion of a phase transition rather than a material change cannot yet be substantiated. On the whole it is reasonable to assume that the continental crust is not found in the true oceans, and that the material beneath the Moho is similar everywhere.

Layer 2 is obviously volcanic in origin in some areas, consisting of erupted material, resting on and depressing the basaltic layer 3 beneath it. It is also possible that in some areas this second layer is composed of hard limestone as seismic waves travel through this rock at about the same speed as through volcanic rock. One possible interpretation of the data is a layer of sediment over the basalt, followed by a fairly thin layer of hard limestone, on which layer 1 rests. This limestone could have been deposited during the Cretaceous period, which was one of extreme development of lime-secreting organisms. The chalk of Europe was laid down at this time and calcium carbonate formation may also have been active in the deep ocean; it was a period of climatic and geological change.

The similarity of this layered structure over wide stretches of the oceans is noteworthy. Another interesting observation is the relatively thin layer of unconsolidated sediments that was recorded. The thickness of these, according to Laughton (1954), varies with the depth of water; it is about 1,000 m. in water less than 4 km. and 380 m. in water depths greater than 5 km. The sediments will be considered in more detail in chapter 7.

(a) Methods of investigation

Before describing the structure of the individual oceans, it is relevant to mention briefly the methods used to obtain information concerning the structure, as this will indicate some of the limitations imposed by the character of the observational techniques. A number of different techniques are used to study the structural character of the ocean basins, but one of the most useful methods of investigating the interior structure is by the seismic technique. Gravity surveys also yield useful information while the newer methods of magnetic and heat flow studies give additional evidence, all of which may be fitted into an analysis of the ocean basin structure and characteristics.

i. SEISMIC STUDIES. Information concerning the structure of the deep oceans can be obtained by either the reflection or refraction methods. In order to be able to deduce the structure from a seismic reflection shot, it is necessary to know the speed of travel of the primary, or P, waves, which are like sound waves, through the layers of rock. This difficulty does not affect the value of the ordinary echo-sounder, now used extensively to measure the depth of the sea, because the speed of the waves travelling through water is known. It is, however, a less effective technique for dealing with deep structures. For this purpose the refraction method yields much more information, (Hill 1957).

The refraction method of seismic survey depends on the refraction of waves from layers of differing density, the denser the layer the greater the speed with which the waves pass through it. The experiments carried out by the *Challenger* expedition in all the oceans from 1950 to 1952 used this refraction technique. In these observations four buoys were used, spaced half a mile apart. The distance between the explosion and the receiver buoys can be obtained accurately from the time taken for the sound waves to travel from the explosion, detonated near the ship, to the receiver buoys directly through the water. These buoys, to which hydrophones are fixed, are linked by radio to the ship to enable their information to be received on the ship. This method provided fairly detailed information about the upper layers beneath the ocean floor.

In order to distinguish between waves refracted by different layers it is necessary to place the receiving buoys some distance from the ship near which the explosion is detonated. The waves travelling through the deepest layer then reach the receiving apparatus first, because, although they have travelled farther, they have also moved faster. In this way it is possible to estimate the number of layers of material present and to assign to each a speed of travel of the sound waves emitted from the explosion. This method is also used to obtain information on earth structure from natural earthquakes, but observations made at sea have the great advantage that the exact position of the explosion relative to the receiving apparatus and the time interval is known.

Another technique used by the American oceanographers requires two ships, one to send out the waves, the other to receive them. This method is supplementary; it provides more information of the deeper structure, but less detail of the upper layers. The ships can be farther apart, because weaker waves can be received by a ship than by floating buoys, which are more affected by the surface movement. There is, however, a rather serious limitation to this method, as it can only be carried out in fairly calm weather (Gaskell, 1960, pp. 54–73). Recently a new type of echo-sounder has been developed which gives very detailed information of the structure immediately below the sea bed, the thicknesses of the rocks and their structures; dips, anticlines and synclines, are all directly visible on the record traced out on the revolving drum (Moore, 1960).

ii. GRAVITY SURVEYS. Gravity anomalies are measured by this type of geophysical survey; these are the difference between the observed and computed values. The Bouguer anomaly is one of the most often used methods of expressing the gravity anomaly. This allows for the visible excess or deficit of mass, as well as the latitude and height. It is expressed in milligals, where one milligal is $1/1,000,000$ part of gravity, which is $987 \cdot 048$ cm./sec./sec. at the equator or 987,048 milligals; an acceleration of gravity of $0 \cdot 1$ cm./sec./sec. equals 100 milligals. The extra mass equivalent to about 1 km. of surface rock is about $2 \cdot 5 \times 10^5$ grams/sq.cm. and this increases gravity by 105 milligals.

Over most of the Earth the gravity anomalies are fairly small, showing that the isostatic balance is nearly attained. This is achieved by an excess of density where the mass is reduced, as under the deep oceans, which over large areas may have small negative anomalies, while under high mountains the density is less to a considerable depth below the visible high ground to compensate for the extra mass (Hill, 1957).

Vening Meinesz pioneered the study of gravity anomalies at sea (Vening Meinesz, 1934). He made his observations, using an accurate pendulum, from a submerged submarine to avoid the disturbing effect of surface-wave action. Some of his most interesting results were obtained from the marginal parts of the western Pacific, where narrow zones of considerable isostatic anomaly show that the Earth's crust is not in adjustment. These long narrow zones of negative anomaly are closely associated with the interesting topographic features of the deep-sea troughs. The gravity surveys help to delimit the edge of the truly oceanic segments of the crust, as within this zone the free-air anomalies are often slightly negative.

iii. MAGNETIC STUDIES. The Earth's magnetic field is continually changing, but at any one time the position of the magnetic poles can be fixed by compass readings, while a study of the orientation towards magnetic north and the dip of magnetic particles in suitable modern sediments or volcanic rocks show that these are also orientated in sympathy with the magnetic field. Therefore, by studying the orientation of magnetized minerals in rocks of different geological periods, it is possible to arrive at a picture of the magnetic field in past periods; the position of the magnetic pole in particular may be located. Assuming that the geographical pole, or axis of the Earth's rotation, has remained set at an angle of about $11°$ to the dipole magnetic field, it is possible to obtain information concerning the movement of the pole in earlier geological time. If observations can be obtained from several continents, the relative movement of the land masses and the resulting change in the shapes of the ocean basins can be approximately assessed. These data are of condiserable importance in considering the difficult question of the permanence of the ocean basins, but they give little information on subcrustal structure.

The magnetic field of the Earth is related to the flow of electric currents in the core of the earth, and it has been suggested that the cause of the changes in the magnetic field are probably due to convectional movements in the fluid core of the Earth; without fluid motions in the core it appears that the magnetic field would be dissipated in a few thousand years. A further suggestion is that these movements within the Earth's core are caused by the rotation of the Earth and its movements forced upon it by the action of the Sun and Moon. This would provide a continual source of energy to maintain the magnetic field of the Earth.

It is worth mentioning the major findings of recent palaeomagnetic studies (Cox and Doell, 1960), as they are relevant to the problem of the permanency of the ocean basins. Firstly, during much of the Tertiary period the Earth's magnetic field was much as it is now. Secondly, the observations for the Mesozoic and early Tertiary could be explained either by relatively rapidly changing magnetic field or by large-scale continental drift; the former explanation may be more plausible. Thirdly, during the Permian and Carboniferous periods the magnetic field was very steady and very different from the present. Finally, the pre-Cambrian field was consistent for all continents, but was different from the present.

iv. HEAT-FLOW STUDIES. Most of the heat-flow studies have been made in the Pacific Ocean, with relatively few observations yet available for the Atlantic Ocean. They do, however, give valuable evidence concerning the processes at work beneath the ocean floor. The surprising result of the measurements is that the heat flow under the oceans is almost the same as that under the continents. It would be expected that the heat flow under the continents would be greater than that under the oceans, owing to the concentration of radioactive rocks in the continental parts of the crust. The heat reaching the floor of the oceans appears to come from beneath the crust and not from radioactive disintegration (Mason, 1960).

The heat flow is measured by determining the temperature gradient in the first few feet of the ocean bottom, allowance being made for the thermal conductivity of the material on the bottom. One uncertainty in the analysis of heat flow is the fact that it is not possible to arrive at accurate values of radioactive heat generated by different rocks, although it is agreed that granitic rocks produce about six times as much as basic rocks and more than a hundred times as much as ultra-basic rocks. Bullard (1954) has suggested that the higher temperatures under the oceans at given depths could be caused by convection currents acting deep down in the mantle. These would rise under the oceans and sink under the continents. These currents could bring heat towards the ocean floor and account for the abnormal heat flow recorded here. The patterns of heat flow show that localized zones of high heat flow exist which can be related to smaller morphological features of the ocean floor resulting from crustal movements, as mentioned in chapter 2.

All the methods of investigation described so far provide only indirect information concerning the character of the crust and its structure, and they are liable to misinterpretation, owing to the uncertainty of some of the assumptions which must be made. An attempt is, therefore, about to be made to obtain direct evidence of the thickness of the Earth's crust and the character of the material beneath it, by drilling down to the mantle below the crust. The project, known as the Mohole, must be undertaken in the oceanic area, as there the crust is thinnest. Even so the bore will have to be about 12 km. deep, and the fact that it must be made in deep water provides formidable problems, although it is possible that it could be done from the calm of a coral atoll. (Bascom, 1961)

(b) The Pacific Ocean

The Pacific Ocean is unique amongst the major structural features of the Earth. It covers about half the globe and is the largest single unit of truly oceanic structure. The boundary of the deep ocean type structure is called the Andesite line, shown in fig. 2–1a; inside this line the volcanic material is entirely basic in character and this line delimits that part of the ocean within which no continental type of rock is found. The Andesite line, so-called after the volcanic rock of that name, runs parallel and close to the west coast of South and North America; it then swings westwards, following outside the arcuate string of the Aleutian Islands west of Alaska, and turns abruptly south-west along the ocean side of the peninsula of Kamchatka, outside the string of the Kurile Islands to skirt the main islands of Japan as far as Tokyo. From there it turns south, running oceanward of the Mariana Islands to reach a position north of New Guinea, where it turns east-south-east towards Fiji Islands, which lie outside it, although the Ellice Islands are inside it, in the true ocean. It then turns south between the Tonga and Cook Islands, the latter being inside it, to leave New Zealand outside. Its position in the south Pacific is not clearly determined. The many islands which are found within this zone are all basaltic volcanoes, of which the Hawaiian Islands are the largest. Some of the volcanic islands are crowned with or buried beneath coral; their foundation is not now visible.

The zones of deep-focus earthquakes are another interesting feature associated with the edge of the Pacific Ocean, and indicate that this is a fundamental structural division of deep-seated significance. Earthquakes are classified according to the depth of focus; the normal earthquakes originate within 35 km. of the surface, intermediate ones occur at depths between 35 and 250 km., while deep focus ones originate at depths between 250 and 700 km. This shows that the Earth's crust and mantle have strength at least to this depth.

Deep-focus earthquakes at the present time are limited to two zones, both of which border the Pacific, one in eastern Asia and the other in South America. Both Japan and western South American countries are noted for their seismic and volcanic activity. Another interesting point about the arrangement of the depth of foci in these zones is that they increase in depth along a plane sloping down towards the continents. It has been suggested (Umbgrove, 1947; Stille, 1955), that these steeply dipping zones of earthquake activity are associated with deep-seated shear zones which have developed at the boundary of the true oceanic and the continental structures. These signs of structural unrest are, therefore, associated with the deeper structural boundary of the large Pacific Ocean. There is also a zone of fold mountains associated with this structural border, mainly on the eastern side of the Pacific, while the island arcs and deep-sea troughs which border much of the western Pacific can be interpreted in terms of the structural processes at the edge of the Pacific Ocean in the structural sense.

The unity of the Pacific basin has been mentioned by Cotton (1958). He compares the character of the Pacific rim at opposite sides of the ocean in New Zealand and California, 7,000 miles apart. Similar large transcurrent or tear faults occur in both these areas. The San Andreas rift in California has caused many earthquakes, and along this zone of dislocation the movement has been in general to the north on the ocean side of the fault relative to the continental side. Both there, and in New Zealand, at the other end of the diameter across the ocean, there has been much recent faulting and upheaval of the land bordering the ocean margin. In New Zealand there is also a major fault system, the Great Alpine Fault, which is partially transcurrent and partly vertical in its movement. It has been suggested that there the vertical movement has been very considerable, even during the last 1,000,000 years, while a lateral movement of about 300 miles over a much longer period has been suggested. The ocean side has moved south relative to the western side, which has moved north.

These movements have led to the suggestion that the rim of the Pacific shows a unity of structure which can be associated with its general character as one structural unit. The direction of the major transcurrent movements give some support to the tentative idea that the body of the Pacific may in some measure be rotating anticlockwise in relation to the lands bordering it.

Within the true oceanic Pacific, inside the Andesite line, the seismic surveys show a fairly uniform type of structure beneath the deeper parts of the ocean. Nine stations there all show the basement layer at depths varying between 0·7 and 2·7 km. below the sea floor. At some stations the thickness of sediment appeared to be very small, amounting to only 100 m. in some areas, which is less than that found in the Atlantic. Volcanic outpourings were found on some sections, while in other areas there was evidence for the presence of consolidated sediment. At two stations near the Mariana trench the Moho was found at the unusually shallow depth of 4 km. below the ocean floor; these stations were outside the Andesite line. Two other stations outside this line, also in the west Pacific, showed an intermediate type of structure, in which a layer of less dense material was suggested. These stations were on banks and it is suggested that this material, which underlies a relatively great thickness of semi-consolidated sediment, may consist of sedimentary rocks. It may, in fact, represent foundered continental type of structure, being part of the lost land of Melanesia; this would agree with geological ideas, and it is interesting that geophysical methods tend to confirm the presence of lost land masses. However, the study of the dispersion of Rayleigh waves, which are surface seismic waves, whose oscillation is partly vertical and partly in the direction of propagation, does not indicate that there are any continental rocks in the Philippine Sea, west of the Andesite line, where the former observations were made. Stations near the American coast also show indications of the presence of continental rocks at depth, although there the sea is not so deep.

Studies of the dispersion of Rayleigh waves suggest that the structure of the Pacific and Atlantic oceans is similar; neither shows evidence of a submerged land mass of continental dimensions, but thin layers of continental rock could escape detection. The results for the Atlantic do not suggest any difference between the eastern and western basin. This method gives some indication of a greater thickness of unconsolidated sediment than the seismic refraction results suggest.

(c) The Atlantic Ocean

A very considerable amount of gravity and seismic work has been carried out off the eastern United States (Worzel and Shurbet, 1955). The results show that the continental boundary ends at the 1,000 fathom depth contour. Towards the ocean the continental crust thins abruptly to merge into the thin oceanic crust in a horizontal distance of about 200 km. Ewing and his co-workers have made many seismic refraction studies on the ocean margin, particularly in the western Atlantic. Their results show a wedge of unconsolidated sediments, thinning offshore, which overlie a lense of consolidated sediments, beneath which the continental basement thins out rapidly towards the ocean, where it is replaced by the oceanic crust at the foot of the continental margin. The sediments and sedimentary rocks approach 9 km. in thickness, and it is interesting to speculate whether this will ever form a mountain range. This structure is shown in fig. 1–2. It indicates that the sediments filling the marginal trench are truly geosynclinal in nature, and it appears that the maturity of the feature increases towards the north; off Puerto Rico the margin appears young in character, in the Blake Plateau–Bahama region it is in late youth or early maturity, while off north-east U.S.A. the continental margin is in late maturity or old age, as it is off Newfoundland. It is possible that these deposits will at some future geological period form a new mountain range.

In the deep Atlantic Ocean true oceanic structure is found, and results for the western Atlantic, derived from various sources, agree well. The 1950–2 *Challenger* results in the west Atlantic show the existence of three layers of material; the sediments were between 500 and 700 m. thick, in the region around Bermuda. Beneath the sediment there was layer 2, whose thickness was between 1·7 and 2·6 km. This second layer may well be volcanic in type, as the Island of Bermuda, which itself contains andesitic material and is not truly oceanic, is volcanic. This material is, however, found farther from the volcanic islands than in the Pacific, and this may indicate extensive volcanic phenomena in this part

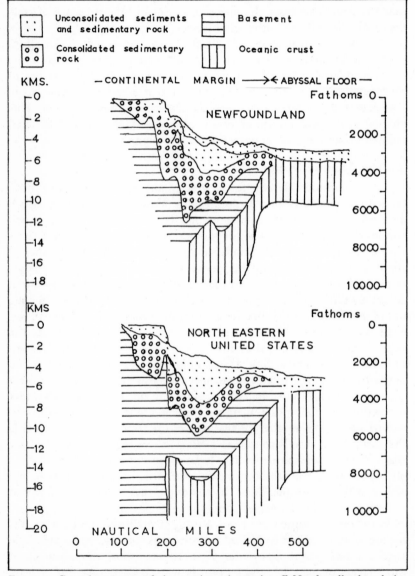

FIG. 1–2. Crustal structure of the continental margin off Newfoundland and the north-eastern United States. (After Heezen, Tharp, and Ewing.)

of the ocean. Below the second layer there is a dense basement layer 3, which is probably basaltic type of material. It extended to the Moho at depths of 11·2 to 18·2 km., rather deeper than in the Pacific, although there was no evidence of continental type granitic rocks. The western Atlantic, with its genuine oceanic type of structure, is separated from the eastern Atlantic by the mid-Atlantic ridge, which is a zone of great seismic activity. Katz and Ewing have given a typical deep-ocean section in the Sohm abyssal plain south of Newfoundland; the sea is 4–5 km. deep, layers 1 and 2 are 0·5–1 km. thick and layer 3 is 3–4 km. thick, beneath which is the Moho and layer 4.

In the eastern Atlantic a considerable number of stations were occupied during the *Challenger* cruise, and it is in this part of the ocean that different interpretations of the structure have been suggested. The results of the *Challenger* seismic work showed that the conditions in the eastern Atlantic were in general similar to those of the other deep-ocean basins. They showed a layer of unconsolidated sediments, overlying a second layer and a basement layer. The most northern stations were situated in rather shallower water on the plateau extending from Greenland to Scotland, south of Iceland. The sediment layers here ranged around 700 m. in thickness, being rather thinner than values to the south-east. Beneath this a volcanic layer was identified, which outcrops at the surface in Iceland and Rockall, although the material could also have been consolidated sediment, or alternating layers of the two. The second layer was rather thicker than in the western Atlantic or Pacific. In the third layer the speed of wave travel was considerably greater than that in continental rocks, therefore it is assumed that the North Atlantic Plateau, below which this layer lies, does not represent a foundered land mass; it is more likely to be continuous with the floor of the deep ocean.

Observations farther south, some of which were on the mid-Atlantic ridge, suggest that this relief feature probably does not contain any appreciable thickness of granitic type rock, as the velocities of waves within it are too great. The depth at which the Moho was found in three places was 13·2, 11·4 and 8·8 km., all values more typical of the oceans than of the continents, the larger values being located nearer to the continental slope. These results suggests that there is no fundamental difference between the structure of the deep oceans in the western and eastern Atlantic and that this is similar to the Pacific oceanic structure.

Rothé has suggested (1951, 1954), however, that there is some affinity between the structure of the eastern Atlantic and that of the neighbouring continental areas. He points out that the basin structure of Africa has its counterpart in the eastern Atlantic; thus the Karroo basin has its counterpart in the Cap Basin, while the Congo Basin corresponds with the Angola Basin offshore, the two oceanic basins being separated by the Walvis ridge. But on the whole the more recent detailed work does not support the hypothesis of Rothé, and it may be assumed that the eastern and western Atlantic are structurally similar.

(d) The Indian Ocean

Most of the observations made by the *Challenger* survey in the Indian Ocean, with one exception, were made in the eastern half of the ocean. The only observation near the west coast of the ocean was made in the Seychelles. These islands contain granite, which supports the view that continental type structures may be present in the western Indian Ocean. The seismic studies in the eastern Indian Ocean, just south of the Equator, showed that the thickness of sediment varied from about 400 m. to a thickness of about 1,100 to 1,600 m. in two positions; this is thicker than in most of the deep-ocean stations. Beneath the sediment, at two stations, a thick layer was identified, nearly 3 km. in one place, through which waves travel faster than in the equivalent layer in the Pacific, but it probably consisted of the same basic volcanic material or lithified sediments. The great thickness may have been due to the proximity of a sea mount. One of the stations had a thick layer of material in which the wave velocity indicated material which was probably volcanic. The deeper layer, in which the waves travelled faster, was almost certainly basic rock as in the Atlantic and Pacific, but the station nearest the Equator, and farthest west, recorded a rock which might possibly be granitic, under considerable pressure. The waves passed through it only slightly faster than through the granite of the Seychelles. Much detailed oceanographical work is being planned for the Indian Ocean, which may help to solve some of the outstanding problems of the structure of this part of the oceanic crust.

From these results it seems that in all the oceans there is a large area which is truly oceanic in the structural sense—only in the western Indian Ocean is there some evidence of continental type of structure; the evidence for the eastern Atlantic is rather conflicting, but on the whole conforms with the other areas. The zone outside the Andesite line in the Pacific also has transitional or continental characteristics in parts.

2. *THE PERMANENCY OF THE OCEAN BASINS*

That the structure beneath the oceans and continents differs fundamentally is agreed by most authorities, but the problem of the permanence of the oceans and the mobility of the continents is still very far from being solved. Nevertheless some of the views, which have been advanced in support of both ideas, may be put forward, and the evidence on which they are based discussed. The ingenious theory that the Moon was born out of the Pacific Ocean must be discarded, on the sound evidence, put forward by Jeffreys (1950), that if the crust was mobile enough for the material to be drawn out from the earth, it would have healed over the scar which was left very fast.

There are various other possibilities to be considered; either the continents and oceans have remained more or less in their present positions throughout geological time, in other words they are permanent features in the pattern of the earth's structure, or another possibility is that the continents started as two units, originally under the oceans, and subsequently appeared above the sea to form the land masses. This is the basis of Hills' theory (1947) of the formation of the continents by convection.

Another idea is the well-known view of Wegener (1922) and others that the continents originated as one large unit, which subsequently split up and drifted apart to form the present pattern. According to Wegener this split did not take place till the Cretaceous period, since when the Atlantic and Indian Oceans have formed. Various paths of polar wandering have also been suggested to account for different palaeogeographical facts.

(a) Theories of permanency

The fact that there is a fundamental difference between the structure of the oceans and continents has led some workers to think that the two must always have remained more or less in their present positions. A distinction must, however, be drawn between the true deep oceans and those areas which are of intermediate structure and situated near the continental margins.

It is quite clear from the distribution of marine sedimentary rocks on the Earth's surface that much of the area which is now dry land has at one time been beneath the sea, but only a shallow sea adjacent to the land from which the sediment could be derived. Some rocks were laid down in the clear shallow water environment, such as most of the limestone now exposed on the land.

It is equally certain that some areas which are now within the oceans must at one time have been dry land; this applies particularly to those areas marginal to former geosynclines, from which sediment must have been derived to fill the sinking geosynclines. One example, Melanesia, in south-east Asia has already been cited, others which are known on very good evidence are Atlantis, which lay to the north-west of Europe during the filling of the Caledonian geosyncline, and Appalachia, from which sediments were derived to fill the Appalachian geosyncline from which the Appalachian Mountains were eventually built. Cascadia off north-west America has also disappeared into the Pacific Ocean.

It is obvious, therefore, that our modern shorelines are very far from being permanently in their present position. On the other hand, there is much evidence that the deep oceans have never been dry land, nor the continents true deep oceans. It is also certain that during the span of geological time, since the oldest rocks now visible on the continents were formed, none of these has escaped, at one time or another, severe contortion and disturbance by earth movements, although large areas, now forming the Shields, have been relatively stable since the beginning of the palaeozoic period about 600 million years ago. It seems likely that similar upheavals may have taken place in the oceanic sections of the crust.

In considering the probability of permanence of the oceans, it is necessary to consider the original state of the Earth when such permanent oceans would have been initiated. Lees (1953) has pointed out that there are two possibilities; either the Earth started, as is usually assumed, as a hot liquid, which then developed a solid crust through heat loss due to radiation, or, secondly, the Earth may have formed by accretion of gaseous matter, of dust and cold solid particles, which have subsequently compacted to form the planets.

If the second hypothesis is true, the Earth must have gained heat by adiabatic compression and impact heating, at least to the extent that rocks could liquefy to form the fluid lava flows which have been active throughout the Earth's history. Although Lees favours the second general hypothesis, he does not show how it would lead to the differentiation of the oceans and continents. His views are, however, provocative and original, and he does not consider the geological interpretation of the geophysical evidence is always justified, suggesting that perhaps there is no fundamental difference between the oceans and continents. He suggests that the Atlantic Ocean may be due to down warping of the intercontinental area, using as evidence the way in which the continental structures strike out into the Atlantic to disappear into the sea.

Returning to the first possibility of the liquid Earth, some of the various possible methods of ocean and continent differentiation may be considered. At the present time the force which is normally invoked to explain this separation into two distinct structural and material types is that of convection currents. Those who favour the permanence of the oceans point out that their pattern, and the arrangement of the continents, is such that most of the land masses are grouped in the Northern Hemisphere, situated around a polar ocean, while in the Southern Hemisphere there is the most continuous stretch of ocean in high southern latitudes, around the South Polar continent. This more or less antipodal arrangement has led Vening Meinetz (1944) to suggest that it could be due to the action of a series of convection currents. Supposing that these currents extend down to the limit of the Earth's mantle, where, at a depth of 2,900 km. below the surface, it meets the core, he suggested that the probable arrangement of the currents would lead to eight cells, four rising and four sinking. Each cell would occupy one octant of the globe, as shown in fig. 1–3, and the light material would

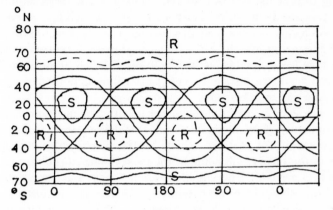

FIG. 1–3. Theoretical arrangement of convection cells. R indicates rising currents and S sinking currents.

tend to accumulate at those positions where the currents are sinking, while the rising cells would help to disperse the light continental material. This light material would eventually consolidate to form the continents, which have been shown to consist of less dense rocks.

On the assumption that two of the cells are arranged along the axis of rotation, it is suggested that the sinking cells are situated symmetrically around the North Pole, while the fourth sinking cell would be found at the opposite end of the axis, round the South Pole. The rising cells, now the oceans, would have been situated at the North Pole and symmetrically around the southern continent. Thus the continents would be concentrated in the Northern Hemisphere. In this way the basic arrangement of land and sea could be accounted for; but the theory is lacking in proof, and is very speculative.

One of the arguments put forward by those who favour permanence is the fact that deep-water sediments are never found on land, nor are continental rocks found in the true oceans. Another argument concerns the capacity of the ocean basins in relation to the amount of water; large changes in the area of land and sea would upset the sea-level. One of the stronger arguments in favour of permanence is the negative one, that there is no mechanism yet discovered by which continents and oceans can be moved. While the very different structure of the oceans and continents does point to their permanent role on the Earth, this does not necessarily imply that their positions relative to one another must have been static all the time.

(b) Theories of drifting continents and changing oceans

The original theory of Wegener, in which he proposed the idea of the drifting continents, was put forward to explain the distribution of the deposits of the Permo-Carboniferous Ice Age, which interested him as a meteorologist. He assumed that all the continents were grouped together as one unit, which he called Pangaea; this was centred around the South Pole, then situated, according to his view, off South Africa. This explained neatly the distribution of glacial tillites in South Africa, India, South America, and Australia.

The evidence in favour of the theory may first be mentioned and later the arguments against it can be raised. It is not necessary to consider all the very abundant material which has been assembled by those in favour of the theory, but some of the most important points are worth taking into account. The climatic evidence is in some ways the most difficult to explain by other hypotheses, particularly the distribution of the glacial deposits, already mentioned. On this point it may be mentioned that it cannot be assumed that the climate has remained similar to the present climate throughout geological time; different distributions of the shallow seas and variations in the height of land masses as well as extra-terrestrial factors may well have played their part, while developments in vegetation can also have had an effect. Ice ages are rare phenomena in the history of the earth; one occurred in late pre-Cambrian time, but only two have occurred since the Cambrian in the last 600 million years, in the Permo-Carboniferous and the Pleistocene. They exert a powerful influence on the world climate.

The arrangement of rock types and structures on either side of the Atlantic Ocean, which according to Wegener was formed by the splitting up of Pangaea, is also of interest. The similarity of structures on either side of this ocean is indeed striking at first sight. For example, the Caledonian folds and Variscan trend approach in Britain, but their crossing takes place in eastern North America. The superficial similarity of the shape of the coastlines on either side of the Atlantic and elsewhere suggests the fitting of the land masses into one unit, but this is not strong evidence in favour of the theory, as the splitting is supposed to have taken place in the Cretaceous period, when in any case the coastline was not the same as it is now.

Perhaps the strongest evidence which has been put forward recently in favour of the theory of continental drift is that derived from palaeomagnetic studies. These have already been mentioned and it has been suggested that an abrupt change in the magnetic field took place between the steady state of the Permo-Carboniferous period and that of the Tertiary. This change could be interpreted as the result of continental drift, although this is not the only possibility. Collinson and Runcorn (1960) have assembled palaeomagnetic evidence which they feel shows some evidence in favour of drifting. They show that the position of the pole relative to America has been moving about in the Pacific. In the late pre-Cambrian it was situated in the tropical central Pacific, it then moved across the tropical Pacific westwards towards Asia in the late Palaeozoic and early Mesozoic, and thence across the north Pacific to its present position. This route is displaced relative to that worked out from observations in Europe. From this evidence it is calculated that the displacement of America relative to Europe has been 30° of longitude since the Mesozoic. The movement appears to have started at the end of the Palaeozoic. This evidence again suggests active movement during the Mesozoic period. The palaeomagnetic evidence has given renewed vigour to the drifting theory, by providing at last what appears to be positive evidence in its favour, although the interpretation of the results is not entirely without possible alternatives. The difficulties facing the hypothesis must, therefore, be considered.

The major one of mechanism has already been mentioned, and this, according to Jeffreys, is difficult to overcome. The drift also has other implications; if the theory were correct, the Atlantic and Indian Oceans must be very much younger than the Pacific, having been formed by rifting in the Cretaceous and later periods. There is, however, no evidence that they contain much less deep-sea deposits, which might be expected. Also it has been pointed out that the movement of the Americas westwards to form the Atlantic should have piled up a heap of sediment on their west coasts in the Pacific, but there is no evidence of this, and what is more, the Andes are not a marginal mountain range, but originated in an intercontinental geosyncline, according to Lees (1953). The sunk land of Cascadia has already been mentioned in this respect. This does not support the idea that this mountain range was formed by the pressure of America against the Pacific margin, in its westward travel, during which its leading edge became crumpled to form the Andes and Rockies.

One difficulty about the continental drift theory as proposed by Wegener is the fact that it must have taken place fairly suddenly during the Mesozoic and subsequently, while no similar movement took place during earlier geological time. It is very difficult to think of any possible reason why this should have been so, and what force could have become active suddenly about this time.

Other theories, which do not come strictly into the permanency category, because they allow some drifting, include that of Hills (1947).

o.–c

His theory is thought to be possible by Jeffreys (1950). Hills suggests that the continents were formed at an early stage in the history of an originally molten earth. At an early stage the convection currents would be active and Hills suggests that these might have carried the hot material towards the poles, where it would tend to concentrate the floating crystals of lighter material. As the currents slowed down, due to increasing viscosity, the light material, which by this time would have accumulated in the form of rafts floating on a denser substratum, would tend to drift away from the poles towards the Equator. Two continents of about equal size, called Laurasia and Gondwanaland, would result.

At first these light continents would be floating on the denser substratum and would be about 10–15 km. thick. It is suggested that they would float with a free board of $1\frac{1}{2}$ km. in a universal ocean 3 km. deep. Their elevation above the surface of the ocean, to form the first continents, would come about by the expansion of the thick continental-type rocks by radioactive heating, as it is in this type of rock that the radioactive material is concentrated. Hills considered that the Atlantic was a rift ocean formed by the splitting of Laurasia.

This hypothesis is intermediate between that of Wegener and that of permanency, advocated by Umbgrove and Jeffreys. It gets over some of the difficulties of Wegener's theory, but it also fails to account for some of the facts that fit in well with the Wegener drift hypothesis. The problem is an extremely difficult one, but nevertheless it is also very fascinating. The modern tendency seems to be veering rather towards the drifting hypothesis again, largely on account of the findings of the palaeomagnetic studies. This follows a period when serious doubt was cast on the theory of drifting, mainly because of the lack of a sufficient mechanism to account for it. If, however, the suggestion of the rotation of the Pacific within its basin is taken into consideration and the evidence accepted, this shows that large-scale horizontal movements of the Earth's crust have, in fact, taken place, which lends further support to the drifting theory.

Dietz (1961) has recently suggested that many features of the ocean floor and its borderland region could be explained by the action of convection currents, rising under the centre of the oceans and sinking under the continental edge. This process would allow some continental drift as the continental blocks are dragged, by the currents, on the moving mantle, in which the currents are operating. He has suggested that the ocean floor could be the outcropping mantle, moving slowly at a few cm./year towards the margin, leaving ridges in the centres of the oceans and adding to the continents at the edges. This would help to account for the apparent post-Mesozoic age of much of the sea-floor deposits and their relative thinness. If the continental blocks move along with the ocean floor, a stable Atlantic-type margin is formed, but if the ocean floor slips under the continental block, a Pacific type of margin, with deep trenches, island arcs and mountain ranges, is formed.

3. THE ORIGIN OF THE OCEAN WATER

The estimated volume of the water in the ocean according to Kuenen (1950) has a total of $1,370 \times 10^6$ cu. km. at the present time. The origin and rate of collection of this water into the ocean receptacles is worth comment. Water which enters for the first time into the hydrological cycle is termed juvenile water; it is this water which has throughout geological time built up the vast store of the ocean supply. Its source lies in the igneous rocks, which are either intruded into or extruded upon the Earth's crust. Juvenile water is now being added to the oceans at the rate of not more than $0 \cdot 1$ cu. km./year and probably less. This estimate is based on the amount of volcanic activity now in progress; this, together with igneous intrusions, has been estimated to produce at most 2 cu. km. of rock annually. The maximum amount of juvenile water which could be released from this quantity of igneous rock is thought to be not more than 5 per cent. Hence the annual production of $0 \cdot 1$ cu. km. or $1/40$ cu. mile of water.

Assuming 600 million years since the Cambrian period started, the water in the ocean must have increased by 60×10^6 cu. km. during the period. At the beginning of the Cambrian period, therefore, the amount of water in the ocean must already have exceeded 1,300 million cu. km. if these calculations are approximately correct. The most doubtful point in this analysis is the amount of volcanic and plutonic activity which has taken place during this long period of the Earth's development. To take the present as an average over the period is about the best estimate which can be made, because, although some geological periods may have been more active in this respect, others may have been more quiescent. It seems fair to assume that the oceans have had very nearly the same amount of water in them since the beginning of the Palaeozoic.

Not all authorities agree with this view, however, and Twenhofel has suggested that the amount of water in the oceans has been increasing steadily throughout geological time, with an accelerating rate of increase in the Mesozoic, as shown in fig. 1–4. Kuenen's view, on the other hand, holds that the increase was very rapid indeed in the early stages of the Earth's history, but the increase has only been at the slow rate mentioned above during the last 1,000 million years or so. Walther has put forward an even more extreme view than Twenhofel, in which he considers that the oceans contained very little water before the beginning of the Mesozoic, some 200 million years ago, when they suddenly increased rapidly in water content. His argument is based on the absence of deep-sea fauna in the fossil record until after the Palaeozoic period, from which he concluded that the deep-sea environment did not then exist. There are, however, many other ways in which this phenomenon could be explained; deep-sea deposits are rarely found on land and hence would not be expected in the fossil record, while climatic conditions may well have been such that cold deep water could not form in high latitudes, and the whole oceanic circulation may have been so sluggish that the deep-ocean basins were almost stagnant and unsuitable for deep-sea life.

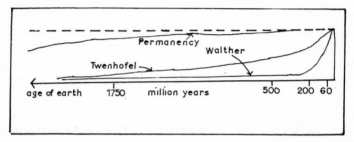

Fig. 1–4. Different views on the changing volume of ocean water. (After Kuenen.)

On the whole it seems reasonable to assume that the content of the oceans has not changed very much during and since the Palaeozoic era; the amount suggested above would be sufficient to raise the ocean level, at its present size, by about 400 ft. This implies that the ocean basins must have been available during this period to accommodate the water. The Pacific holds about half the present ocean water; it is clear, therefore, that either the Pacific was larger by a considerable amount, if the Atlantic did not exist, or the other oceans must have been in existence since this time. This is due to the fact that the level of the sea relative to the land has not changed substantially during this period; at times parts of the present ocean have been land, at times the continental margin has been flooded by shallow seas, geosynclines have developed, but on the whole sea-level has not changed very much during the period, although earth movements have caused considerable local elevations or depressions of the land.

4. CHANGES IN SEA-LEVEL DURING THE TERTIARY AND QUATERNARY PERIODS

Changes of sea-level can be the result of many different causes, so that the level is unlikely to remain static for long, even if the amount of water remains constant. Before considering the changes taking place during the Tertiary and Quaternary periods, some of the factors affecting sea-level may be mentioned. Some of these factors lead to local changes, such as the rising of areas isostatically following deglaciation, or the sinking of some geosynclinal regions, such as the southern North Sea. Other movements are associated with local tectonic instability; for example, the change in level in Wellington Harbour, following the 1851 earthquake. Others influence the world-wide sea-level and these are called eustatic changes.

Sea-level may change differentially in different zones, as a result of geodetic changes. For instance, an increase in the speed of rotation will affect the centrifugal force and alter the geoid, causing equatorial swelling and polar shrinking. The hydrosphere will react differently to the lithosphere, causing zonal sea-level fluctuations. Polar shift will also cause similar regions of transgressions and regression. A sudden shift of $10°$ in the pole would cause an equatorial rise of sea-level of 2,450 m. (8,050 ft.), and a $1°$ shift would raise the level by 245 m. (805 ft.), with equal regression $90°$ away.

Eustatic changes may be caused by a change in the capacity of the ocean basin; a negative change can be the result of the formation of basins and is called tectono-eustatism by American workers. A positive world-wide change could result from sedimentation, called sedimento-eustatism. If all the land were peneplaned, sea-level would rise 250 m. (820 ft.). At the present rate of denudation, estimated at 12 km³./year, sea-level would rise about 3·3 cm./1,000 years.

During the last one million years a more obvious and rapid cause of eustatic change has been glacio-eustatism, due to the repeated growth and decay of ice sheets. Other related effects include that of the change of ocean temperature; a rise of the whole water column of $1°C$ has been stated to lead to a rise of sea-level of 2 m. (6·5 ft.) (Fairbridge, 1961). The changing volume of ice sheets has been the most important influence in the Quaternary period, while tectono-eustatism dominated the Tertiary period and carried on into the Pleistocene, in combination with the glacio-eustatic factors, in connexion with the Alpine orogenic upheavals.

(a) Tertiary changes

During the Tertiary period much of Britain was land and the changes of sea-level there during this period can best be studied by the methods of geomorphological analysis. This aims to establish an estimate of the former base levels by studying the erosion surfaces, formed either just below sea-level by earlier and higher seas, or by subaerial forces, which reduced the land to near base level. The results of the study of denudation chronology suggest that sea-level fell intermittently during the major part of the Tertiary period. Surfaces now 2,000 feet or more above sea-level are thought to have been formed during this period. The major problem which remains is to ascertain whether this relative fall of sea-level was accomplished by the elevation of the land, by the fall of sea-level, or by a combination of both movements.

If the main movement was due to a general world-wide tectono-eustatic fall of sea-level, all stable land areas must have been affected similarly. In which case it should be possible to correlate variations of base level by height from place to place. This has, in fact, been attempted and cross-Channel correlations between Europe and Britain have been suggested as well as transatlantic correlations. However, the Tertiary period was one of great tectonic activity, when the main Alpine earth movements took place, which influenced many parts of the world. Thus few places escaped some tectonic disturbance during this phase; folding was active in southern Britain, while, in the early Tertiary, volcanic activity was widespread in northern Britain. All this tectonic unrest makes it fairly certain that, at least during the early Tertiary, movements of base level were probably a combination of tectono-eustatic and local tectonic effects. It is thus not surprising that the old base-levelled surfaces which were near sea-level during this period are now no longer horizontal.

Many geomorphologists would consider that at least since the 1,000 ft. surface was eroded in Britain, probably in the Mio-Pliocene, the movements of base level have been on the whole fairly uniform throughout the country, and therefore most likely eustatic in origin. Some parts of the country, particularly in the east, can clearly not be included in this generalization, as there deposits of the Pliocene and Pleistocene periods have been warped down below sea-level. This region, according to Wooldridge and Henderson (1955) lies to the east of a north-south line, north of the Thames, running through Braintree in Essex. To the west and south of this line there is clear evidence, in the form of marine deposits belonging to the latest Pliocene and earliest Pleistocene, that sea-level at this time stood about 600 ft. higher than it does now.

Over much of southern Britain the geomorphological evidence of this higher phase of marine transgression lies at about this height, and elsewhere around the coast of England and Wales remnants of the effects of a higher sea-level can be found at about this altitude. There is a strong suggestion, therefore, that over some of the country at least the land has been stable and the sea-level has fallen since this time. These remarks only apply to the relatively stable parts of the British Isles and other stable land areas, and some places, such as parts of New Zealand, have been uplifted by up to 10,000 ft. and greatly warped during the late Tertiary and Quaternary period.

The reason for the generally falling base level of the Tertiary period may well be related to the very widespread land uplift that took place during this period and the sinking of tectonic basins into which the ocean water could withdraw. Material at depth must move to beneath the continental area to make the elevation possible; the source from which this material was likely to be derived was under the oceans, which would therefore deepen, with a consequent withdrawal of water from the coastal areas. The great elevation of land in the late Tertiary also helped to initiate the Pleistocene glaciation. This in its turn has played a very important part in the fluctuation of sea-level during the ice age.

(b) Pleistocene changes

As the ice sheets grew, which eventually covered vast areas of Europe and North America, they abstracted more and more water from the oceans, which was locked up in the solid state on land; this led to a considerable fall of sea-level. The exact amount of the maximum change of sea-level, as a result of the growth of ice sheets, is difficult to estimate, because although the area covered at their maximum is fairly well known, the thickness of the ice can only be estimated approximately. Apart from the water locked up as ice, much was held on land in the form of temporary lakes, some of which were very large. The sinking of the crust isostatically under the weight of the overlying ice must displace deeper-seated material, which will have an effect on sea-level, while it also means that the ice sheets were bi-convex not plano-convex in shape. Another difficulty is that the ice sheets need not all have their maxima simultaneously.

Because of these uncertainties it is not surprising that several different estimates of the maximum fluctuation of sea-level, as a result of the growth of ice sheets, have been put forward. Antevs (1928) suggested a value of about 93 m. (305 ft.) for the last glaciation and 120–130 m. (395–427 ft.) for the maximum glaciation. Daly (1934) gives the value of 75 m. (246 ft.) for the last glaciation and 90 m. (295 ft.) for the maximum glaciation. Penck suggested 100 m. (328 ft.) for the maximum reduction of sea-level. Other values almost double this. It seems that about 100 m. (328 ft.) is a reasonable estimate, supported now by many lines of evidence, for the greatest fall of sea-level as a result of the formation of ice-sheets. This low level was probably attained during the last glaciation, owing to the superimposition of the tectono-eustatic curve on the glacio-eustatic one. This more than compensated for the smaller ice volume during the last glaciation, as shown in fig. 1–5a.

Sea-level changes during the Pleistocene ice age were not all negative, when the ice melted and interglacial conditions prevailed; the climate was probably milder than at present at times, and there was less ice than now. This resulted in a higher sea-level than at present. The effects of these changes of sea-level have been numerous. At times of low sea-level, during glacial advances, much of the shallow sea bed of the continental shelves was above sea-level. Rivers extended their courses across such areas. In many of the major river valleys of the British Isles and elsewhere there is evidence of the lower sea-level in the form of buried channels. The Thames cut down its bed to form a deep and narrow channel, subsequently filled with later deposits during a phase of higher sea-level. This is a good indication of low sea-level; as this area was not overrun by ice, the channels must, therefore, be the work of a

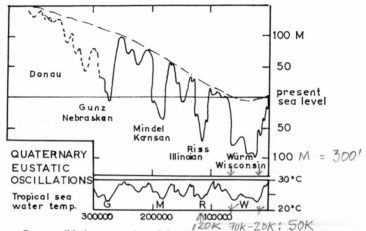

FIG. 1–5a. One possible interpretation of the eustatic changes in sea-level during the Quaternary period, using the correlation with tropical sea-water temperatures, as given by Emiliani. It should be noted that other interpretations, which are equally possible, give a time scale for the Pleistocene period almost twice as long. (After Fairbridge.)

river graded to base level. Elsewhere overdeepened channels may be the work of glacial scour, which can take place well below sea-level, as, for example, the fjords of Norway and elsewhere. At the time of the low glacial sea-levels and even subsequently the Straits of Dover and the southern North Sea were dry land and Britain was joined to the Continent, an important fact with regard to the immigration of men, plants and animals. Glacial drift was widely deposited on the continental shelf around Britain during the low sea-level periods. Since the rise of sea-level this has initiated entirely new coastlines, which have been rapidly modified as sea-level has risen, owing to their generally non-resistant character.

The higher interglacial sea-levels have also left their mark conspicuously in many coast areas and have extended their influence far inland in the form of river terraces, aggraded to the higher sea-level. That these can be associated with the warmer interglacial periods is clearly demonstrated by their associated fauna and flora. A number of high interglacial sea-levels have been recognized; one of these, the Great Interglacial (Yarmouth interglacial in North America), has been correlated with the deposits of the Holstein Sea in Europe. It represents the interglacial between the Mindel and Riss glacial advances. At this period sea-level was about 100 ft. higher than it is now, which is indicated by the aggradation of the gravels of the Boyn Hill terrace of the Thames to this level above the present flood plain.

The last major interglacial, between the Riss and Würm advances (Sangamon in North America), is correlated with the Eemian Sea deposits on the European continent and with various aggradational terraces in Britain, such as the Taplow terrace in the Thames. It is also probable that the well-known raised beach of southern Britain, at about 10 ft. above the present sea-level, dates from this interglacial. It is found from Sewerby in Yorkshire, where it is covered by Newer Drift, to the south coasts of England, Wales, and Ireland.

Much evidence shows that there has been a steady fall in the high level of the interglacial periods, and of the low glacial sea-levels; this is the result of tectono-eustatic effects, due to basin formation and other processes, superimposed on the glacio-eustatic effects. The following heights and fig. 1–5a illustrate these points:

Gunz (Nebraskan) Glacial +30 m.
Gunz-Mindel Interglacial (Sicilian of Mediterranean) +100 and +80 m.
Mindel (Kansan) Glacial −5 m.
Mindel-Riss, Great Interglacial (Milazzian of Medit.) +55 m.
                    Late Great Interglacial (Tyrrhenian of Medit.) +30 m.
Riss (Illinoian) Glacial −75 m.
Russ-Würm Interglacial (Monastirian of Mediterranean) +18 m., +8 m., +3 m.
Würm (Wisconsin) Glacial −100 m.

(c) Late and post-glacial changes

The changes in sea-level during the last major ice advance and the phases of deglaciation are better known than those of the earlier glacial advances. The evidence is more clearly preserved, while more precise dating has been possible. During the last decade the carbon[14] technique has been supplementing and defining more precisely the earlier estimates, based on such methods as pollen analysis and archaeological evidence. The phases of high sea-level can be clearly identified in the raised beaches, cut during the times of relatively high-water level, while well-preserved submerged forests give good evidence of the times during which sea-level was lower than at present.

In considering the changes of sea-level in areas which were previously glaciated, it is very necessary to take into consideration the uplift of the land following deglaciation, due to isostatic recovery. This movement, which causes an apparent fall of sea-level in the areas of recovery, must be considered in conjunction with the eustatic changes. The latter have been on the whole positive, causing a rising sea-level, as the water returns to the ocean as the ice melts. The apparent changes of sea-level in Scotland are very different from those in south-east England, during the late and post-glacial period, because of the interaction of these two factors, and even greater contrasts are found between central Scandinavia and Holland. As examples of these two contrasting types of sea-level change the former two areas may be considered briefly.

In Scotland isostatic recovery has been active, but there is a difference of opinion as to whether it is still continuing. During the late glacial period, however, there is evidence that sea-level was much higher relative to the present level. This is seen in the marine deposits at Paisley, now 40 ft. above sea-level, which contain arctic fauna; there are also well-marked raised beaches at about 100 ft. above present sea-level. These higher beaches do not penetrate to the heads of the sea lochs, which is generally assumed to be due to the presence of glaciers at their heads. The 100 ft. beach was cut before isostatic recovery had become rapid, and it owes its present altitude above sea-level to its elevation due to this process.

At a lower level is a so-called 50 ft. beach, although it actually varies considerably in altitude, due to differential isostatic uplift. A recent account of some of the raised beaches of Scotland by Donner (1959) shows the higher beaches to be warped, so that in the area peripheral to the maximum isostatic recovery they become mixed with the lower beaches. One of the most conspicuous lower beaches is the 25 ft. beach; this is again a misnomer, as although the beach appears to be fairly horizontal at this altitude in the central area of isostatic recovery, around the Mull of Kintyre and south Inverness-shire, it is found at lower levels in the regions peripheral to the main ice centre. The warping of the strandlines gives evidence of the position of the area of maximum recovery due to isostacy, which was probably also the area of maximum ice thickness. The '25 ft.' beach is found almost at present sea-level in north-east Ireland, and south of Dublin, and in Anglesey. From the archaeological remains associated with it, the beach seems to date from the late Mesolithic and Neolithic periods, being formed rather earlier in the central area, near Oban in Scotland, than near the southern limit at Larne in Northern Ireland. This suggests that the maximum post-glacial submergence was earlier in the central than the peripheral areas.

The east and south-east coast of England was not seriously affected by isostatic movement; the changes of sea-level there will, therefore, represent much more closely the eustatic changes of the sea. The tendency of the southern North Sea area to subside geosynclinally must, however, be taken into account, in interpreting the changes of sea-level in this area. Godwin (1940) and Swinnerton (1931) have elucidated the changes of sea-level in the Fens and Lincolnshire coast, respectively, arriving at very much the same conclusions. The evidence is provided by differing types of deposits; peat was formed during periods of low sea-level, while when sea-level was rising salt marsh silt was laid down. ✓ℳ 18K BC = 300′ ↓

Godwin (1940) has indicated that about 8000 B.C. sea-level was approximately 180 ft. lower in the North Sea than it is now. In fact, the whole southern North Sea was dry land and trees grew on the Dogger Bank. Sea-level rose very rapidly during the period up to about 3000 B.C., in what is known as the Flandrian transgression. At this time sea-level stood about 20 ft. lower than at present, but rose to about 2 ft. above the present level around 1600 B.C. and 5 ft. above at A.D. 0. The sea was relatively low around 700 B.C. and 800, A.D. but only by 15 and 8 ft. respectively.

More recently these dates have been checked by using all the relevant radio-carbon dates (Godwin *et. al.*, 1958). This evidence shows that sea-level rose at the rate of about 3 ft./century during the period from 14,000 to 5,000 years ago. This is the period during which ice started to retreat very rapidly, with a slight re-advance following the mild Alleröd period, which lasted from about 12,000 to 11,000 years ago. From this evidence it is suggested that sea-level reached within a few feet of its present level some 5,000 years ago. Data from southern Louisiana, also based on radio-carbon dating, (McFarlan, 1961) in general confirms this picture. Broecker (1961) considers that sea-level rose by 50 ft. between 16,000 and 13,000 years ago and 150 ft. between 13,000 and 11,000 years ago, when the climate was warming rapidly.

A detailed account of the post-Pleistocene changes of sea-level is given by Fairbridge (1961). His results show that since 13,000 years ago, when sea-level was 50 m. lower than now, it has risen rapidly, but with many minor fluctuations to reach its present level 6,000 years ago. Since this time it has oscillated up to 10 ft. above and below its present level, with gradually decreasing swings to either side of the present level, as shown in fig. 1–5b.

There is good evidence that more recently, anyway on the south-east coast of England, sea-level has risen appreciably. In Lincolnshire sea-level has risen by about 3 ft. during the last 750 years. This is indicated by the difference in level of the silt marsh, reclaimed during the medieval period, and the modern actively growing salt marsh, which is 3–4 ft. higher, and still flooded by high spring tides. This rise of sea-level which is still continuing has very serious consequences on the low coast

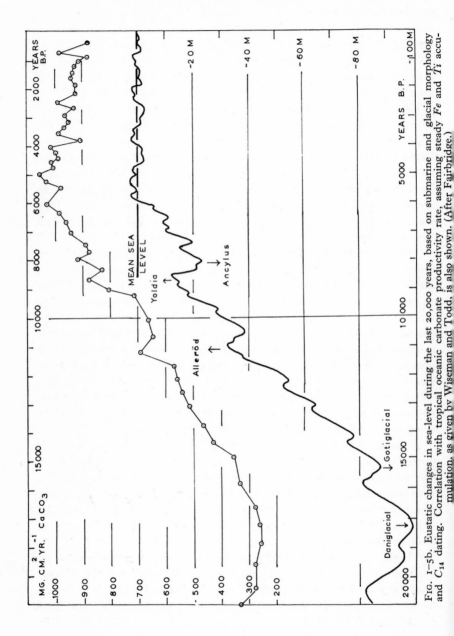

Fig. 1-5b. Eustatic changes in sea-level during the last 20,000 years, based on submarine and glacial morphology and C_{14} dating. Correlation with tropical oceanic carbonate productivity rate, assuming steady *Fe* and *Ti* accumulation, as given by Wiseman and Todd. is also shown. (After Fairbridge.)

of part of east England and Holland, where the hinterland is becoming increasingly below high tide level; sea floods become more and more disastrous for this reason.

(d) Present trends in sea-level changes

The evidence of the tide gauges around the British Isles shows that the south-eastern part of the country is suffering from a slowly rising sea-level. The most accurate tide gauges at Newlyn in Cornwall and Felixstowe in Suffolk show a rise of 2·3 mm./year and 1·7 mm./year respectively (Valentin, 1954). The major part of this rise is due to the eustatic rise of sea-level which is now in progress, as a result of the very general glacial retreat, which has been particularly active since the 1930s. The line of no change, according to Valentin, runs north–south between Aberdeen, which is rising at 0·5 mm./year, and Dundee, which is sinking by a similar amount. It then runs south-south-west to Anglesey and from here probably turns north again around Scotland, although the evidence for the rise of central Scotland is conjectural, and Hafemann (1954) considers that Scotland has not risen isostatically since the first century A.D.

A somewhat similar pattern is found on the coast of north-west Europe. Rapid uplift is still active around the Gulf of Bothnia, where isostatic recovery is not yet complete; the line of no change runs through extreme south-west Norway, across north Denmark and southern Sweden. The maximum rate of sinking occurs in south Denmark and north Germany on the North Sea coast, where sea-level is rising at 3 mm./year; all of the coast of Holland and Belgium is also sinking at a rather slower rate. Apart from those areas still undergoing isostatic recovery, which include Alaska, Canada north of 46½°N., and Scandinavia, most other areas are affected by the eustatic rise of sea-level, and hence have a rising sea-level. This applies to all the coasts of America, where the Gulf coast is subsiding very fast at 5·5 mm./year; this is partly tectonic, due to delta formation. However, even on the Atlantic coast the mean rise amounts to 3·9 mm./year. ≐ *1 in./6 yrs.!*

The present eustatic rise of sea-level has been estimated at 1·12 mm./year by Fairbridge (1961) and 1·18 mm./year by Wexler (1961), the latter discusses some of the factors on which this estimate depends. The basis of his argument rests on the estimated changes in volume of the Antarctic ice sheet, which is by far the largest in the world, and its variation will clearly have an important effect on sea-level. It has been estimated that if it all melted, sea-level would rise by 100 m. (328 ft.), which would flood many of the major cities and all the ports of the Earth.

Various estimates of its state of balance or budget have been put forward during the last few years, the majority suggest that the ice is growing in volume, although two consider the ice sheet to be static and one suggests that it is losing material. Taking the mean of the results, however, it does appear that the ice volume here is increasing; this might well accompany the warming, which is well established in the glacial areas of the Northern Hemisphere, where retreat is rapid at present. This is because in the extreme cold of Antarctica a slight rise of temperature would enable the air to hold more moisture, without raising temperature above freezing-point.

Nearly all the recent estimates of the eustatic change of sea-level suggest that it is rising, which is the opposite movement which would be expected if the ice of the Antarctic were increasing in volume. The processes which can help the balance the estimated growth of the Antarctic ice sheet, to cause the measured rise of sea-level, are the melting of the Northern Hemisphere ice, which is well substantiated, and the warming of the ocean; the last factor has already been shown to cause a rise of sea-level, but its exact part in the present eustatic change of ocean level is not well known, although it may well be an important one.

Glacio-eustatic effects will continue to operate until all the ice now on the continents finally melts. There are two alternatives for the near future: either the ice will continue to melt and sea-level to rise, or it is possible that the present is an inter-glacial period, and sea-level may fall as ice again builds up to form new ice sheets over north-west Europe and north America.

REFERENCES

Antevs, E., The late-glacial and post-glacial history of the Baltic, *Geog. Rev.* **12**, 602–12, 1922.

Antevs, E., The last glaciation, *Amer. Geog. Soc.* Res. 17.

Bascom, W., *A hole in the bottom of the ocean.* Weidenfeld and Nicolson, London, 1961.

Broecker, W., Discussion of radio-carbon dating of Late Quaternary deposits, S. Louisiana, *Bull. Geol. Soc. Am.* **72**, 159–61, 1961.

Bullard, E. C., The flow of heat through the floor of the Atlantic Ocean. *Proc. Roy. Soc. A* **22**, 408, 1954.

Charlesworth, J. K., *The Quaternary era.* Arnold, London, 1957.

Collinson, D. W., and Runcorn, S. K., Palaeomagnetic observations in the United States. *Bull. Geol. Soc. Am.* **71**, 915–58, 1960.

Cotton, C. A., The rim of the Pacific, *Geog. Journ.* **124**, 223–31, 1958.

Cox, A., and Doell, R. R., Review of paleomagnetism, *Bull. Geol. Soc. Am.* **71**, 645–768, 1960.

Daly, R. A., *The changing world of the ice age.* New Haven, Conn., 1934.

Dietz, R. S., Continents and ocean basin evolution by spreading of the sea floor, *Nature* **190**, 854–7, 1961.

Donner, J. J., Late and post-glacial raised beaches in Scotland, *Suolmal. Tiedeak.* (Tom. Ann. Acad. Sci. Fenn.), Ser. A III Geol. Geog. **53**, 5–25, 1959.

Ewing, M., and Press, F., Geophysical contrasts between continents and ocean basins, *Geol. Soc. Am. Sp. Pap.* **62**, 1–6, 1955.

Fairbridge, R. W., Eustatic changes in sea-level. Reprinted from *Physics and Chemistry of the Earth*, Vol. 4, Pergamon Press, 99–185, 1961.

Gaskell, T. F., in A discussion on the floor of the Atlantic Ocean, Part II. The deeper structure of the Atlantic, *Proc. Roy. Soc. A* 222, 287–407, (356–61), 1954.

Gaskell, T. F., *Under the deep oceans*. Eyre and Spottiswoode, London, 1960.

Gaskell, T. F., Hill, M. N., and Swallow, J. C., Seismic measurements made by H.M.S. *Challenger* in the Atlantic, Pacific and Indian Oceans and in the Mediterranean Sea 1950–1953. *Phil. Trans. Roy. Soc. A* 251, 23–83, 1958.

Godwin, H., Studies of the post-glacial history of British vegetation, III and IV, *Phil. Trans. Roy. Soc. B* 230, 239, 1940.

Godwin, H., Suggate, R. P., and Willis, E. H., Radio-carbon dating of the eustatic rise in ocean level. *Nature* 181, 1518–1519, 1958.

Heezen, B. C., Tharp, M., and Ewing, M., The floors of the oceans—1, North Atlantic. *Geol. Soc. Am.* Sp. Pap. 65, 122, 1959

Hess, H. H., in A discussion on the floor of the Atlantic Ocean, Part II, The deeper structure of the Atlantic, *Proc. Roy. Soc. A* 222, 287–407 (341–8), 1954.

Hill, M. N., Recent geophysical exploration of the ocean floor, Chap. 5, Vol. 2. *Physics and Chemistry of The Earth*. Pergamon Press, 129–63, 1957.

Hills, G. F. S., *The formation of the continents by convection*. Arnold, London, 1947.

Jeffreys, H., *Earthquakes and mountains*, 2nd ed., Collins, London, 1950.

Kuenen, P. H., *Marine geology*. Wiley, New York, 1950.

Laughton, A. S., Laboratory measurements of seismic velocities in ocean sediments. *Proc. Roy. Soc. A.* 222, 336, 1954.

Lees, G. M., The evolution of a shrinking Earth. *Quart. Journ. Geol. Soc.* 109, 217–57, 1953.

Mason, R. G., Geophysical investigations of the sea floor. *Liverpool and Manchester Geol. Journ.* 2, 389–410, 1960.

McFarlan, E., Radio-carbon dating of Late Quarternary deposits, S. Louisiana. *Bull. Geol. Soc. Am.* 72, 129–58, 1961.

Moore, D. G., Acoustic-reflection studies of the continental shelf and slope off Southern California. *Bull. Geol. Soc. Am.* 71, 1121–36, 1960.

Rothé, J. P., La Zone séismique médiane Indo-Atlantique. *Proc. Roy. Soc. A* 222, 387–97, 1954.

Swinnerton, H. H., The post-glacial deposits of the Lincolnshire coast. *Quart. Journ. Geol. Soc.* 87, 360–75, 1931.

Umbgrove, J. H. F., *The symphony of the Earth*, 1947.

Umbgrove, J. H. F., On the origin of continents and ocean floors. *Journ. Geol.* 54, 169–78, 1946.

Un. Geog. Geoph. Inter., 1954, Assoc. d'Oceangr. Sci. Pub. 13, *Secular variations of sea-level*.

Valentin, H., Present vertical movements of the British Isles, *Geog. Journ.* 119, 299–305, 1953.

Vening Meinesz, F. A., Gravity and the hypothesis of convection currents in the Earth, *Proc. K. Akad. Wetensch.*, Amsterdam, 37, 1934.

Wegener, A., *The origin of continents and oceans*, 1922.

Wexler, H., Ice budgets for Antarctica and changes of sea-level. *Journ. Glaciol.* 3, 867–72, 1961.

Wooldridge, S. W., and Henderson, H. C. K., Some aspects of the physiography of the London Basin. *Trans. & Pap. Inst. Brit. Geog.* 21, 19–32, 1955.

Worzel, J. L., and Shurbet, G. L., Gravity anomalies at the continental margin. *Proc. Nat. Acad. Sci.* 41, 488–459, 1955.

CHAPTER 2

THE GEOMORPHOLOGY OF THE OCEAN FLOOR

INTRODUCTION

THE relief features which are found on the ocean floor rival the major topographic features on land, from the point of view of size and interest. However, these features have only been revealed in some detail since modern techniques of echo-sounding, underwater photography and sampling have been used extensively from about 1930. They are of great interest for their own sake and because they affect the circulation of ocean waters. As more and more observations become available, the character of the relief is found to be more and more complex and intricate; nevertheless, certain well-defined relief features, both positive and negative, can be distinguished.

The area of deep abyssal plain has been getting gradually smaller on charts of the ocean as more and more detail is becoming known. There are, however, large areas which appear to consist of smooth, deep-sea floor, which are very flat. Bordering these abyssal plains, particularly along the edge of the Pacific Ocean, are the deep-sea troughs, in which the greatest depths have been recorded. These are intimately related to the island arc festoons, so characteristic of the western border of the Pacific. All the oceans contain major submarine mountain chains in the form of submarine ridges. Their character suggests that these features do not all have a common origin, there being several types of ridges, probably formed by different processes. The major relief slope of the Earth, along the edge of the ocean, links the two fundamental levels of the continents and the deep oceans; this is the continental slope. The origin and character of this feature has again been interpreted differently in different areas. It leads up to the continental shelf, which forms a zone of shallow water, varying greatly in width and character, and probably should be considered as part of the continent structurally. It is of great importance from the point of view of many types of fishery. Other features of interest deserve special study, as they provide valuable evidence of the processes at work in the oceans; these include submarine canyons, sea mounts and similar features, and coral reefs and atolls.

One point in which submarine features differ from those on land is that they are not affected by subaerial weathering and erosion, thus they retain their original shape, and their formation can more easily be appreciated; on the other hand, in some circumstances they may become buried beneath a mantle of sediment.

1. *THE ABYSSAL PLAIN AND ABYSSAL HILLS*

Considerable areas of deep ocean floor consist of broad elevations and depressions, at depths between 3 and 6 km. According to Mason (1960), this type of surface amounts to 80 per cent of the oceans, but this seems excessive. In the Pacific off western United States, which has been studied in detail, it has been shown that extensive areas of smooth flat plain exist, for example in the Gulf of Alaska (Emery, 1960). These areas can be directly correlated with the rate of deposition of sediment; where a deep trench has intercepted the sediment the sea floor beyond is very much more irregular. Most of the sediment in the area off Alaska and northern California has been supplied from the land. It is where the supply of sediment is plentiful that the irregularities of the sea floor have been buried to produce the flat, even deep-sea bed. Further offshore the abyssal plain is largely blanketed by organic sediment or volcanic material.

The large areas of very flat gradient that have been revealed by echo-sounders have a slope between 1:500 and 1:5,000, decreasing away from the source of sediment. Heezen *et al.* (1959) define an abyssal plain as 'an area of deep-ocean floor in which the bottom is flat and the slope of the bottom is less than 1:1,000'. These features have been found in all oceans, but only since World War II have sufficiently accurate deep-water echo-sounders been available to delimit and study them. Abyssal plains have been found in the Bay of Bengal and the Weddell Sea as well as in the major oceans. Those in the Atlantic are fairly well known and include many small plains, of which the Sohm abyssal plain may be taken as an example. This occurs south of Newfoundland, and is 200 miles wide at a depth of 16,200 to 18,000 ft. (4,940 to 5,500 m.) and towards one of its margins submarine peaks protrude through it. Its eastern and western boundaries are formed by scarps 1,200 to 4,800 ft. (366 to 1,460 m.) high, but to the north it merges gradually with the continental rise. Its gradient decreases southwards from 1:3,000 to 1:5,000. Recent work in the Arctic Ocean (Dietz and Shumway, 1961) has revealed extensive abyssal plains on either side of the central Lomonosov Ridge. The largest is the Canada Basin, which has a very flat floor at 3,820 m. (12,520 ft.) and is 1,100 km. (660 miles) from north to south. The very flat floor found in all the Arctic abyssal plains is probably due to a thick layer of sediment. Another smaller flat plain is called the Central Arctic Basin, while the Eurasian Basin is the third; this last is equally smooth and almost as large as the Canada Basin.

Associated with the abyssal plains are abyssal hills, rising from a few

O.–D

fathoms to a few hundred fathoms above the floor. They are frequently found near the edge of the plain and are particularly common where trenches or ridges isolate the basins. They form two strips in the north Atlantic, parallel to the mid-Atlantic Ridge.

It is generally agreed (Menard, 1959; Laughton, 1959) that the smooth areas are the result of an even blanket of sediment over the area, which has been spread by turbidity currents. The evidence includes (1) the presence of coarse sand and shallow water fossils in the sediments, (2) the thickness of the sediments suggests rapid deposition, which is greater than the rate of sedimentation in the normal deep-sea environment, and (3) they only occur where turbidity currents can spread out from the land. They do not occur where deep-sea trenches can intercept the sediment; thus they are more common in the Atlantic than the Pacific. They indicate that a drainage pattern of channels and fans extends down to a depth of more than 5km. Abyssal plains are particularly well developed in the Atlantic, where they occupy 15 per cent of the ocean floor; there are two large ones in the western Atlantic, but more numerous, smaller ones in the east, where the basin type structure is better developed. In the north Pacific soundings suggest large areas of very little relief in broad basins; there are also basins of low relief in the south-west and south-east Pacific. A level-floored basin at a depth of 3,400 m. occupies the Arabian Sea.

2. DEEP-SEA TRENCHES AND ISLAND ARCS

The deep-sea trenches are narrow, curved deeps, most of which are situated near and just on the landward edge of the structural limit of the deep oceans. They are arranged in festoons around the western Pacific, while there are deep-sea trenches off central and south America, in the Pacific. There are also deep-sea trenches in the Atlantic, outside the Antilles and in the south Atlantic between Tierra del Fuego and the Islands of South Georgia, South Sandwich group, and the Falklands Islands; they are shown in fig. 2–1a. The greatest depth known is situated in latitude 11°20′N, 142 to 143°E, in the trench south of Guam in the Mariana Island group; this depth is nearly 1,000 ft. deeper than the previously recorded deepest sounding in the Philippine trench, and was sounded by the *Challenger* in 1950–2. A sounding of 5,900 fathoms (10,800 m., 35,400 ft.) was recorded in this very deep trench off Guam, but in 1960 the bathyscaphe *Trieste* descended to the bottom of this trench, and found it to be 6,300 fathoms (11,500 m., 37,800 ft.) deep; it is now known as the Challenger deep. The part of the trench deeper than 5,900 fathoms was half a mile wide and twenty miles long, which indicates the elongated nature of these deep troughs. They are arcuate in plan, and normally occur on the deep ocean side of the island festoons, forming the island arcs, to which they are parallel. They are situated near the continental side of the Andesite line, which forms the limit of the truly oceanic structure, with their convex side facing the deep ocean.

The gravity surveys of Vening Meinesz have shown that the deep trenches are associated with strong belts of isostatic anomaly; some of these negative anomalies lie symmetrically over the topographic deeps, others are asymmetrical, with the maximum negative anomaly on the continent side of the deep trough. The Yap deep (see fig. 2–1a) is an

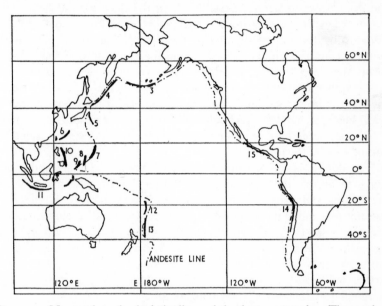

FIG. 2–1a. Map to show the Andesite line and the deep-sea trenches. The numbers refer to the following trenches:

1 Puerto Rico.	6 Riu Kiu.	11 Sunda.
2 South Sandwich.	7 Nero.	12 Tonga.
3 Aleutian.	8 Yap.	13 Kermadec.
4 Kurile.	9 Pelew.	14 Peru and Chile.
5 Japanese.	10 Philippine.	15 Middle American.

example of the former and the Nero deep, off Guam, of the latter. This anomaly indicates that there must be a deficiency of density, maintained by some force which prevents the establishment of isostatic equilibrium. From the position of these arcs near the edge of the true ocean, it seems likely that they are associated with the junction zone between the continents and the oceans, where the continental crust is thin, if it is present at all.

According to Vening Meinesz and Umbgrove, there are two types of island arcs; there are the single island arcs, with their associated deep trenches, which lie nearer to the margin of the true ocean, for example the Mariana Islands, and the more complex double island arcs, which also have their associated trenches, such as the deep south of Java in the East Indies, which are found in the continental section of the ocean margin area.

The theory put forward to explain them by Vening Meinesz and Umbgrove (1947) seems to account very plausibly for their main characteristics, but later geophysical evidence does not altogether support it. They suggested that a downwarp of the crust takes place at the edge of the deep ocean structure, possibly along the deep-seated shear zones associated with the deep-focus earthquakes. The downwarp could be initiated by the underthrusting of the oceanic basement beneath the continental crust. This could account for the great depth of water, which forms the deep trench, while the buckling down of the crust could account for the isostatic anomaly. On the continental side of the trench the crust is upwarped, but owing to its thinness it does not emerge. It does, however, tend to crack, and volcanic activity produces volcanoes which may extend above sea-level to form the island festoons, along the curved crest of the upwarp.

The double island arcs are thought by Vening Meinesz and Umbgrove to occur where compression causes buckling in areas where the continental crust is rather thicker. The outer arc is the non-volcanic one, while the inner one is essentially volcanic in character. The Aleutian Islands illustrate both types; at their western end this is a typical single arc, with the deep trench lying close to the island chain, but as the arc is followed eastwards it becomes double; the deep moves farther out from the inner volcanic arc, taking on the character of a marginal deep in front of a non-volcanic arc.

The idea that the island arcs and deep trenches are associated with deep-seated structural forces is widely supported. Benioff (1954) has suggested that the deep-sea troughs and island arcs are surface phenomena, related to deep-seated reversed faults, extending down to 650 km. in the mantle. These faults are thought to dip at 61° in the true oceanic area of the western Pacific, but in the marginal zone the upper part is thought to dip at 33° to a depth of 300 km. and then 61° to 700 km. The volcanoes are arranged on the curved uplifted block, parallel to the strike of the fault, and coincide with the highest elevation of the overhanging block. Stille (1955) has shown that some of the trenches are fairly recent; the New Pommeranian-New Hebrides deep in Melanesia is definitely post-Tertiary. He points out that there are four features associated only with the Pacific border, which are (1) deep trenches, (2) Meinesz negative anomaly zones, (3) active volcanoes and (4) deep-focus earthquakes, all of which could be accounted for by thrusting of the continents over the ocean floor.

More recent work has thrown doubt on the essence of the earlier interpretation of the deep-sea trenches. Seismic surveys have shown that there is little evidence for a thickening of the continental crust beneath the deep trench. Three trenches have been studied in detail: the Tonga trench in the west Pacific, the Middle America Trench off western central America and the Puerto Rico trench in the West Indies. The Tonga trench is the deepest, going down to 10,800 m. (35,400 ft.) ±200 m. A seismic cross section shows that the Moho is 20 km. below sea-level under the trench, rising oceanward to 12 km. in only 70 km. horizontally to the east. There is no evidence of thickening of the crust below the trench, in relation to the area to the west. It is interesting to note that there is very little sediment in the trough, indicating its recent age (see fig. 2–1b).

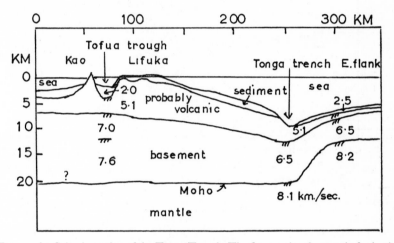

FIG. 2–1b. Seismic section of the Tonga Trench. The figures give the speed of seismic waves in km./sec. (After Raitt *et al.*)

The Middle America trench has been studied by Shor and Fisher (1961) and Fisher (1961). This trench is almost continuous for 1,260 miles at a depth greater than 4,400 m. (14,400 ft.) and is more than 5,500 m. (16,400 ft.) deep over a distance of 380 miles in the Guatemala deep. The Moho is 9 km. deep in the Pacific basin to the west, 10 km. under the outer ridge of the trench, 16 km. under the trench and 17 km. under the shelf. The total crustal thickening in this zone is from 5–7 km. to 10–17 km. The trench is older to the north, where it is U-shaped and partially filled with sediment, while to the south it is V-shaped. It has many features of the island arc sequence, including the negative anomaly, but there is no evidence of a crustal downbulge into the mantle. This deepens landwards of the base of the continental slope off

California, while off Guatemala the deepening of the mantle takes place seaward of the trench, as in the very deep Tonga trench.

The Puerto Rico trench in the West Indies has also been studied in detail. North of the trench the structure is typically oceanic, with no continental crustal material. The gravity anomaly of −226 mgls. over the trench is explained by the very thick sediments in it; these were thought to be 12 km. thick, but more recent estimates suggest only 4 to 8 km. thickness. A section through the deep, shown in fig. 2–1c, shows a basaltic layer beneath the trench and island of Puerto Rico, with a layer of metamorphic material beneath the island, which outcrops

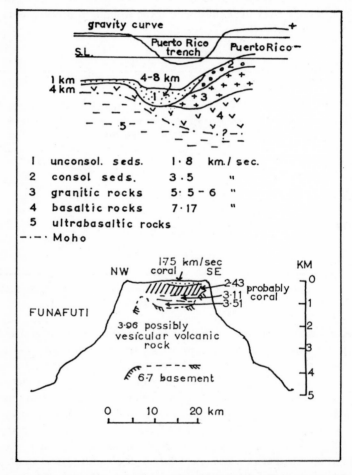

FIG. 2–1C. Seismic section of the Puerto Rico Trench (after Ewing), and of Funafuti coral atoll (after Gaskell, Hill, and Swallow). The thickness of sediment in the trench is indicated in the upper diagram, while the lower shows the speed of travel of seismic waves.

at the surface. Ewing and Heezen (1955) have suggested that the negative anomaly could be explained by a thin crust and a thick layer of sediments. This could be the result of crustal tension, an idea supported by Worzel and Shurbet (1955), but not generally accepted and probably not the best explanation of the data. The recent views, however, seem to be turning away from the idea of a downwarped tectogen to account for the negative anomaly, which can be adequately explained by the deep water and the lower level of the Moho under the trench, although it does imply some force to maintain this anomaly in these youthful features.

Dietz (1961) has drawn these ideas together in a recent theory of the possible effect of a series of convection cells, with currents rising beneath the central area of the oceans and sinking along their border, where there are zones of compression as a result, in which the deep trenches occur. This theory was mentioned in chapter 1. The low heat flow recorded over the trench and arc areas also fits in with the idea of a downward convection current at the oceanic border (Menard 1959).

3. *SUBMARINE RIDGES*

The same theory of Dietz (1961) can also help to account for the median ridges, which would be associated with the uprising currents in the centre of the ocean basins. It is a conspicuous feature of all the oceans that they have a ridge running almost centrally through the ocean as shown in fig. 2–2. The Mid-Atlantic ridge has already been mentioned; this is a very large relief feature, running north–south through the ocean and connecting by Kerguelen Island and St. Paul Island to the Indian Ocean ridge. A branch of this ridge diverges from St. Paul Island south-east to bisect the southern Indian and Pacific Oceans, and to swing north-east and north to Easter Island. From this point other ridges divide the Pacific fairly equally, one running northwest to Christmas Island, and further west, while another runs northeast towards the coast of Mexico. The Arctic Ocean is also divided by the Lomonosov Ridge, which was revealed by Russian surveys from stations drifting across the Arctic Ocean on the pack-ice. This ridge runs almost directly under the north pole from the Novo Sibirsk Islands to Ellesmere Island, north of Canada. The character of this ridge, as revealed by recent work (Dietz and Shumway, 1961) suggests that it is a faulted feature or a slightly overturned and folded geanticline. There is no evidence that it is volcanic. Its upper surface is truncated in part at 1,400 m. depth, suggesting that sea-level relative to the crest is now much higher than formerly. The earth movements associated with this ridge are continued in the Novo Sibirsk Islands and in Ellesmere, where they are thought to be Mesozoic in age. The submarine ridge, unlike its continuation on land, shows most of its original relief, having been protected from erosion, while the similar features on land have been deeply eroded, and reduced to a low level. The submarine ridge has a total relief of more than 3,000 m. (9,840 ft.).

There are other ridges of importance from the point of view of the circulation of the ocean, such as the Wyville Thomson ridge, which runs from Greenland via Iceland to Scotland, shutting off the Norwegian Sea from the deep Atlantic. Other ridges run up the Norwegian Sea, coming

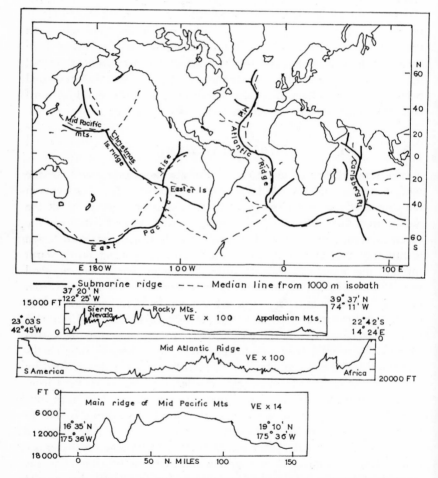

FIG. 2–2. The mid-oceanic ridges are shown in relation to the median line. Characteristic cross-section of the mid-Atlantic is compared with the Rocky Mountains. (After Menard.)

The lower section shows the main ridge of the Mid-Pacific Mountains. (After Dietz *et al.*)

above the surface in Jan Mayen. The ridges which divide the eastern Atlantic and western Indian Oceans into basin structure have already been mentioned.

Many of these ridges are major relief features, sometimes rising more than 10 km. above the adjacent sea floor (32,800 ft.), often more or less continuously for up to 60,000 km. (37,500 miles). A profile across the Mid-Atlantic ridge is similar to one drawn across the Rocky Mountains, as shown on fig. 2–2.

The ridges differ in character, and it is, therefore, unlikely that any one hypothesis will account for all the major ocean ridges. The different theoretical methods of ridge formation, as proposed by Hess (1954), may be mentioned and examples of them can be sought and examined. The first method supposes the ridge to be the result of large outpourings of basalt along linear fissures, which build up into piles of basalt lavas and pyroclastics; the peaks of some of the larger volcanoes may emerge to form oceanic islands of basic rock. The pile of material which results from prolonged eruption is lenticular in form, as its base depresses the oceanic crust on which it rests, but owing to its porosity it may be less dense than the original material from which it was derived, and thus it makes a conspicuous relief feature. Once formed, this pile of material would be liable to slow subsidence. This type of ridge may be associated with quiet tectonic conditions and possibly with transcurrent or tear faulting, which would help to form the rift or fracture along which the deep-seated material could move.

The second method by which submarine ridges may form, according to Hess, is associated with forces which produce tension in the crust, possibly due to rising convection currents. This process is associated with the breaking up of the substratum, which is probably peridotite, and its mixture with the basaltic crust under the ocean. There is some evidence for this possibility in the blocks of peridotite which have been found on St. Paul's Rock. At a time when the hypothetical convection current was rising actively, the height of the ridge would on the whole be higher and part of it might well emerge, while a reduction in vigour of the current could well lead to rapid subsidence. At all stages the density of the disturbed part of the crust would tend to be lower than the adjacent areas, enabling it to stand higher than its surroundings and thus forming a positive feature on the ocean floor.

The third possibility is associated with the area in which possible convection currents turn downwards into the deeper regions of the mantle. This process would tend to thicken and buckle the basaltic crust, which might well be associated with andesitic vulcanism and diorite nitrusion. It is, in fact, a process rather similar to that which was thought to initiate island arcs. These possibilities are illustrated in fig. 2–3.

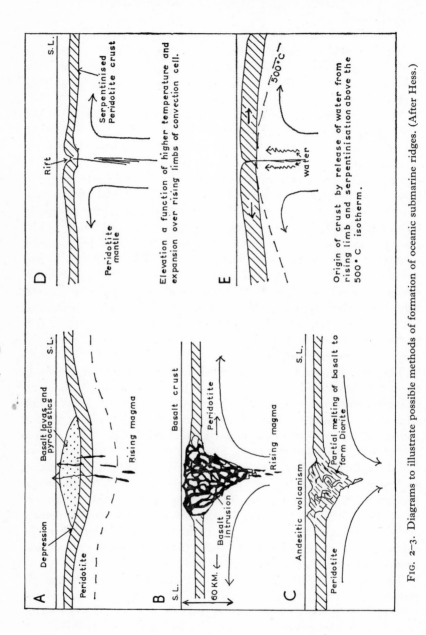

Fig. 2–3. Diagrams to illustrate possible methods of formation of oceanic submarine ridges. (After Hess.)

Hess suggests that an example of the first process may be found in some of the Pacific Ocean ridges, many of which are crowned with volcanoes erupting basic rocks. The second type he considers explains some of the features of the Mid-Atlantic ridge, while a possible example of the third process may be the Walvis ridge, which links the Mid-Atlantic ridge to the coast of Africa, where it is continued in an ancient fold of late pre-Cambrian date in South West Africa.

Further possibilities are suggested by Hess, which are all illustrated in fig. 2–3, D and E. They illustrate the possible formation of submarine ridges by rising convection currents; the former, D, occurs in association with expansion, resulting from the higher temperature. The latter, E, suggests that serpentinization is effective in forming the crust in the zone above the 500°C isotherm; this is caused by the release of water from the rising limb of the convection cell.

The median ridges in many parts of the oceans are broad, gently sloping rises, but in the north Pacific there are steep-sided, narrow submarine mountains. It is interesting to note that the former type is associated with a continuous narrow band of earthquakes and much volcanic activity, while the latter appears to be in regions of tectonic quiet. Heat flow observations under the broader ridges have shown zones of very high heat flow. The southern east Pacific rise is a good example of the broad type, being very wide, and it is associated with seismic activity, volcanoes and sea mounts, while the Mid-Atlantic ridge is much steeper and narrower; it has volcanic islands and guyots (flat-topped sea mounts). It is narrower and steeper in the north Atlantic at 30°N than it is at 10°S.

Menard has tentatively suggested (1958) that the different form of the ridges may indicate a difference of age and stage of development. The gentle rise is the early stage, and the steep type, exemplified by the Mid-Pacific Mountains, a later stage. If this is so, submarine ridges may not be permanent features of the ocean floor. They do not appear to differ fundamentally from the material of the surrounding ocean basin; it is possible that broad rises may be temporary features, which are first elevated and then subside to leave a narrow ridge, capped with guyots.

Points that are worth noting in connexion with the characteristics of submarine ridges include: (1) the fact that the position of the ridge is related to the margin of the ocean as defined by the 1,000 m. (3,280 ft.) depth line; (2) the forces responsible for determining the oceanic limits must operate over vast areas, i.e. from the median ridge to the margin of the Pacific basin, a distance of more than 5,000 km. (3,000 miles); (3) the process appears to act intermittently, and (4) it acts simultaneously on both sides of the basin. A force which would satisfy these conditions is that of convection currents. The high heat flow through the ridges would imply rising currents there, while sinking currents might be expected at the margins of the basins. This could be related to the formation of island arcs at the edge of the ocean and movement along the Pacific fracture zone.

There are certain corollaries to these arguments which are of interest. The hypothesis suggests intermittent movements, with the ridges extending at times above sea-level. In this state they would form convenient stepping-stones by which fauna and flora could be dispersed around the oceans and continents. Thus Easter Island could be connected across the Pacific with South America or Japan. The problem of the age of the ridges and rates of development is significant in this respect and here evidence is scanty. It is known, however, that the Mid-Pacific Mountains were above sea-level in parts in the late Cretaceous and have since subsided. The question of continental drift is also associated with the position of the ridges. The Mid-Atlantic ridge lies midway between Africa and America, and could, therefore, be related to their former closer proximity, but on the other hand there are also median ridges in all the other oceans, so that this argument is no longer valid. The Mid-Pacific Mountains, which have been shown to be earlier in origin than the late-Cretaceous, are centrally placed in the Pacific, but according to the proponents of continental drift the disruption of the continents did not take place till Cretaceous or later times. They could not, therefore, have been central originally if the continents moved after their formation.

There are certain other characteristics, shown particularly clearly by the Mid-Atlantic ridge, which give useful support to the convection current hypothesis. This ridge is a broad, fractured arc, occupying the central third of the ocean. It has been most studied between 17°N and 54°N, where it is 800 to 1,400 km. (500 to 875 miles) wide and 2·5 km. (8,200 ft.) to 4 km. (13,100 ft.) high (Mason, 1960). It rises in the form of a series of three steps, becoming more rugged towards the crest. At the crest there is a deep rift valley; this is 1 to 4 km. (3,280 to 13,100 ft.) deep and 25 to 50 km. (16 to 31 miles) wide. The floor is rough and contains some mountainous zones. This feature is a very striking aspect of the relief of the whole ridge. The rift valley is the centre of seismic activity and in the adjacent rift mountains and high fractured plateau bare slopes are common and flat-floored intermontane basins are lacking; this suggests that the ridge is of recent date. Most of the rocks obtained from the ridge are basic or ultrabasic rocks, although Tertiary limestone has been collected in one sample (Heezen *et al*, 1959).

The structure of the ridge has been worked out by seismic observations, which show that near the crest the sediment layer may be missing, and rocks, in which the seismic waves travel fairly slowly, and are therefore not very dense, may be exposed at the surface. This rock is 2·8 km. thick and rests on a denser material beneath, in which the waves travel faster than in the normal basaltic ocean crust. This denser material could originate in several ways. It could represent an abnormally low mantle velocity, or a mixture of mantle and crustal rocks due to intensive intrusion or volcanic activity, or it could be due to serpentine formation, as suggested by Hess (1954). This process involves the formation of serpentine from olivine and water, which takes place with an increase of volume of 25 per cent, which would account for the density intermediate between that of the crust and mantle. This process could explain the elevation of the ridge, but it fails to explain the high heat flow measured there, which is more than six times the average value.

Another point about the unusual character of the central part of the ridge is the high magnetic anomaly there, which suggests that it is underlaid by highly magnetic intrusive rocks. It has also a small negative isostatic anomaly. The significance of the serpentinization idea is that the process operates at relatively low temperatures mainly, that is below 500°C, but with the high heat flow, temperatures could be raised above this and the process could then reverse, leading to shrinking and hence subsidence of the ridge, a process aided by the liberation of water in diserpentinization.

In many ways the Mid-Atlantic ridge resembles the African Rift Valley, which appears to be a feature resulting from tension in the crust. If this analogy is sound it suggests that tension is also a factor to be considered in the central parts of the oceans. This could be a general tension, such as would result in the drifting apart of America and Africa to widen the Atlantic, but this can clearly not apply simultaneously to all the oceans, unless they are growing at the expense of the continents, for which there is no evidence, and, in fact, the opposite is much more likely. The idea of local tension as a result of rising convection currents fits in with the position of the zones of excess heat flow and with other factors, as already mentioned. On the other hand, the results could be due to local uplift, as a result of crustal differentiation. Until more is known it will not be possible to decide which, if either, of these ideas is correct.

4. THE CONTINENTAL SLOPE AND CONTINENTAL RISE

All around the deep ocean basins, separating them from the continents, is the continental rise and the continuous continental slope, the latter is the largest relief feature of the Earth. Average values of the slope are given by Shepard (1959) as 4° 07′ from the edge of the continental shelf to the 6,000 ft. depth contour; the slope is not uniform, but is usually diversified with valleys or basins. The gradient increases to 5° 40′ off faulted coasts, but is reduced to 1° 20′ off large rivers. One of the most spectacular slopes is that found off west Florida, where an escarpment descends very abruptly from 3,600 ft. to more than 9,600 ft.; it is more than 500 miles in length and the level drops more than one mile in height in less than two miles horizontally. This very steep slope, which cuts off a gentle slope very abruptly, is due to a fault. Another great fault scarp, which forms the continental slope, is that which descends to the Bartlett Trough off Santiago; this slope has a gradient of 45° and a vertical difference of 20,000 ft. On the whole the slopes of the continental border seem to be rather steeper in the Pacific at 5° 20′, than in the Atlantic, where they average 3° 05′ and the Indian Ocean, where they average 2° 55′.

The continental rise links the deep ocean floor to the continental slope. It has a gradient between 1:100 and 1:800 and is up to a few hundred miles in width. This rise is very well developed, for example, off North Africa near Dakar, where it is over 400 miles wide, but it disappears off the Bay of Biscay to reappear again off England, as a narrow feature 70 miles wide, sloping at 1:250 to 1:800.

Different types of slopes can be recognized in different areas. The continental slope off the north-eastern United States is fairly steep, but its major characteristic is the very large number of submarine canyons which dissect it. These descend to at least 6,000 ft. The rocks exposed in them show that the continental margin is built of sedimentary rocks varying in age from the Miocene to the Cretaceous. Farther south the slope is of interest, as there the wide Blake Plateau is found part way down the slope. From the continental shelf the slope drops off steeply from 300 ft. to 2,400 ft. to the Blake Plateau, which slopes gently down to 3,600 ft. over a horizontal distance of about 300 km. (188 miles) in latitude 28° to 30°N. At the outer edge of the plateau there is another abrupt break of slope, with a gradient about 15° falling to a depth of 15,000 ft. The surface of the plateau is of resistant material, probably rock of Cretaceous to Miocene age. ✓

The most likely explanation of this feature seems to be related to the position of the Gulf Stream, which flows very rapidly along the inner edge of the plateau. Shepard suggests that the stream has prevented the building up of more recent sediments over the older deposits; this deposition has taken place farther north, where the Gulf Stream leaves the continental slope. This explanation seems more probable than the suggestion that the plateau has actually been eroded by the Gulf Stream, as its surface is too smooth for this explanation to be likely.

A different slope type is found off Louisiana and Texas, where the slope becomes gentle, but west of the Mississippi river the slope becomes much more irregular, with elongated hills and basins of irregular, but generally elongated, form. The basins are about 1,500 ft. deep and 30 miles long. It seems that these basins may be blocked-up remnants of former valleys, as they are elongated in the direction of the slope; landslides have been suggested as a possible process, but the slopes are too gentle for this to be likely. The lower parts of these slopes are in general smoother, but the hills and basins descend some way down them.

Off California the offshore areas and continental slope have been intensively studied by the Scripps Institute of Oceanography. Here the slope lies from 50 to 160 miles from the coast (Emery, 1960). It trends N25°W and is broken by five gaps which are probably tectonic in origin, as they are unrelated to submarine canyons. The slope itself is about 10 miles wide, dropping to a depth of 12,000 ft. In general its profile is straight, but minor irregularities do occur, while at its base is a shallow depression, which has the appearance of a filled-in deep sea trough. Northwards, off San Francisco, this depression is replaced by an apron, indicating a later stage of development, while to the south, off Mexico, an earlier stage is found, where the depression is deeper. This indicates a gradual transition northwards up the coast. This difference is probably related to the rate at which sediments are supplied to the trough; off Mexico the dry climate prevents perennial streams, while off northern California the streams are perennial and the hinterland is high and erosion more rapid. Off southern California the rate of trough formation at the base of the slope is about equal to the rate of sedimentation in this area.

This particular slope is not a depositional one, as rock is found near the top of the slope and the topography inshore is very complex. It is not easy, however, to give definite views of its origin. It seems most likely that faulting has played a part in its formation, but there is no proof of this.

Not many continental slopes are known in detail, but several observations off the west coast of Britain have given some useful data concerning the character and method of formation of the slope in this environment. Here the continental shelf is very wide and the slope drops down steeply beyond it from a depth of 200 m. (650 ft.) to 4,000 m. (13,120 ft.).

Seismic data give evidence of the structure in this zone; this is particularly valuable in giving an insight into the structural changes which take place at the continental slope. This feature must be in some way connected with the change-over from the continental structure, with its thick layer of less dense, acidic-type crustal rocks, to the deep-ocean structure, with its thinner layer of basic rocks, overlying the ultra-basic mantle. The results obtained from these surveys showed that in

the deep ocean beyond the slope the sediment ranged from 0 to at least
2·8 km. in thickness and probably more in places. Beneath this, at the
foot of the continental slope, was a layer, presumably of continental
type, of 8.1 km. thickness, below which the Moho was found at a depth
of 13·2 km. below sea-level. This is transitional between the structure
on the inland side of the slope and that beyond it, where the layer
beneath the sediment is oceanic crustal rock with a thickness of 4·2 to
5 km., the Moho being at only 11·4 km. below sea-level. Near the edge
of the shelf several layers are indicated, which are probably sediments in
various stages of consolidation. The basement rock beneath these
sediments slopes gently down from a depth of about 2½ km. south of
Plymouth to about 4½ km. at 10°W, at the top of the continental slope,
while at its foot the basement is about 5 km. below the surface. This
structure is shown in fig. 2–4, and is very similar to that off the northern
part of eastern United States, where the basement rocks are also buried
under a great thickness of later sedimentary rocks; in both areas these
are mainly Mesozoic and later sediments.

From these data it is possible to suggest various theories of the
possible origin of the continental slope. As with so many other features,
it is unlikely that any one explanation will account for all the continental
slopes of the world, which have been shown to vary considerably in
type. It is important to bear in mind that this major relief feature often
lies at or near the junction of the two fundamental structural types, with
their very different characteristic levels. This fact alone would account
for the presence of a major slope, so that some of the suggested explanations seem to be unnecessarily complex. The commonest origin for the
shelf and slope, as formerly suggested, is that they result from the
building out of sediment from the land, the slope being the foreset beds
of a vast deltaic-type of sedimentation. In many instances it can be
shown quite clearly that this explanation cannot hold, where old rocks
outcrop at the top of the slope; nevertheless in some areas it has some
truth in it.

In this connexion it is relevant to consider the character of benches
associated with the continental shelf and slope (Heezen *et al.*, 1959).
These may be of several origins: (*a*) ancient coastal features, (*b*) structural or rock benches, (*c*) block faulting, and (*d*) landslide or slumping
scars. Those features found at depths down to 70 to 100 fathoms, at
constant levels, can best be explained as beaches cut during phases of
low glacial eustatic sea-level. These were probably formed between
12,000 and 5,000 years ago. Those benches which are found lower down
the slope at depths of 1,500 fathoms are more probably rock benches of
structural origin, although some may be formed by step faulting. The
structural benches are found on the slope off Cape Hatteras, where

Cretaceous and Tertiary strata dip gently seawards, parallel to the shelf surface, but are abruptly truncated by the steep slope, on which the harder rocks outcrop as steps. This slope is so steep that no recent sediments can accumulate on it. This may also be a factor helping to account

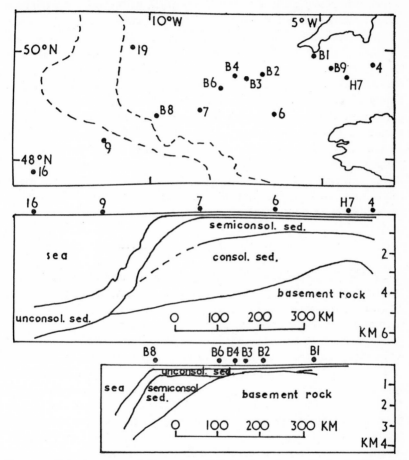

FIG. 2–4. Seismic surveys of the continental shelf off south-west England. (After Hill and Laughton.)

for the Blake Plateau. A similar feature has been recognized on the slope off the west coast of Europe, where a bench at 1,600 fathoms on the slope may represent the outcrop of the metamorphic basement beneath Palaeozoic and Mesozoic sediments, which form the upper part of the slope.

This implies that in these areas the slope is a structural or erosional feature, and is only thinly covered by recent sediments if at all, as these are removed by turbidity currents, ocean currents or slumping. There

O.–E

is a fundamental structural break at the continental margin, which has already been mentioned, and faulting may have played an important part in the early development of this marginal zone. Its present character, however, can be explained by alternating periods of sedimentation and marine planation on the continental shelf, with erosion by the processes already mentioned taking place on the continental slope. General and prolonged subsidence has also taken place in these marginal areas.

Shepard has suggested that faulting may be an important factor in the formation of some slopes. This may be in the form of a series of step faults, or one major low-angle fault, although the latter is less likely. Examples of this type of fault slope may be cited as the 6° slope off north-west Peru, and the very steep slope leading straight down to 12,000 ft. off the fault coast of the south-west South Island, New Zealand, where the slope drops to more than 12,000 ft. only 15 miles offshore. Seismic activity associated with some of these slopes supports this hypothesis, as do rock outcrops. The trenches at the foot of many slopes are also evidence in favour of faulting, according to Shepard (1960), although they can also be explained in other ways.

5. *THE CONTINENTAL SHELF*

Closely associated with the continental slope and linking it to the land is the continental shelf. This zone of shallow water varies very much in dimensions from place to place. It is also of considerable importance from many points of view; for economic reasons the shelf is important, the major fisheries are associated with it, and considerable oil supplies may be obtained from it. For this reason the United States in 1946 extended their mineral rights to cover the continental shelves adjacent to their territory, by a presidential decree. The shelf was defined for this purpose as an area extending out to the 600 ft. depth line.

On the other hand, the shelf is defined scientifically as the flattish area extending out to the top of the continental slope, where there is a sudden increase of gradient. The depth at which this change of slope takes place is very variable, and so is the width. The average value of 42 miles given by Shepard (1960) for the width and 0° 07′ or 10 ft./mile for the gradient of the shelf, does not really give much information concerning its character. The form and material of the shelf is also very variable. It is, however, possible to relate different shelf types to different coastal types.

(a) Shelf types

i. GLACIATED SHELVES. One of the most characteristic types of shelf is that found off coasts which have been glaciated. These shelves tend to be very irregular, the deep glacial valleys and fjords of the land extend some distance across the shelf, often becoming shallower towards the edge of the shelf. At their deepest the shelves often exceed 100 fathoms, and contain many basins in which mud tends to settle. There are also many hills on the shelf, often rising as banks nearly to sea-level, along the outer part of the shelf; banks of this type include the Georges Banks off New England, the Grand Banks off Newfoundland and others, which are all very important for the fishing industry, as their elevation raises them into the region of more active currents, by which nutrients reach the area. Such features clearly owe their origin to the selective scouring action of glaciers, working at a time when sea-level was considerably lower than at present by up to 300 or more feet.

The enclosed basins and troughs are analogous to the lake basins in glaciated valleys on land. The ice could continue to erode below sea-level, as it does not float until the depth exceeds 8/9 of its thickness, which in many areas was very considerable, its activities were not limited to the times of lowest glacial sea-level. Glacial deposition also had its effect on the shelf area, as many of the banks may be of morainic or other glacial deposits, somewhat modified by the strong currents which frequently occur on the shelves. Another characteristic of these glaciated shelves is that there is no orderly grading of the material in diminishing size offshore; in fact, the coarser sediment is often found at the edge of the shelf.

The glaciated shelves cover considerable areas offshore. They are in general very wide, averaging 100 miles, widening appreciably as the glaciated areas are approached. The average depth at the edge of the shelf is 112 fathoms (672 ft.). The widest known shelf is in the Arctic in the Barents Sea between North Norway and Novaya Zemlya; it stretches 750 miles offshore, at a depth between 100 to 200 fathoms (600 to 1,200 ft.) as far as Spitzbergen, and has troughs and banks.

ii. LARGE RIVER SHELVES. Other shelf types include those found off large rivers; these are also very wide. They are more commonly found off rivers which do not have large deltas, as in this case there is usually a uniform slope downwards from the edge of the delta, which may be partly the result of subsidence. Wide shelves off rivers are found in the Yellow Sea, off northern Siberia, and the Alaskan side of the Bering Sea, and in the Gulf of Siam. These shelves tend to be fairly shallow, extending down to about 330 ft. The inner edge of the shelf may often be fairly smooth, while beyond there may be hills on the shelf.

iii. OTHER SHELF TYPES. Some shelves have a pattern of dendritic valleys, which are shallow in contrast to the deeper troughs of the glaciated shelves. The best example of this type is the Sunda Shelf, which lies between Borneo, Java and Sumatra, with the Malay Peninsula forming the other boundary. Kuenen (1950) has described this shelf; the branching pattern of the Sunda River, flowing north between Borneo and Sumatra, has been reconstructed, while another river is indicated, flowing eastwards between Borneo and Java. These are inferred as the channels formerly used by rivers. They extend to a depth of about 328 ft. (100 m.), while the surrounding shelf into which they are cut is about 50 to 80 m. (164 to 262 ft.). It is thought that this pattern can be explained by the submergence of the river valleys by a rise of sea-level of about 90 m. (295 ft.). These channels do not contain basins, but grade smoothly offshore; this is good evidence for their being river valleys, cut during the period of glacially lowered sea-level, which is of the correct order. The distribution of fresh-water fish in the western rivers of Borneo are very similar to those found in Sumatra, which supports this theory.

Other characteristic shelf types include those formed of coral reefs. The major characteristic of this shelf type is the very shallow water at the edge of the shelf, as reef-forming corals cannot grow in deep water, while the offshore slope may be very steep; the depth at the edge of this type of shelf is about 20 m. (66 ft.). Off coasts of young mountain ranges the shelf is usually very narrow, averaging 10 miles in width. An example of this shelf type is found round much of the Pacific coastline. Such shelves also tend to be fairly deep, their edge being at about 480 ft. (80 fathoms).

(b) The origin of the shelf

The shelf is the complementary part of the steep continental slope, which has already been discussed, and the problem of its origin can be seen in the light of the character of the slope. Four possibilities can be suggested for their formation. Firstly they could be constructional features, built up by deposition from the land. Secondly, they could result from the planing off by marine erosion of offshore islands, the intervening basins becoming filled with finer sediment; a third possibility is that they are submerged deltas, as, for example, the Mississippi delta. A final idea is that they may be submerged and downwarped wave-cut terraces.

From what has been said of the slope off western Britain it seems that the geophysical evidence there favours the first possibility, while an example of the second type may well be found off California. The fourth method of formation has been particularly advocated by Bourcart, in his theory of continental flexure (Bourcart, 1950). This hypothesis has interesting implications on the development of certain features in river valleys. Bourcart has suggested that the continents may flex about the position of the present sea-level, the inland area tending to rise, while the offshore zone tends to sink. There is certainly evidence for the sinking of the offshore areas, as seen in the sediments of shallow water, now deeply buried by later deposits off the east coast of the United States. If this movement were to take place intermittently, it would help to account for the alternating periods of regression and transgression. At times when the shelf sinks and the land is elevated inshore a regression results; inland slopes are steepened, coarser sediments are brought down and at this stage coarse gravel and sands are laid down, perhaps as basal conglomerates. These are associated with the period of regression, when the sea floor sinks and the sea withdraws. At this period rejuvenation will be active inland, if this area is rising at the same time.

During periods of quiet sedimentation, which follow the flexing, the land is worn down, finer sediments are brought down to the sea, which tends to rise at this stage, resulting in a transgression. It depends on the position of the line of flexure in relation to the coast whether the change at the coast itself is one of emergence or submergence. If the line of flexure is offshore, this will cause a withdrawal of the sea as the land tilts, but if it is inland the tilt will cause drowning of the coast, at the same time as rejuvenation takes place inland.

As evidence in favour of his theory he discusses the character of the coast of Morocco; he suggests that there is evidence for the down-warping of a succession of three continental shelves, whose margins are now found at 180 m., 500 m. and 1,000 m. (590, 1,640 and 3,280 ft.); in each shelf as it is traced offshore the slope becomes steeper. This type of warping is probably only applicable to limited areas, and even in this particular part of Morocco the evidence has been interpreted differently by other workers. It is, however, an interesting theory, which may well have played a part in the making of continental shelves in some areas, where there is evidence of downwarping offshore and elevation inland. The latter can be in the form of elevated erosion surfaces, such as the Schooley Peneplain in the Appalachian region.

As examples of shelves and associated areas, which show very different characteristics, and which are known in some detail, two areas will be described. The shelf and continental borderland off southern California has been studied in great detail, and this area can be contrasted with the wide shelf and adjacent basins round the British Islands.

(c) The southern Californian borderland

The relief off the southern Californian coast is complex, and although the continental shelf itself is narrow, the zone between the major escarpment of the continental slope and the shore, known as the continental borderland, will be considered (see fig. 2–5). The shelf itself ranges from less than 1 mile wide to 15 miles in width, the average being only 4 miles (Emery, 1960). There are other shelves around the offshore islands, such as San Clemente Island, and these become wider round the western islands. This may be due to the greater exposure of the outer islands, which are also composed of less resistant rock, although in general elsewhere there is no close correlation between shelf width and degree of exposure. Other flat-topped banks in this area are similar to

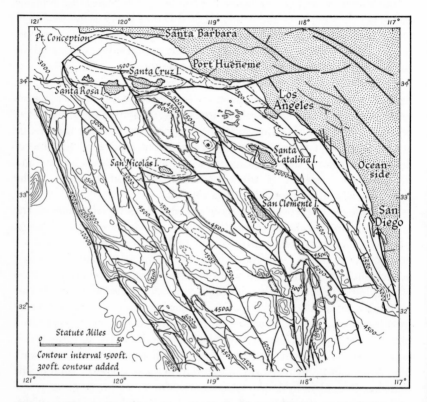

FIG. 2–5. Map to show the structure and character of the Californian Borderland. Primary faults are shown by wide lines and secondary faults, some of which may prove to be limbs of folds, by narrow lines. Based largely on sea-floor relief. (After Emery.)

the shelves around the islands and mainland; the whole area of banks, islands and basins of the borderland extends over a zone about 150 miles wide to the edge of the continental slope. The flat tops of some of the banks are up to 8 miles wide and on these rock outcrops are very numerous, rock also outcrops on the island and mainland shelves; where it does outcrop the rocky bottom is irregular.

Erosional terraces are found on some of the shelves, where the deposits, which are usually thin, may include rounded gravel. Many of these terraces are probably related to eustatic changes in sea-level, having been formed during the glacial lowering of sea-level. The shallowest one occurs at a depth of 50 to 60 ft. Its Pleistocene age is indicated by the truncation of rocks of Pliocene age. Many of the terraces are wider and flatter than those which are now emerged above sea-level, being up to 5 miles wide and having a slope of 1°, as opposed to the maximum width of ½ mile and 3° slope of the emerged terraces. These terraces are probably younger than the main diastrophic movements on this coast, which are responsible for some of the deeper features and terraces. Some evidence of warping is given by the increasing depth offshore of the terraces, between the shore and the offshore islands and banks. The difference is greater as the terraces become deeper, which shows that the deeper terraces have been downwarped to a greater degree in the offshore zone, than the shallower ones farther inland.

Between the shelves and banks there are basins and troughs. The depths of the basins below their sills lie between 496 and 290 ft. The depth of the sills lie mostly within a height range of 120 ft., for some unknown reason. Those basins nearer the shore have flatter floors, often filling the whole area below the sill. Farther offshore the floors are only about half covered below the sill. This difference is due to the greater rate of sedimentation in the basins nearest to the shore. The basins mostly trend north-west to south-east, being angular in shape in many instances; in this they resemble the land basins on the adjacent shore. The nearshore basins are probably filled largely by the action of turbidity currents, but this method is not so effective in the offshore basins, where sedimentation is by organic material and by the deposition of fine detritus brought in suspension from the shore.

The continental borderland of this area is composed mainly of sedimentary rocks of Tertiary age, although volcanic and older metamorphic rocks also outcrop. Over these solid rocks, whose structure is complex, rests an uneven covering of sediment of recent date, which is not yet consolidated. A new acoustic technique of surveying the shelf sediments (Moore, 1960) shows not only the thickness of the sediment, but also the structure of the underlying rocks. The modern shelf deposits are often lense shaped, thinnest near the outer edge of the shelf. At times coarse deposits of Pleistocene age are found on the edge of the shelf and at the shore, while the intervening area is covered by a thin layer of more recent finer sediments.

The structure of this area is very strongly influenced by faulting which shows distinctly in the relief pattern. In the submarine environment faults can be most easily recognized by the topography, which is not modified by subsequent erosion as it is on land, but where it is much more difficult to obtain detailed geological data. A fault scarp remains a conspicuous feature of the submarine relief. Seven major faults, all trending north-west to south-east, occur between the shore and the continental slope, while one trending east-west occurs near Los Angeles. These primary faults are connected by shorter faults, and in this way the basin and bank structure of this area has been formed; movement has been both vertical and horizontal along these faults (see fig. 2–5).

Geophysical work shows an increase in the depth of the Moho from 13 km. below sea-level on the abyssal plain to 18 km. at the top of the continental slope and 32 km. on the coastline at San Diego, near the Californian-Mexico boundary. This correlates with the positive gravity anomaly which increases from o milligals along the coast to 80 to 100 milligals on the upper edge of the slope (Bouguer anomaly). The faulting which gave rise to this complex structure took place around the Miocene period. Since the blocking out of the basins and banks in the Miocene, the outer part of the continental borderland has been downwarped, a process which has been going on into the post-Pleistocene period. The displaced material at depth may have helped to build up the uplifted inland area, but its bulk is greater than can be accounted for in this way. This gives some support to the idea of continental flexure.

(d) The continental shelf and adjacent shallow basins around Britain

Very different is the character of the shallow sea floor round Britain; the shelf extends out for a distance of about 300 miles off Lands' End and the adjacent basins cover the whole of the North Sea and English Channel. The outer limit of the shelf is marked by the 100 fathom (600 ft.) line.

i. CONTINENTAL SHELF. The structure of the shelf has already been mentioned in connexion with the discussion of the continental slope in this area. It has been shown that the shelf off Land's End consists of a deep basement rock, which has been built up to its present shallow depth by deposition throughout long ages by sediments which become more and more consolidated with depth. The relief of the area covering the Western Approaches to the English Channel and Irish Sea has been discussed by Robinson (1952), who shows that to the west of Land's End a series of north-east to south-west running troughs dissect the shelf and descend to 15 to 20 fathoms (90 to 120 ft.) below its surface. It is suggested that these banks and intervening troughs may have a similar origin as the rias of south-west Ireland, being due to folding in the Armorican orogeny. Subsequent deposits, if there were any, have been removed, possibly by selective marine erosion or subaerial erosion during low glacial sea-levels. South-east of these banks and troughs, off the entrance to the English Channel, the shelf is smoother and slopes very gently seawards. It is in this region that the seismic surveys suggest a great thickness of sedimentary rocks, overlying the basement rocks. This is confirmed by the work done in the English Channel (Hill and King, 1953, and King, 1954), which shows that there is over 3,000 ft. of New Red Sandstone over a considerable width of the western Channel, but its base rises to above sea-level on the shores of the Channel.

The shelf off western Ireland and Scotland shows evidence, in the form of deep clefts and troughs, of the characteristic features of glaciated shelves. Some of these clefts, as in the Inner Sound of Raasay may be tectonic features, modified by glacial erosion (Robinson, 1949).

The North Sea is very shallow, very little of it being more than 300 ft. (50 fathoms) deep, except for a few deep holes. Only the northern part of the sea can be considered as continental shelf; the shallow southern area is better described as an adjacent basin. The deeper northern part, where the depth is rather greater, may be taken as extending northwards from the Forties, in the latitude of south Scotland. The depths here vary between about 40 and 50 fathoms, except for the deeper Norwegian Trench, which follows the southern coast of Norway and penetrates about 550 miles into the shelf. It is deepest at its head, where the water is 2,538 ft. (423 fathoms) deep, while near its mouth, in the neighbourhood of Bergen, it is only 600 ft. (100 fathoms) deep. Holtedahl has suggested that this trench is of tectonic origin, and earthquakes still take place along it. It may have originated by the tilting of Scandinavia north-east and east in the early Tertiary. More detailed surveys of the trench show it to be double, and it has no doubt been altered to some extent by the ice sheets which passed south across it.

ii. ADJACENT SHALLOW SEA AREAS. The southern North Sea is very shallow, much of it being under 20 fathoms (120 ft.) deep. It also shows clearly the influence of the glacial period, during the advances of which it must have been dry land, overrun by ice. Rings of stony ground, which continue the lines of the end moraines of Jutland, seem to be the seaward continuation of these features, now submerged beneath the sea. Some of the trenches, cut across the North Sea floor, may represent parts of the courses of the Thames and Rhine, which at times of low sea-level joined to flow north to the open sea. The latest date at which this took place was during the low sea-level of the Mesolithic period about 8000 B.C.

The east-west trend of the Silver Pit, south of the Dogger Bank, has been interpreted as an old urstromtal, cut by melt-water flowing along the edge of the retreating North Sea ice sheet. The Devil's Hole, which is 780 ft. deep (130 fathoms) in an area only 240 ft. (40 fathoms) deep, is more difficult to explain; it may have been formed by glacial melt-water flowing beneath the ice sheet under pressure; it is not being modified now to any extent.

The Dogger Bank has recently been interpreted as the remains of a glacial moraine by Stride (1959). This is based on seismic survey of the area, which failed to reveal solid rock in this vicinity. This shoal area, which is more than 60 ft. above its surroundings, is 60 miles wide at 120 ft. depth, and is less than 60 ft. (10 fathoms) deep at its crest. The moraine was probably deposited by the last glaciation ice sheet and the ridge has not been much modified since then, as early post-glacial peats are still found on its top and flanks. The offshore banks, which are so characteristic of the southern North Sea, are shaped mainly by tidal currents, and will be considered in chapter 5, with other tidal features.

The southern North Sea is structurally a geosynclinal area, which has been subsiding slowly for a very long period, as indicated by the character of the Mesozoic and later sedimentary strata of Holland. The tide-gauge data show that this area is still sinking, as sea-level is rising more rapidly there than on the more stable parts of the coastline of Europe. It is, therefore, a basin of considerable antiquity, associated with the subsiding area of the Rhine deltaic region.

From the geological evidence (King, 1954) and the geophysical data, it seems that the English Channel is also a very old feature. It has been subsiding geosynclinally for a long period and accumulating sediments, while the adjacent areas of south-west England and Brittany have remained relatively high. Subsidence has been particularly active in the region of the Isle of Wight, as shown in fig. 2–6, where the sub-New Red Sandstone floor is estimated to be at 12,000 ft. below the surface.

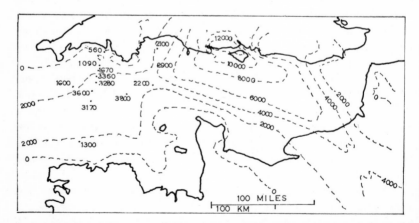

FIG. 2–6. Contour map of the sub-Mesozoic—New Red Sandstone floor in the English Channel area. The depths are in feet, derived from seismic survey. (After King.)

While the Channel has been sinking at intervals, to accumulate sediment, the adjacent land areas have on the whole been rising, although they may not always have been much above sea-level. Tertiary deposits are much thicker in the Isle of Wight basin than elsewhere on the Channel floor, in the former area, they attain 2,000 ft. in thickness. Some folding took place during the Miocene earth movements, and chalk now outcrops over much of the floor of the central part of the Channel.

One of the most intriguing characteristics of the floor of the Channel is its extremely flat nature and the absence of any thickness of modern sediments over large areas. It varies only within one or two fathoms across its whole width, and is only interrupted by one deep trough, the Hurd Deep, which is 94 fathoms (564 ft.) deep, situated in a very gently sloping floor which falls from about 20 fathoms (120 ft.), at the east end to about 50 fathoms (300 ft.) between Land's End and Brest, where the true shelf may be considered to start. All the flat area of the Channel would have been exposed during the low sea-level of glacial times, and it is possible that its flatness is partly due to erosion by the strong, laterally swinging melt-water streams which overflowed through the then dry Straits of Dover and along the Channel. It would also have come under the action of the waves of the transgressing sea as it rose during the inter-glacial periods; the flat area may represent, therefore, a plane of marine erosion, trimming a fluvio-glacial valley. Such a plane can only be cut effectively over a wide area during a period of rising sea-level.

The origin of the Hurd Deep is more difficult to suggest, as it cannot have been cut by ice action and it does not appear to be structural in origin. Tidal currents have been suggested by Shepard (1960), but it is difficult to see how they could have cut a deep trench in this position. The trench is 100 miles long, but only 4 miles wide, and is asymmetrical, having a steeper northern slope.

The Irish Sea, according to the suggestion of Linton (1951), may have originated as the result of subsidence of the key-stone of an arch elevated during the Tertiary, of which England, Scotland and Wales form the eastern slope. This suggestion follows Cloos's idea of the structural history of dome-shaped uplifts. There is, however, much evidence to suggest that ancient basins of sedimentation, as in the English Channel and southern North Sea, also existed in the Irish Sea area from at least Mesozoic times onwards.

6. OTHER SUBMARINE FEATURES

Various other submarine features, which have given rise to much speculation, have only so far been mentioned in passing, but they are worthy of more detailed analysis. Perhaps the best known of these, and those which have aroused most controversy, are the submarine canyons. Lately, however, the great number of submarine hills of different types have become objects of interest, which can give useful information about submarine processes. These hills include those now beneath the ocean surface, in the form of sea mounts and guyots, and those still exposed as coral atolls.

(a) Submarine canyons

i. DISTRIBUTION. As more and more of the coasts of the world are surveyed in detail, the distribution of submarine canyons becomes known to be wider and wider. These deep valleys, which cut across the continental shelf and incise the slope, often extending far out into the abyssal plain, are found off all different types of continental shelf. They occur in the Arctic (Carsola, 1954), off straight coasts, in both stable and unstable areas, areas of uplift and subsidence, off deltas, associated with estuaries, in enclosed seas such as the Mediterranean, where they extend far below the sill depth. Many canyons are associated with the mouths of large rivers; these include the Congo, the Indus, the Ganges, the Columbia, the Hudson, the Mississippi, the Yukon, the Susquehanna, the old mouth of the Tagus, the Adour and others. Some canyons are not, however, connected with the mouth of a large river. Where canyons appear to be lacking, this may well be due to inadequate soundings. Recent work has shown that in the north Atlantic canyons can be traced far out on to the abyssal plains.

ii. TYPES OF CANYONS. There seem to be three broad types of canyons; the first are fairly small gorges, which originate near the edge of the continental shelf and run down the slope to a great depth. The second type is rather similar in form, but these canyons extend right across the shelf and often start near the mouth of a large river. The third type has a branching, dendritic pattern which is deeply incised into the edge of the shelf and slope. Examples of these may be described to give the data on which an interpretation of their origin may be based.

iii. EXAMPLES OF SUBMARINE CANYONS. The Oceanographer Canyon may be taken as an example of the first type. It cuts into the New England shelf, heading 13 miles inside the edge of the shelf, at a point 100 miles from the land; it is the largest of a series along this shelf, many of which only head 5 to 10 miles from its edge. The floor has an average gradient of 1 in 23 to a depth of 6,600 ft., while at its head its depth is 360 ft. It reaches a maximum depth of 4,980 ft. below the surrounding shelf. In cross-section it is V-shaped and Cretaceous rocks outcrop on its walls, together with late Tertiary and glacial material.

The Congo Canyon may be cited as an example of a canyon associated with the mouth of a large river; in fact, it extends 20 miles up the estuary of the river. This canyon is also V-shaped, unlike the flat-floored Mississippi and Indus canyons, and can be traced for 145 miles, to a depth of 1,260 fathoms (7,560 ft.). Its longitudinal gradient is $\frac{1}{2}°$, and it seems to be the only canyon along a considerable stretch of shelf to north and south which is lacking in large rivers. It appears that the canyon floor and walls are now being covered by mud; although sand and silt are carried down the river and alongshore, these materials do not seem to find their way into the canyon. It has been suggested that only during the last few thousand years has the canyon started to be filled.

The Hudson Canyon is of particular interest, as it is one which has been traced to great depths and in which very interesting evidence of the deposition at the mouth of the canyon has been studied by Ericson, Ewing and Heezen (1951). This canyon originates off the coast north of Boston, Mass., and has been traced to a depth of about 16,000 ft., its length being about 180 miles; it forms one of a series linking up with canyons coming down into the western Atlantic basin from Greenland, the whole series having a length of about 1,200 miles.

The bottom sampling carried out by Ericson *et al.* off the mouth of the Hudson canyon has given important information concerning the character of the sediments associated with the canyons. Cores were taken beyond the mouth of the canyon, in what was a submarine delta at a depth of 15,000 ft. These showed layers of sand, varying from thin films to layers 6 m. (20 ft.) thick, which were interbedded with abyssal clays. The sand was well graded and bedded, but was not at uniform levels, while material of Eocene age from the canyon walls was included in the sediment. Even in the mid-oceanic basins the canyon had steep sides, but there it had a flat floor 3 to 5 miles wide and from 60 to 600 ft. below the smooth basin floor. This evidence shows that material from a source near the shore or inland can be carried right out to the centre of the deep ocean basins along the submarine canyons, which helps to account for the smooth character of some of the abyssal plains.

The third type of dendritic canyon is very well illustrated in those off the coast of southern California, which have been studied in great detail. Of these the Monterey canyon is one of the best known; it can be traced right up on to the beach and extends for 50 miles offshore to where the depth is 9,000 ft. A profile across it is very similar to one across the Grand Canyon of Colorado. It heads near the Salinas river, but its gradient is much steeper than that of the river; it has a gradient of 1 in 10 for the first $\frac{1}{2}$ mile, and 1 in 25 for the next 45 miles, compared with 1 in 1,666 for the lower Salinas River. It is joined at a depth of 6,600 ft. by the Carmel Canyon. The rocks of its walls include Miocene

sediments and granite at a depth of 3,000 ft., while samples from its
floor at 4,800 ft. show graded bedding, each layer becoming progressively
finer upwards. It looses its V-shaped character at a depth of 9,000 ft.
and runs into a trough which continues to a depth of 12,000 ft., terminat-
ing in a fan, which is cut by shallow trenches, with levees on either side.
Fig. 2–7 illustrates the character of these canyons.

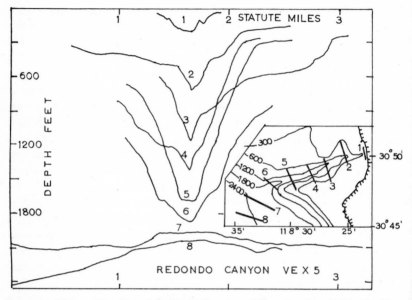

Fig. 2–7. Map and profiles of Redondo Canyon, off Los Angeles, California. Note
submarine fan shown in profile 7. (After Emery.)

Many of the canyons on the Californian Borderland have large fans
at their lower ends; in many instances the volume of the fan is greater
than that of the canyon above it (Emery, 1960), as shown by the following figures:

Volume of fans and canyons					10^9 cu. yds.	Ratio of fan to canyon
Hueneme-Mugu	Fan	33	Canyon	18		1·8
Dume		2·3		0·7		3·3
Redondo		20		11		1·8
Carlsbad		37		1·3		28
Coronado		22		7·8		2·8

This shows that the canyons are used as routes for the transport of
sediment from shallower depths. In some canyon fans shallow channels
are eroded across the fan; these are mostly only 50 to 300 ft. deep and
0·2 to 2 miles wide. Some information concerning the age of the canyons

is given by the age of the rocks through which they are cut; the La Jolla canyon cuts through Cretaceous shales and sandstones, others cut through Eocene, Miocene and Pliocene strata, while the heads of some of the canyons are cut through Pleistocene sediments. On the whole the older rocks occur farther from the shore in deeper water. It can be concluded that at least part of some of the canyons were cut during and after the Pleistocene.

iv. ORIGIN OF SUBMARINE CANYONS. The problem of the origin of the submarine canyons is one which is a long way from being completely solved. However, there is no lack of hypotheses to explain them. These can be broadly divided into two groups; those which propose a subaerial origin for the canyons and those which consider they are the result of submarine processes. As with other features, there is probably something in favour of both theories. It is quite certain that sea-level has oscillated through about 300 to 400 ft. vertically during the Pleistocene period, while tectonic movements can account for further changes of level in some places. On the other hand, now that it is known that submarine canyons can be traced right out into the abyssal plain at very great depths it is very difficult to reconcile a subaerial origin for the whole length of the canyon. If this were so the oceans would have had to be very nearly dry.

The subaerial theories were initiated when the comparison of some submarine canyons to youthful land valleys first showed the striking similarity in form of the two types of valleys. At first it was thought that sea-level could be lowered enough by assuming that the volume of ice had been very great, as suggested by Shepard in 1948. This, with the addition of marginal warping, could have allowed sea-level a fall of about 6,000 ft., of which 4,000 ft. was thought to be due to the locking up of water in ice sheets. This fall of sea-level is more than ten times that normally allowed, and it seems very difficult to envisage enough ice to allow this fall. Shepard (1952) has himself abandoned this idea and has put forward a much more likely theory, which considers that the canyons are formed by a number of composite processes.

Even if all the canyons have not been formed by subaerial processes, it seems likely that some have originated in this way. There are a series of canyons off Corsica which seem to prolong land valleys and which are very similar in form to them. Here it is probable that the canyons were cut by normal rivers and have been subsequently downfaulted to reach their present position. The geophysical evidence favours this view (Gaskell, 1960), and the presence of hard rock on the walls of the canyon can most easily be explained in this way.

It has been shown that there is some evidence in favour of the idea of continental flexure, with downwarping of the sea and upwarping of the land; this process could also help to increase the depth at which canyons originally near sea-level are now found. Other more extreme views on the subaerial origin of canyons have been put forward by Landes (1952), but his ideas are very hypothetical.

It is clearly necessary to consider possible submarine processes. A number of these have been suggested, but the only one for which there is much evidence, and which is generally considered as likely to be applicable over wide areas, is the turbidity current theory. This idea was originally put forward by Daly (1936) and has since been strongly advocated by Kuenen (1950) and many others. The principle on which this process is based is the fact that water with a load of sediment in it is denser than clear water; it will, therefore, flow down slope. As it flows, providing it is above a critical velocity, it will tend to gather more sediment; the density again increasing will render the effect cumulative. In this way such currents once started are self-generating.

An increasing number of observations are showing that some such process is active in the ocean. The smoothness of the abyssal plain in those areas to which such turbidity currents can reach indicates their effectiveness in spreading out a large volume of material over a wide area as they disperse on the bottom of a depression. The character of the sediments which have been found on the floor and beyond the mouth of many submarine canyons show that material can be carried from shallow water along these valley systems, to accumulate at their mouths in the form of fans. The formation of graded bedding can be explained by the gradual settling out of mixed material when a turbidity current gradually disperses on the ocean floor as its velocity is lowered. This process can explain the characteristics of rocks now found on land, as discussed by Jones (1954); but some of these structures may well be due to slumping over a wide area of the submarine slopes, although some could be explained by the action of turbidity currents.

Also there is experimental evidence, derived from model experiments carried out by Kuenen (1948), that turbidity currents can operate in water mixed with sediment, and that they can attain very great velocities. The velocity increases with the effective density of the current. He estimated that on a slope of $3°$ a current 30 cm. deep should be able to attain a velocity of 0·9 m./sec. By anology with experimental values, and extrapolating the data further, the conclusion was reached that dense currents, of considerable thickness could transport, large boulders; thus a current on a slope of $3°$ could carry 10-ton blocks with a velocity of 4 m./sec. if it were 16 m. thick and had a density of 1·5. Although it is generally agreed that turbidity currents can carry much material, it is much less certain whether they can erode the material across which they are moving, particularly if it is solid rock. The fact that the size of the canyons is smaller than the fans at their mouths indicates that turbidity currents are more effective as transporting agents than eroding agents.

Daly originally suggested that during the low sea-level of the glacial period much of the continental shelf was laid bare; the sea churned up the sediment to which the lowered base level gave it more effective access; this created zones of denser water, which flowed over the edge of the shelf as turbidity currents, cutting the canyons. In view of the doubtful capacity of the currents to erode the materials of the shelf and slope, this theory is not fully satisfactory.

The newer ideas of Shepard (1952), however, use this principle with other factors to arrive at a composite idea of canyon formation. In this connexion it is worth observing that the age of the canyons varies throughout their length, some parts of their courses being older than others. The lower parts of the canyons off the eastern United States at a depth of 6,500 ft., are cut through Cretaceous rock of shallow water origin. In the head of the Monterey Canyon, wells in the mouth of the Salinas valley show an old canyon, 5,000 ft. below sea-level, filled with shallow-water Miocene sediments. The land must have stood higher in relation to sea-level when this canyon was cut. This suggests that part of the canyon is an old feature.

Shepard has suggested that at one time the shelf and slope may have been elevated above sea-level and subaerial canyons were cut across them, with fans forming offshore. Subsidence then caused the shelf to sink, and some of the canyons were kept open by turbidity currents, while others were buried. Meanwhile, as subsidence continued, the shelf around the canyon was built up by progressive deposition, thus deepening the canyon. After the glacial period the open canyons extended headward across the Pleistocene deposits, cutting the upper and youngest part of the canyons through deposits left on the shelf during periods of low glacial sea-level. Although this method of formation may well apply in some areas, it may not account for all canyons, and many problems remain to be solved concerning their formation. The evidence on the whole does point to a considerable downwarping or downfaulting of the continental margin in many areas. It is also clear that much material is transported through the canyons to the deep ocean floor.

(b) Sea mounts and guyots

Since the relief of the ocean floor has become better known a very large number of submarine hills of different types have been discovered. These hills are particularly numerous in the Pacific Ocean, although they also occur in the Atlantic. A sea mount, which has more than 1 km. local relief, is differentiated from a guyot by the fact that the latter has a flat top, while the former may have a sharp crest. It is estimated that

O.–F

there are 10,000 sea mounts and guyots in the Pacific alone, some of
which rise 10,000 ft. above the adjacent ocean floor (Menard, 1959).
These features are also associated with the coral atolls, which will be
considered subsequently.

The distribution of the three features is of interest. Menard has
shown that the coral atolls are all concentrated in the south-western part
of the Pacific and in a line extending west-north-west from Hawaii,
with only a few exceptions. The distribution of sea mounts, on the other
hand, is much more extensive, although they are found in greater
number in the centre and particularly in the north-eastern part of the
ocean, while the guyots are concentrated in the west and in the area
south of Alaska, as shown in fig. 2–8. When their distribution is considered in detail it is found that in many areas they show linear patterns.
The distribution of the three features indicates that different parts of
the Pacific basin have been volcanically active at different periods.

There seems to be little doubt that both sea mounts and guyots
originated as volcanoes, erupted beneath the ocean. They are often
circular in plan, their slopes tend to be steeper than land volcanoes

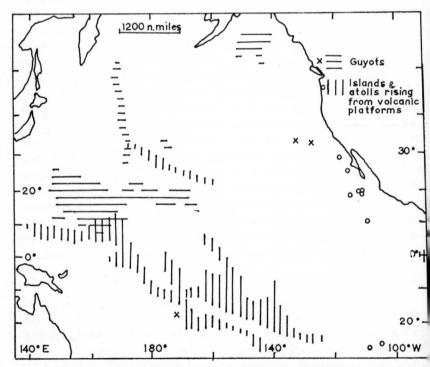

FIG. 2–8. Map to show the distribution of guyots and islands, including atolls, rising
from a volcanic platform. (Adapted after Menard.)

owing to the more rapid solidification of the lava in sea water. The difference between the pointed sea mounts and the flat-topped guyots is due to the elevation of the guyot above sea-level at some stage in its development, during which period it suffered subaerial erosion and marine planation, the top being truncated in this way (see fig. 2–9). Its

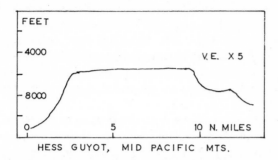

HESS GUYOT, MID PACIFIC MTS.

Fig. 2–9. Section surveyed across a guyot, flat-topped sea mount, from which mid-Cretaceous reef-coral fauna was dredged. (After Dietz *et al.*)

present depth below sea-level is the result of subsequent sinking. The tops of many guyots are now about 4,800 ft. below sea-level; the variation in depth, which is considerable, probably reflects a variation in age, the deeper ones being the older, as subsidence has continued longer. The guyots are grouped in three main areas; there is a north-south line running from Kamchatka to the latitude of Hawaii, a group south of Alaska, and a large group west of Hawaii, running from the Mariana Islands to the Marshall Islands. Those in the Gulf of Alaska average 3,000 ft. depth.

The depth over the guyots can be explained either by a rise in sea-level, which has drowned the guyots, as suggested by Revelle, or by their foundation having subsided; this is the most probable explanation, and is favoured by Menard, as well as being supported by geophysical evidence. The denser basic substratum of the ocean is shown to be bent down under the weight of the overlying erupted material, which is of relatively lower density of 2·4, and can, therefore, form a positive feature. Once erupted the volcano tends to sink as the weight of the lava depresses the crust into the void left by the erupted material.

The Hawaiian chain illustrates the stages well; there volcanic activity has shifted south-eastwards along the linear group. At the north-west end the volcanoes are oldest and these now form atolls, the central section consists of volcanoes, now no longer active, while the south-eastern end has the active volcanoes of the Hawaii Islands. Further evidence in favour of the sinking of the volcanoes to form guyots is the frequent occurrence of a trough of deeper water around the foot of the extruded material, where the crust has been bent down.

The linear arrangement of the sea mounts and guyots may be related to elongated zones of upwarping in the ocean floor. This process generates heat, which may help to account for the subsequent volcanic activity. Some of the many sea mounts of the eastern Pacific are related to the four east-west zones of fracture in this area. These zones are 100 km. wide and 2,000 km. long, the Murray fracture zone is a good example of these features. That there has been considerable lateral movement along this zone is clearly shown by the horizontal displacement of 160 km. (100 miles) of magnetic anomalies by the fracture. This fracture zone forms a steep asymmetrical ridge, with a total relief of 1,600 m.

Many of the sea mounts and guyots seem to be fairly old. From the crests of some of them shallow water Cretaceous material has been dredged, including corals, indicating that the guyot summit was near sea-level at this time. Miocene material has been obtained from others. At the present time the central Pacific is on the whole quiet seismically; there are only a few active volcanoes within the Andesite line. However, considering that all the sea mounts and guyots must have been active volcanoes at one time, the Pacific cannot always have been as quiet as it is now, unless the period over which the 10,000 volcanoes formed is a very long one. At the present time there are four active clusters of volcanoes within the Pacific; assuming that there are twenty volcanoes to each cluster, there must have been 500 active clusters to form the submarine hills. It is suggested by Menard that all the large volcanoes of the Pacific basin could have been produced since the Cretaceous period at the present rate of volcanic activity.

(c) Coral atolls and other reefs

The formation of coral atolls was at one time a problem which aroused much interest and rival theories were hotly debated. These features, which are again much more numerous in the Pacific than elsewhere, are closely associated with sea mounts and guyots, as far as their formation is concerned, although the resulting feature is very different. The distribution of coral atolls and coral reefs is determined by the conditions which the coral polyps and associated reef-building organisms require for successful growth. They need a water temperature averaging 70°F or over; clear water, which is not deeper than 150 ft. is also essential. They are, therefore, restricted to the shallow water of the tropical zone, and only rarely extend beyond 20° north and south. There are some coral formations up to 30°N near Hawaii, in the West Indies in the Atlantic, and around the Indian Ocean, although they do not

COLT 45

form typical atolls in these areas. The true atolls are nearly all restricted to the tropical Pacific. The point that corals will only thrive in shallow water is a very important one from the point of view of the rival theories originally put forward to account for the atolls. These features consist of a ring of reef coral, growing actively on the seaward margin and enclosing a lagoon in the centre; no solid rock is visible in the true atoll.

The two major theories were proposed during the nineteenth century. Darwin, who studied coral formation during the voyage of the *Beagle*, suggested that the coral atoll was formed from the simple fringing reef which develops round an emergent island. The fringing reef widens to a barrier reef as the island round which it is forming slowly subsides, until the island completely disappears below the surface and an atoll surrounds the lagoon over the former position of the island, as illustrated in fig. 2–10. This theory was supported by Dana and Davis, the latter adding the geomorphological arguments in favour of subsidence; for example, the lack of cliffing in the barrier reef stage and the drowned nature of the valleys, which often were found to have a great thickness of alluvium in them.

The opposing theory was put forward by Murray, supported by Agassiz and Semper; their idea was that any submarine platform could be built up by deposition, or lowered by erosion, until it was at a suitable

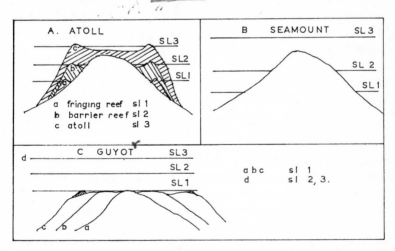

FIG. 2–10. Schematic diagram to illustrate the formation of A, an atoll on a slowly subsiding volcanic foundation. B shows the formation of a peaked sea mount, resulting from rapid subsidence, which was too fast for coral growth to keep pace, or where conditions were not suitable for coral growth. Such features may also form if the peak never reaches shallow enough water. C, possible formation of a flat-topped guyot; stage a, volcanic island growing up to sea-level; b, erosion by waves keeps pace with growing volcano; c, flat-topped area near sea-level is formed as volcanic activity ceases; coral may grow on this platform; d, sea-level rises to drown the guyot, as its foundation subsides. If coral growth is active atolls may form in this way.

elevation for corals to grow; these then built up an atoll, which developed
a lagoon as the reef-building corals on the edge grew more vigorously
than those in the centre. Their observations were mainly made in the
East Indies, and their arguments may well apply correctly to some of the
reefs in this area and in the Indian Ocean, where there is in some instances evidence of emergence rather than submergence.

An early attempt to show which of these theories accounted best for
the Pacific atolls was made in 1901, when a bore-hole was put down to
a depth of 1,114½ ft. on the atoll of Funafuti; throughout this depth
coral material was passed through. This lent strong support to the subsidence theory, but it was argued by the opponents that the coral was
in the form of talus, which had slipped off the edge of the submarine
platform, rather than being in the position of growth, but for this there
was little or no evidence.

More recently further experiments, including bore-holes and seismic
studies, have thrown further light on the formation of atolls; these have
shown that in the deep Pacific Ocean the atolls are almost certainly the
result of subsidence of a volcanic cone, at a rate at which the reef-
building organisms could maintain their hold. However, the rising
sea-level, due to subsidence, has not been the only process operating.
As was pointed out by Daly long ago, the sea-level was lowered during
glacial times and the temperature fell; these changes must have had
some effect on the development of the atolls, and in the areas near the
limiting temperature control the sea probably became too cold for coral
growth. The corals there may have died off, leaving their island foundation to be trimmed by the waves; when the sea rose again as deglaciation
took place and the water became warmer, the corals returned in some
instances, and built up a new atoll on the planed-off island. In this type
the coral need not be very thick to form an atoll.

In other areas the reef corals perhaps never returned, and the island,
now sunk beneath the surface due to the rise of sea-level, will form a
guyot. At times coral atolls become drowned; a recently described
example (Fairbridge and Stewart, 1960) lies in the Alexa Bank on the
Melanesian Border Plateau. This submerged bank has a raised rim, as
do true coral atolls, and it lies at a depth of 70 ft., while the central
depression is at 100 ft. depth. The outer slopes of the bank drop away
steeply at 30° to 40° for thousands of feet. The reason why the corals
deserted this bank is not easy to find; it is in equatorial waters, so a
lowering of temperature is not likely to be the cause. On the other hand,
corals can be killed either by emergence for a short period or too rapid
submergence, so that their upward growth cannot keep pace. Other
possibilities suggested are the deposition of too much volcanic ash, or
the formation of foul water in enclosed basins, which are found in this

vicinity. However, many corals escaped being destroyed with the changing sea-level and other conditions, as shown by the many atolls now present in the Pacific.

Recent surveys and bore-holes may be considered. The island of Funafuti has now been explored more thoroughly by seismic survey. This showed that there were several thousand feet of material having a low velocity of wave travel, which is probably coral rock; this extended all across the lagoon of Funafuti, while similar results were obtained from the islands of Bikini and Eniwetok, as shown in fig. 2–1c. At this last island the results were also confirmed by a bore-hole which penetrated to the base of the coral (Kuenen, 1954). This core gives some evidence of the rate of sinking of the island. Bore-holes were put down on both sides of the atoll; these reached volcanic rock beneath coral formation at depths of 4,200 and 4,600 ft. The coral appeared to be in the position of growth.

The top of the Miocene was found on this atoll at a depth of 600 ft., indicating a subsidence of 50 to 60 ft./million years. The top of the Eocene was found at 2,800 ft., which corresponds with a subsidence of 60 to 70 ft./million years. The rate of upgrowth during the Quaternary must have been much more rapid, as the glacial changes of sea-level were much more rapid than the Tertiary rate of subsidence; this supposes that the coral formed at the high pre-glacial sea-level was destroyed as sea-level fell to its low glacial level. Thus the corals building up the atoll during the post-glacial rise of sea-level must have been working 200 times faster than those in the Tertiary, and although this is quite possible, the results remain tentative. It is clear, however, that glacial changes of sea-level must be taken into account in the consideration of atoll formation.

Shepard has suggested that the foundations of many of the atolls were formed during volcanic activity in the Cretaceous period. Those volcanoes which emerged were attacked by the agents of erosion and truncated. Where the conditions were favourable corals grew on the banks around the islands, which have slowly subsided since. In some instances the reef-building organisms have kept pace to form atolls; in others they did not gain a foothold before the water was too deep, and the truncated islands have now become guyots. The subsidence is shown by the lowering of the Moho by 2·5 to 3 km. beneath them.

It has been suggested that coral atolls develop from the preliminary features of fringing and barrier reefs, the atoll forming the final stage, when all the original foundation has disappeared below sea-level. Fringing reefs may either form facing the open sea or be protected by a barrier to seaward. On the exposed side of the reef, as with other reef types, the outermost feature may be an algal ridge, formed predominantly of calcareous algae, and not corals, of which *Porolithon* is common. Corals flourish on the inner slope of the reef flat, which is built up of dead coral, sand and other detritus, interspersed with some living coral. The lagoon, separating the reef from the shore, is often flat floored, its depth varying between 30 and 100 m., although in places coral may still grow within it.

The largest barrier reef is that off the Queensland coast of Australia, extending from 9°S to 22°S. The feature is not a continuous barrier reef, but, in the south especially, consists of many reefs spread over an irregular platform. To the north, however, the reefs become more linear in pattern, facing the ocean and separated by narrow channels. The width of the barrier is 80 miles near Torres Strait in the north, and narrows southwards to 20 to 30 miles wide near Cairns, increasing again southwards to about 100 miles in width.

The origin of this great barrier reef zone is related to the structure of the Queensland coast; the offshore zone has been faulted down in the recent past, probably at the end of the Tertiary period. It has been suggested that a fault system let down a peneplaned surface to a suitable depth below sea-level for reef-building organisms to become established, in an area in which other conditions necessary for their growth were favourable. The flat and shallow floor between the reefs can probably be explained by sedimentation in the lower areas and coral growth.

REFERENCES

Benioff, H., Orogenesis and deep crustal structure—additional evidence from seismology. *Bull. Geol. Soc. Am.* **65**, 385–400, 1954.

Bourcart, J., La Théorie de la flexure continentale. *Compte Rendu Inter. Geog. Un.* **16**, Lisbon, 167–90, 1950.

Carlson, R. O., and Brown, M.V., Seismic refraction profiles in the submerged Atlantic coastal plain near Ambrose Lightship. *Bull. Geol. Soc. Am.* **66**, 969–76, 1955.

Carsola, A. J., Submarine canyons of the Arctic Slope. *Journ. Geol.* **62**, 605–10, 1954.

Daly, R. A., *The changing world of the ice age*, 1936.

Davis, W. M., *The coral reef problem*, 1928.

Dietz, R. S., Geomorphic evolution of the continental terrace (continental shelf and slope). *Bull. Am. Ass. Petrol. Geol.* **36**, 1802–19, 1952.

Dietz, R. S., Continents and ocean basins, evolution by spreading of the sea floor. *Nature* **190**, 854–7, 1961.

Dietz, R. S., Menard, H. W., and Hamilton, E. L., Echograms of the Mid-Pacific expedition. *Deep-Sea Res.* **1**, 258–72, 1954.

Dietz, R. S., and Shumway, G., Arctic basin geomorphology. *Bull. Geol. Soc. Am.* **72**, 1319–30, 1961.

Emery, K. O., Continental slopes and submarine canyons. *Geol. Mag.* **87**, 102–4, 1950.

Emery, K. O., *The sea off southern California*. Wiley, New York, 1960.

Ericsson, D. B., Ewing, M., and Heezen, B. C., Deep-sea sand and submarine canyons. *Bull. Geol. Soc. Am.* **62**, 961–6, 1951.

Ewing, M., Heezen, B. C., Ericsson, D. B., Northrop, J., and Dorman, J., Exploration of the north-west Atlantic mid-ocean canyon. *Bull. Geo. Soc. Am.* **64**, 865–8, 1953.

Ewing, M., and Heezen, B. C., Puerto Rico Trench, topographic and geophysical data. *Geol. Soc. Am. Sp. Pap.* **62**, 255–68, 1955.

Ewing, M., and Worzel, J. L., Gravity anomalies and structure of the West Indies, Part I. *Bull. Geol. Soc. Am.* **65**, 165–74, 1954.

Ewing, M., Worzel, J. L., Steenland, N. C., and Press, F., Geophysical investigations in the emerged and submerged Atlantic coastal plain. *Bull. Geol. Soc. Am.* **61**, 877–92, 1950.

Fairbridge, R. W., and Stewart, H. B., Alexa Bank, a drowned atoll on the Melanesian border plateau. *Deep-Sea Res.* **7**, 100–16, 1960.

Fisher, R. L., Middle America Trench: Topography and structure. *Bull. Geol. Soc. Am.* **72**, 703–20, 1961.

Gaskell, T. F., Seismic refraction work by H.M.S. *Challenger* in the deep oceans. *Proc. Roy. Soc. A* **222**, 356–61, 1954.

Gaskell, T. F., *Under the deep oceans*. Eyre and Spottiswoode, London, 1960.

Gibson, W. M., Submarine topography in the Gulf of Alaska. *Bull. Geol. Soc. Am.* **71**, 1087–1108, 1960.

Heezen, B. C., and Ewing, M., Turbidity currents and the 1929 Grand Banks earthquake. *Am. Journ. Sci.* **250**, 849–84, 1952.

Heezen, B. C., Tharp, M., and Ewing, M., The floors of the oceans: 1, North Atlantic. *Geol. Soc. Am. Sp. Pap.* **65**, 122, 1959.

Hess, H. H., Geological hypotheses of the Earth's crust under the oceans. *Proc. Roy. Soc. A* **222**, 341–8, 1954.

Hill, M. N., and King, W. B. R., Seismic prospecting in the English Channel and geological interpretation. *Quart. Journ. Geol. Soc.* **109**, 1–20, 1953.

Hill, M. N., and Laughton, A. S., Seismic observations in the eastern Atlantic 1952. *Proc. Roy. Soc. A* **222**, 348–56, 1954.

Jones, O. T., Continental slopes and shelves. *Geog. Journ.* **97**, 80–99, 1941.

Jones, O. T., The characteristics of some of the Lower Palaeozoic marine sediments. *Proc. Roy. Soc. A* **222**, 327–33, 1954.

King, W. B. R., The geological history of the English Channel. *Quart. Journ. Geol. Soc.* **110**, 77–102, 1954.

Kuenen, P. H., *Marine geology*. Wiley, New York, 1950.

Kuenen, P. H., Turbidity currents of high density. *Internat. Geol. Cong.* 18 Session, G. B. **8**, 44–52, 1948.

Kuenen, P. H., Eniwetok drilling results. *Deep-Sea Res.* **1**, 187–9, 1954.

Kuenen, P. H., and Menard, H. W., Turbidity currents, graded and non-graded deposits. *Journ. Sed. Pet.* **22**, 83–96, 1952.

Landes, K. K., Our shrinking world. *Bull. Geol. Soc. Am.* **63**, 225, 1952.

Laughton, A. S., The sea floor. *Sci. Prog.* **186**, 230–49, 1959.

Linton, D. L., Problems of Scottish scenery. *Scot. Geog. Mag.* **67**, 65–85, 1951.

Mason, R. G., Geophysical investigations of the sea floor. *Liverpool and Manchester Geol. Journ.* **2**, 389–410, 1960.

Menard, H. W., Development of median elevations in ocean basins. *Bull. Geol. Soc. Am.* **69**, 1179–86, 1958.

Menard, H. W., Deep sea channels, topography and sedimentation. *Am. Assoc. Petrol. Geol. Bull.* **39**, 236–55, 1955.

Menard, H. W., Geology of the Pacific Sea floor. *Experientia* **15**, 205–13, 1959.

Moore, D. G., Acoustic-reflection studies of the continental shelf and slope off southern California. *Bull. Geol. Soc. Am.* **71**, 1121–36, 1960.

Raitt, R. W., Fisher, R. L., and Mason, R. G., Tonga Trench. *Geol. Soc. Am. Sp. Pap.* **62**, 237–54, 1955.

Robinson, A. H. W., Floor of the British seas. *Scot. Geog. Mag.* **68**, 64–79, 1952.

Robinson, A. H. W., Deep clefts in the Inner Sound of Raasay. *Scot. Geog. Mag.* **65**, 20–25, 1949.

Shepard, F. P., *Submarine geology*. Harper, New York, 1948.
Shepard, F. P., Composite origin of submarine canyons. *Journ. Geol.* **60**, 84–96, 1952.
Shepard, F. P., *The earth beneath the sea*. John Hopkins Press, Baltimore, 1959.
Shor, G. G., and Fisher, R. L., Middle America Trench: Seismic refraction studies. *Bull. Geol. Soc. Am.* **72**, 721–30, 1961.
Stille, H., Recent deformations of the Earth's crust in the light of those of earlier epochs. *Geol. Soc. Am. Sp. Pap.* **62**, 171–92, 1955.
Stride, A. H., On the origin of the Dogger Bank. *Geol. Mag.* **96**, 33–44, 1959.
Umbgrove, J. H. F., *The pulse of the Earth*. Martinus Nijhoff, The Hague, 2nd Edition, 1947.
Worzel, J. L., and Shurbet, G. L., Gravity interpretations from standard oceanic and continental crustal sections. *Geol. Soc. Am. Sp. Pap.* **62**, 87–100, 1955.

CHAPTER 3

THE WATER OF THE OCEANS

INTRODUCTION

THE oceans contain about 97 per cent of all the water on the Earth; they are the great store of water, which is always available for evaporation into the atmosphere and precipitation on to the land. Water as a substance has some interesting properties; it is the only natural substance to be found in all three states, solid, liquid and gaseous, while it is one of the very few inorganic materials in nature which is liquid at normal temperatures and pressures. Its other special properties include its very great solvent power, which makes it indispensable for life; in this property it exceeds any other liquid. It also has a higher surface tension than any other liquid and has an exceptionally great capacity for absorbing heat. It requires a large amount of heat to change state from solid, through liquid, to gas. Water heats and cools more slowly than other liquids; as a result it exerts a very important modifying effect on the Earth's temperatures, while the heat of vaporization also exerts a strong influence on temperate extremes in some areas, by using heat from the atmosphere for evaporation.

The maximum density of pure water is at $4°C$, but with sea water the density increases steadily to its freezing-point, which is lowered as the salinity increases. Thus sea water can reach its greatest density as it is about to freeze at temperatures around $-2°C$. This means that very cold sea water can be formed which is also very dense and can, therefore, sink to the bottom of the ocean basins. Another property of interest is the compressibility of sea water; this is small, but it is enough to make the surface of the oceans 100 ft. lower than it would be if it were completely incompressible.

Water achieves almost all the natural transport of solid material in the world, whether on land or in the sea, but on land the air plays a minor part. The ultimate source of all the energy on which the work of water depends is the Sun, although the Moon plays an important part in the generation of tidal energy. The energy of the Sun is imparted to the oceans in the form of heat received, and this is then transferred to the atmosphere, which is more or less transparent to short-wave radiation. Heat can lead to evaporation, which carries the ocean water into the atmosphere, from where it can be transferred to the land. The

79

atmosphere also affects the movement of the ocean waters via the wind, which exerts a direct stress on the water surface.

1. *OCEANOGRAPHIC INSTRUMENTS*

The density of the water is of great significance in the circulation of the ocean; this depends on the temperature and salinity. It is necessary, therefore, to determine with the greatest possible accuracy, and at as many depths and positions as practicable, the characteristics of the ocean water, with particular stress being laid on its temperature and salinity. It is, therefore, worth mentioning the instruments with which these observations are made.

The temperature at the surface can be measured easily by using an ordinary thermometer, but for subsurface measurements other instruments must be used. There are two alternatives: either a sample may be brought to the surface in an insulated bottle, for measurement at the surface, or a reversing thermometer may be used. This latter instrument is so arranged that when it is turned upside down the mercury breaks at a constriction in the tube. The thermometer is reversed by the action of a weight sent down the wire cable on which the sampling bottle and thermometer are fixed. This causes the thermometer to turn over.

The salinity must be measured in a laboratory, and for this purpose it is necessary to bring up samples of water from definite depths. It is also essential to measure the temperature and salinity at the same position, in order to obtain the correct density. For this purpose the reversing thermometers are usually attached to the sampling bottles; the weight which reverses the thermometer at the same time automatically closes the sampling bottle, by reversing it. Two thermometers are usually used, one of which responds to the pressure and the other which does not. The protected thermometer eliminates the effect of hydrostatic pressure, while the unprotected one gives a fictitious temperature, the pressure of the overlying water causing a higher reading, owing to the contraction of the thermometer. Thus the difference between the two thermometers gives a determination of the depth, which can give a more accurate depth than the length of wire paid out, on which the thermometers were fixed, as the wire is rarely vertical. It is important to be able to measure the water character at several depths in any one position, and in order to accomplish this a series of sampling bottles and thermometers are fixed to the wire; when one is reversed by the weight, this releases another weight, which reverses the next bottle beneath it and so on.

Once the water samples have been brought to the surface they can be analysed to give a value of their salinity and other properties, both chemical and biological. It is, therefore, the thermometer and sampling bottles which enable the essential information concerning the characteristics of sea water to be determined. These characteristics play an important part in the subsequent movement and fertility of the water with regard to the production of the lower forms of marine life, on which the larger creatures depend. The plankton in turn may assist in tracing the water movement.

2. THE CHARACTERISTICS OF SEA WATER

Before dealing with the fundamentally important properties of sea water, temperature, salinity and oxygen content, which are vital to an understanding of the oceanic circulation, some of the minor elements which are important in other respects may be mentioned. Normal sea water, with a salinity of 34·33 grams per thousand grams by weight, contains 18·98 g./kg. of chlorine and 10·561 g./kg. of sodium, the elements which produce the common salt of the sea. The next most common elements are magnesium at 1,272 mg./kg., or parts per million; sulphur, 884 mg./kg.; calcium, 400 mg./kg.; and potassium 380 mg./kg. The amounts of other elements falls off sharply, but even some of the trace elements may be of considerable importance biologically, or even commercially, in time. Silver, gold and radium occur in sea water, but in minute proportions, which are respectively 0·3, 0·006 and 0·000,000,2 mg./metric ton (parts per thousand million). The proportion of the main constituents remains very constant in sea water from different areas and with a different total salinity.

Some of the important elements in sea water are those used by living organisms for growth or reproduction and are called nutrients. They vary inversely in quantity with the abundance of living organisms at any place; these elements include silicon, 0–4·0 mg./kg.; nitrogen 0–0·7 mg./kg.; phosphorus, 0–0·1 mg./kg.; other elements, in smaller quantities, include arsenic, iron, manganese and copper. Where the nitrates, silicates and dissolved oxygen, necessary for life in the sea, cannot be replaced as they are used up the sea is relatively barren, but where they can be replaced by upwelling water from below the sea is fertile. The zones of fertile water are greenish blue, on account of the large number of small organisms in the water, while the deep blue of some tropical waters indicates paucity of organic matter.

In some areas the sea supplies the needs for common salt, and other elements are becoming commercially important. Magnesium is one of these; the oceans hold enough of this to cover the dry surface of the earth to a depth of 20 ft., while the salt would cover the surface to a thickness of nearly 200 ft., according to Krümmel. Bromine is also extracted from sea water. Another element which would be very valuable as a fertilizer, if it could be extracted from the sea, is potassium.

It is the total salinity which is used to describe the water of the sea; recent developments in technique have both speeded up and made this determination more accurate. An electric salinity meter has been developed at the National Institute of Oceanography and in America; that from the former can determine the salinity to an accuracy of $\pm 0 \cdot 003\%_0$, by measuring electrical conductivity, and the operation is speeded up to allow about 200 determinations to be made in a day. The normal method of determining salinity gives results to $\pm 0 \cdot 02\%_0$. The salinity and temperature of the water together determine its density. As the salinity increases and the temperature decreases, so the density increases. The surface distribution of both salinity and temperature is closely related to climatic factors. From these data the formation and character of the deeper water of the oceans can in part be determined and explained.

(a) Temperature of the ocean water

The temperature of sea water is measured in degrees centigrade to an accuracy of $\pm 0 \cdot 02$°C, the range of oceanic temperature falling between -2°C and $+30$°C; at the lower limit ice forms. The conduction of heat through sea water is complicated by the fact that the motion is nearly always turbulent. The specific heat of sea water has recently been re-determined by Cox and Smith (1959). This value states the number of calories required to increase the temperature of 1 g. of water 1°C. Their new value indicates that there is greater adiabatic cooling, as water is raised to the surface, for low temperatures than previously estimated. The specific heat decreases with increasing salinity. Adiabatic heating may lead to temperature increases at the bottom of deep isolated basins; owing to the slight compressibility of water, this process is less important in water than in the atmosphere.

The potential temperature of sea water is defined as the temperature that it would have if it were raised adiabatically to the surface. The freezing-point of sea water depends on the salinity, falling from $-0 \cdot 5$°C at a salinity of 10‰ to just below -2°C at a salinity of about 36‰.

The distribution of temperature in the surface layers of the ocean reflects the general distribution of heat supply from the Sun. The value of heat received from the Sun is greatest at the Equator and falls off towards the poles, while the total heat lost falls off similarly from Equator to poles, but not at the same rate. There is, therefore, a surplus of heat received from the Sun between the Equator and 30° latitude, and a net deficit from there to the poles. The transfer of heat from low to high latitudes is achieved by air currents and water movement, reaching a maximum around 40° latitude. Most of the heat transfer probably takes place in the atmosphere, but at least in some places the oceans play a significant part; for example, in the north Atlantic at about 55°N, 0.3×10^{16}g. cal./min. is carried by the ocean, which is one-tenth of the total transport of heat at this latitude.

The heat budget of the oceans can be given as $Q_s - Q_b - Q_h - Q_e = 0$. Q_s is the heat received and equals 0·221 g.cal./cm.²/min. It is transmitted by radiation from the Sun and sky. Q_b is radiation back from sea surface and equals 0·090. Q_h is the convection of sensible heat to the atmosphere and equals 0·013, and Q_e is the heat of evaporation and equals 0·118; these three together equal 0·221 and thus the budget is balanced. This applies between 70°N and 70°S, according to Mosby (1936). Heat can also be added to the oceans in various minor ways, such as convection of heat through the ocean floor, transformation of kinetic energy to heat, heating due to chemical processes, convection of sensible heat from the atmosphere and condensation of water vapour.

It is only possible to give a generalized picture of the surface temperature of the oceans, because of the variability of the large number of factors which affect the temperature of the oceans. Nevertheless some interesting facts emerge. The figures given for the Atlantic Ocean by Böhnecke (1938) are of value in demonstrating some of these facts. The average surface temperatures for each 10° latitude are as follows:

North latitude		South latitude	
70—60°	5·60°C	70—60	—1·30°C
60—50	8·66	60—50	1·76
50—40	13·16	50—40	8·68
40—30	20·40	40—30	16·90
30—20	24·16	30—20	21·20
20—10	25·81	20—10	23·16
10—0	26·66	10—0	25·18

One of the striking points, which applies not only to the Atlantic Ocean, is the fact that the maximum temperatures occur north of the Equator. The oceanic thermal Equator, therefore lies north of the geographical Equator, and this has interesting repercussions on the movement of water and other factors in the equatorial zone. This maximum temperature zone moves with the seasons, but it never reaches a point south of the Equator, except in a very few areas. Another point, which is readily apparent, is the fact that the temperatures in the Southern Hemisphere are considerably lower than those in the north. This may be due partly to the different atmospheric circulation in the two hemispheres and to the effect of longitudinal land barriers in the north, which deflect warm and cold currents to north and south, while the large mass of the ice-covered Antarctic continent is an additional and important source of cold in the south. The much smaller amount of land in the Southern Hemisphere is very significant in this respect.

The difference between the sea surface temperature and the air temperature over it is of importance; it influences the amount of evaporation and heat transfer to the air and is likely to have an important effect on interchange of energy between the sea and the air. In general heat is given off from the oceans to the atmosphere; this means that the sea surface temperature is on the average warmer than the atmosphere above it. Between 20°N and 55°S in the Atlantic, at a height of 8 m. above the sea surface the air temperature is on the average 0·8°C cooler than the sea; there is, therefore, a fall in temperature in the layers immediately above the water surface. However, the heat given off by the oceans to the air varies greatly with the seasons in middle latitudes, being much greater in winter than in summer, when it is probably negligible or even reversed. This causes the great difference of air temperature over the oceans and continents during the winter season in particular. For example, taking an entirely land meridian, and comparing it with a water one, the temperature difference for January is 22·2°C higher over the water between 80 and 20°N, while in summer, in July, it is 4·8°C lower; the mean annual temperature is 7°C higher over the water meridian. This illustrates the important modifying effect the oceans have on the surface air temperature over them.

Although the sea temperatures do not vary so greatly throughout the year, there is nevertheless an important seasonal fluctuation of surface temperature in the oceans. This varies with a number of factors, such as the ocean currents, prevailing winds and so forth. However, it is generally true that the zones of maximum variation occur in middle latitudes as shown in fig. 3–1: in the Atlantic Ocean the zone of maximum range of over 8°C occurs around latitude 40°N; from this position it falls off steadily to north and south; in the latter direction it reaches its

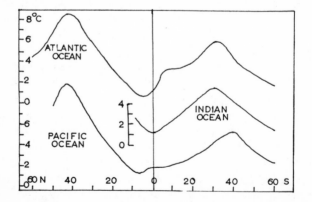

FIG. 3–1. Annual range of surface temperature is shown in the different oceans for different latitudes. (H. U. Sverdrup, Martin W. Johnson and Richard H. Fleming, *The Oceans: Their Physics, Chemistry and general Biology.* © 1942, Prentice-Hall, Inc., U.S.A. Reprinted by permission.)

minimum range of less than 1°C about 5°N. A smaller maximum range is reached in the Southern Hemisphere at 30°S. The Pacific shows interesting variations; in the north Pacific the maximum range is sharper and higher, reaching about 10°C in latitude 40°N; the southern maximum range occurs farther south at 40°S. These values are derived from the observations of Böhnecke (1938) for the Atlantic and Schott (1935) for the Pacific. The cold, continental winter winds of the Northern Hemisphere are an important factor in modifying the winter temperatures of the water on the west side of the oceans, in particular off China, Siberia and North America. The larger amount of land in the Northern Hemisphere is clearly an important factor in these results.

The relatively great depth to which heat is distributed in the oceans as well as the high specific heat of water are factors which make them such an important source of heat. This is reflected in the annual variation of temperature with depth in the ocean. The change of temperature with depth depends on four factors: (1) the variation in the amount of heat absorbed, (2) the effect of heat conduction, (3) lateral displacement of the water by currents and (4) vertical motion of the water. The variation in these four factors means that it is not possible to generalize concerning annual changes of temperature with depth.

One example will, however, illustrate the effect of some of these variables. The water of the Bay of Biscay, studied by Helland-Hansen, illustrates the effect of heat conduction downwards through the water. This area was chosen because the type of water remained the same throughout the year (see fig. 3–2a). The surface layers at a position 47°N, 12°W showed a range from 3°C below the annual mean in January to nearly 5°C above the mean in August, falling again to the December minimum. At a depth of 25 m. the maximum occurred three weeks later and was about $\frac{1}{2}$° less, while the minimum remained at just about 2° below the mean from mid-December to April; at 50 m. depth the maximum was reduced to just over 1°C above the mean and occurred between September and October, while the minimum of about 1° below the mean was still about the same time. At 100 m. depth the whole range about the annual mean was reduced to less than $\frac{1}{2}$°C, the maximum taking place in early December and the minimum about March to April. A similar change has been recorded in deep Scottish lochs.

Other places show a greater range at 100 m. depth, owing to different circumstances, such as cold winter winds, while some places do not show a systematic variation relating to conduction, but are influenced by different waters at different seasons of the year. For example, off California (fig. 3–2b) the range at the surface is about $4\frac{1}{2}$°C, while at 100 m. it is still as much as $3\frac{1}{2}$°C during the year, although the time of maxima and minima differ at different depths.

The relationship between air and sea temperature is responsible for

The Water of the Oceans

sea-fog formation. Sea-fogs are formed when warm damp air passes over a cold sea surface. The sea-surface temperature must be lower than the dew-point of the air, this then becomes cooled below its dew-point and fog is formed. Owing to the small diurnal variation of sea surface temperature, sea-fog is not dependent on daily heating and cooling, and can occur with strong winds. Sea-fogs occur most frequently in spring and early summer, when the air passing off the land may be warm, but the sea is still very cold. They are most liable to occur

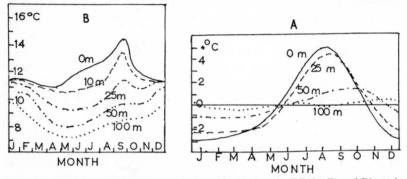

FIG. 3–2. Annual variation of temperature with depth. A. Off the Bay of Biscay in 47°N, 12°W. B. In Monterey Bay, California. (After Sverdrup *et al.*) (H. U. Sverdrup, Martin W. Johnson and Richard H. Fleming, *The Oceans: their Physics, Chemistry and general Biology.* © 1942. Prentice-Hall Inc., U.S.A. Reprinted by permission.)

in high latitudes in summer; the Grand Banks off Newfoundland are notorious for their fogs, which result from the cold water of the Labrador Current flowing alongside the heated land mass and towards the warmer waters of the north-west Atlantic. Only north winds, which blow over the cold water, can prevent fog, which occurs on about 50 per cent of the days of summer. Similar conditions occur in the north-west Pacific, where the cold Kamchatka Current acts in the same way as the Labrador Current.

Coastal fogs also form where offshore winds from the land cause upwelling of colder water, while the land winds are warm. Such coasts lie within the trade-wind belts, on the western side of land masses, and are found along the shores of California, Chile, south-west Africa and Morocco. Around the British Isles fogs form when warm winds are blowing from the south and off the heated continent in spring and summer particularly. Fog is, however, rare in tropical seas and does not often occur in the Mediterranean.

(b) Salinity of the surface water

The amount of chlorine is normally used to determine the salinity, and as its ratio to that of the other chemicals is constant, the total salinity can be obtained. It is expressed as parts per thousand by weight, g./kg. or usually ‰. In the open oceans the salinity normally varies between 33‰ and 37‰, it can reach values below this level where much fresh water enters from large rivers, or exceed it in areas where the influx from the land is negligible and where the surface evaporation is very great, as, for example, in the Red Sea, where it may exceed 40‰. In the open ocean the range is fairly small and the average on the surface for the oceans is 35‰. At depth the salinites range between 34·6‰ and 35‰, and in the deep Pacific are so uniform that the range is reduced to 34·6–34·7‰.

The surface salinity is closely related to the process of evaporation, by which the salts are concentrated. Thus conditions in which evaporation are great will lead to areas of high salinity. The salinity itself will exert some influence on the evaporation, but the relationship between the sea and air temperature is much more important. When the water is warmer than the air evaporation will be facilitated by the instability of the lower layers of air, in which there is a rapid lapse rate near the water surface, leading to instability in the air. Evaporation will be greatest where cold air flows over warm water. However, when the air is very much colder than the water it can contain relatively little moisture, and condensation takes place to form sea-smoke, but this is limited to inland and coastal areas, as only in these can the great extremes that are necessary occur. When the sea is colder than the air turbulence is reduced, and evaporation is only possible if the air is not saturated with moisture.

Taking a section north-south through the oceans, it is possible to determine an average annual rate of evaporation. For example, Wüst has shown that in the Atlantic evaporation falls off rapidly north of 40°N, where it is 94 cm./year, increasing to 149 cm./year at 20°N; falling off again at the thermal Equator to 105 cm./year at 5°N, it increases again to 143 cm./year at 10°S, falling off rapidly farther south to 43 cm./year at 50°S latitude. Similar but rather smaller values hold for the Pacific Ocean. These values are clearly related to the general climatic conditions; the subtropical high-pressure belts and trade-wind zones allow rapid evaporation, while the cloudy skies and calmer conditions of the equatorial zone diminishes evaporation.

Evaporation must be balanced by precipitation before it can be directly related to salinity. From the difference between the two values the net evaporation can be determined, and this shows a linear correlation with surface salinity. Precipitation is on the whole inverse to evaporation; between latitude 40°N and 35°S evaporation exceeds precipitation, except for a narrow belt around 5°N. The curve for surface salinity, shown in fig. 3–3, for all oceans follows very closely the curve for net evaporation, reaching a maximum at 25°N of 35·79‰; a minimum of

34·54‰ is found at 5°N and a secondary maximum in the Southern Hemisphere at 20 to 25°S of 35·69‰; from these subtropical maxima the values fall off rapidly to higher latitudes. Apart from the effects of evaporation and precipitation, salinity at the surface is influenced by mixing with subjacent water; if it is assumed that the salinity of the water beneath the surface is 34·6‰ the correct surface values are obtained in relation to the other two factors. This is the approximate value of the mean salinity at depths of 400 to 600 m., although there are slight variations in the values for the different oceans. The conclusion can be reached that the average values of surface salinity depend primarily on the atmospheric circulation.

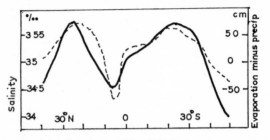

FIG. 3–3. Average values of surface salinity (full line) and evaporation minus precipitation (dashed line) for all oceans. (After Sverdrup *et al.*) (H. U. Sverdrup, Martin W. Johnson and Richard H. Fleming, *The Oceans: Their Physics, Chemistry and general Biology.* © 1942. Prentice-Hall Inc., U.S.A. Reprinted by permission.)

The annual variation of salinity has been calculated for the north Atlantic, where results show that the maximum salinity occurs in March and the minimum in November, when the values are 36·7 and 36·59‰ respectively, although the variations are rather irregular. On the whole they seem to correlate fairly well with the changes in evaporation (which confirms the close relationship between evaporation and surface salinity) and are also associated with small changes of sea-level.

The coastal waters of the southern North Sea show interesting variations in salinity. The salinity is much higher in the water which has penetrated from the Atlantic, via the English Channel or around northern Britain and the northern North Sea, than in the coastal water, which forms a belt of low salinity water extending along the Dutch coast and across the southern North Sea from Holland to East Anglia. The salinity in this coastal water falls below 34·2‰, while the oceanic water exceeds 35‰. This difference is due to the dilution of sea water by river water near the coast.

One of the clearest examples of the effect of evaporation on salinity is found in the Mediterranean. There the character of the water flowing into the Mediterranean is completely altered by the external processes and flows out of the Mediterranean as a completely different type of water. At the Straits of Gibraltar, Atlantic water flows into the Mediterranean, while water of much increased salinity, which is warmer than water at the same depth outside, flows out beneath the inflowing water, because its great increase in salinity increases its density. These changes are due to the great increase of evaporation and the relatively low rainfall and runoff into the Mediterranean area, characteristics which become progressively more effective towards the eastern end of the basin. This is reflected in the increasing salinity and surface temperature eastwards.

Exactly the reverse is found in the Black Sea, however, as there rainfall and runoff from the land greatly exceed evaporation and the surface water becomes much less saline and its density is decreased as a result. This has the effect of making the lower layers of water stagnant, as the surface water never becomes dense enough to sink to the bottom. The bottom water is, therefore, lacking oxygen, and instead contains hydrogen sulphide; this prohibits normal life in the deeper waters of the Black Sea. Oxygen is a useful characteristic of sea water from the point of view of tracing the movement of the waters; it will therefore, be considered in rather more detail.

(c) Oxygen content of the ocean water

Oxygen in sea water is important, not only directly as one of the essential elements of marine life, but also indirectly in that it acts as a pointer to the movement of water, because it is acquired by sea water when it is at the surface and becomes slowly reduced in amount with time since the water was at the surface. Oxygen and carbon dioxide are the two most important dissolved gases in the ocean. The amount of oxygen in water is much less than that in air, the values being respectively 9 ml. and 200 ml./litre. A study of the oxygen content of the deep waters of the oceans gives useful indications concerning the rapidity of deep-water circulation and the renewal of water by new water from the surface.

A few values of the oxygen content of ocean water at different depths and places will illustrate the sort of variation, which will be considered more fully when the deep circulation is discussed. The table of oxygen values, obtained by various expeditions at different dates, shows the general trends in the oxygen content of the Atlantic and Pacific Oceans.

Oxygen Content (ml./l.)
Atlantic Ocean

Depth m.	50°27'N 40°14'W	33°19'N 68°18'W	19°16'N 27°27'W	32°49'S 40°01'W	39°46'S 22°12'E	46°47'S 12°39'E	58°37'S 14°43'E	64°43'S 14°41'E
2,000	6·30	6·08	5·07	4·71	4·70	4·30	4·85	4·68
2,500	6·26	6·04	5·30	5·53	4·99	4·23	4·93	4·51
3,000	6·17	5·99	5·27	5·65	5·14	4·36	5·02	4·89
3,500	6·28	6·03	5·32	5·46	5·04	4·46	4·92	4·89
4,000	6·34	6·06	5·42	4·88	4·97	4·35	5·20	5·14

Pacific Ocean

Depth m.	50°30'N 175°16'W	28°02'N 122°08'W	3°18'N 129°02'E	4°20'S 116°46'E	31°25'S 176°25'W	59°05'S 163°46'W	70°00'S 159°40'W
2,000	1·64	1·89	2·56	2·53	3·32	4·27	4·32
2,500	2·20	2·44	2·82	2·75	3·25	4·33	4·40
3,000	2·58	2·72	3·15	2·86	3·75	4·37	4·49
3,500	3·00	3·00	3·26	2·96	4·27	4·20	4·75
4,000	—	—	3·27	3·00	4·52	4·06	—

It can be seen that at depths between 2,000 and 4,000 m. there is a general diminution of oxygen content southwards in the Atlantic Ocean, except near the Antarctic continent, where sinking water increases the amount. It is interesting to compare the values given for the Pacific Ocean. These values change in the reverse direction to those in the Atlantic; in the Pacific the greater values are found towards the southern part of the ocean, and only there, in about 60°S latitude, do the Pacific values approach those of the Atlantic. The figures show that on the whole the oxygen content of the deep Pacific waters are considerably lower than those of the Atlantic, particularly in the Northern Hemisphere, which can be explained by the sources of deep water and the general circulation of the oceans, which is discussed in chapter 4.

3. WATER MASSES

(a) Definition and Concept

Just as the concept of air masses in meteorology has greatly assisted the description and analysis of the weather, so in the oceans the concept of water masses has proved fruitful. An air mass is a body of air having properties of homogeneity; similarly a water mass is a relatively homogenous body of water, which can be described by its characteristics. The most valuable of its properties from this point of view are its temperature and salinity, and depending on these two, its density. Water masses are therefore, defined by their temperature and salinity. Because the denser water sinks relative to the less dense it is important to determine this property, which can be expressed in terms of temperature and salinity.

The density is usually expressed in terms of sigma$_t$, σ_t, which refers to the density at atmospheric pressure and the temperature at which it was collected. The density of pure water at 4°C is equal to unity, but because of the salt added the density of sea water exceeds that of pure water by a small amount. An average surface density may be about 1·02575. This figure is rather cumbersome and to simplify description it is given in the form, density—1 times 1,000, $\sigma = (\rho - 1) \times 1,000$, thus a density of 1·02575 becomes sigma 25·75. The density depends on temperature, salinity and pressure, and it is given in terms of sigma when it refers to the density at the pressure and temperature where the sample was collected. The term sigma$_t$ is used for this value corrected to atmospheric pressure, while sigma$_0$ refers to the density the water would have at o°C; in this form the density is only a function of salinity. For most purposes sigma$_t$ is the most useful as both temperature and salinity affect density. A knowledge of the distribution of these two factors relative to one another is fundamental to a description of the water masses and to an understanding of their movements relative to one another, particularly in a vertical sense, which depends largely on their density.

In order to describe the water masses in terms of their temperature and salinity, Helland-Hansen (1916) devised a T-S diagram, which relates these two variables together. Density alone, cannot be used to describe a water mass, because two water masses may have the same density but different temperature and salinity; one may achieve its density through low temperature, the other through high salinity. Characteristics of temperature and salinity may be plotted separately against depth, or, as in the T-S diagram, the temperature and salinity may be plotted against each other. The points so plotted usually fall on a well-defined curve, which is often nearly a straight line, in which temperature and salinity decrease together. There is, therefore, only a slow increase of density downwards, as the two factors causing an increase of density are working in opposite directions. Because the density depends on temperature and salinity, it is possible to enter the sigma$_t$ values on the T-S graph; lines of equal sigma$_t$ then fall slowly across the diagram from right to left, the temperature increasing upwards on the abscissa, while the salinity increases to the right on the ordinate axis of the graph as shown in fig. 3–4. The curves show that

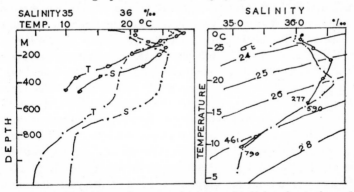

FIG. 3–4. The left-hand part shows temperature and salinity observations plotted against depth in the Gulf Stream off Onslow Bay, while the right-hand part of the figure shows the same data plotted as a T-S diagram. The density line, σ$_t$, is shown. (After Sverdrup *et al.*) (H. U. Sverdrup, Martin W. Johnson and Richard H. Fleming, *The Oceans: Their Physics, Chemistry and general Biology.* © 1942. Prentice-Hall, Inc., U.S.A. Reprinted by permission.)

the same water mass is present at different depths, while the stability of the stratification can be seen from the relationship between the angle of the sigma$_t$ lines and the slope of the temperature-salinity figures.

A water mass is defined by its characteristic T-S curve, though if the water were entirely homogenous it would be possible to define it by one value of the temperature and a corresponding one for the salinity. A straight line T-S relationship results from the mixing of two different water masses, each of which can be defined as a point on the T-S graph.

In considering the formation of water masses, the conditions at the surface are of great importance, as it is here that the water attained its original characteristics of temperature and salinity by the processes already mentioned, while modifications to the original T-S relationships come about by mixing with adjacent water masses, thereby modifying the original T-S character. The mixing takes place either laterally or vertically; in the former, movement is along the sigma$_t$ surfaces, in the latter across them. As mixing proceeds the T-S relationships become modified, and by tracing the changing extremes of one water mass its movement through the ocean can be studied, and the rate of change of its characteristics gives an indication of the amount of dilution with other water masses by mixing which is taking place. This method of tracing water masses by their extreme values of temperature and salinity is called the core method by Wüst (1935); a diagram showing the maximum salinity, for example, of a water mass near its source may be compared with that at the position where it loses its identity; the diminution of this factor at any intermediate point gives a precise value of its dilution, or the percentage of the original water present.

Before considering the character and formation of the different water masses, which have been recognized in the oceans, an attempt to describe the distribution of water in terms of the frequency of temperature and salinity relationships may be mentioned (Cochrane, 1956, 1958; Pollak, 1958, and Montgomery, 1958). The first work of Cochrane deals with the surface characteristics of the Pacific Ocean, and his later contribution with the other waters of this ocean, while Pollak discusses the Indian Ocean and Montgomery the Atlantic and world ocean. The technique used is to work out the number of observations of temperature and salinity which fall within certain divisions of a T-S diagram; the ranges used were 2°C for temperature and 0·4‰ for salinity for the coarse-scale graph and 0·5°C and 0·1‰ for the fine-scale graph. The results are worked out for different seasons of the year. Isopleths are drawn round the frequency values, which indicate clearly the most common values of temperature and salinity relationship at different seasons and in different areas.

The results for the surface of the Pacific Ocean show that the maximum number of observations of high temperatures is much greater in the north than the south Pacific; this is partly due to the great width of the north Pacific in low latitudes, and the inclusion of the Antarctic region accounts for the concentration at low temperatures in the south Pacific. In the north Pacific the salinities are concentrated in the higher values, with a secondary concentration at lower values, while in the south Pacific the salinity range is smaller. On the whole the densities of the north Pacific exceed those of the south Pacific.

In dealing with the deeper waters of the Pacific Ocean the temperatures are naturally much lower. One interesting point emerges, and this is the concentration of T-S values around 1·5°C and 34·65‰ salinity; 33 per cent of the observations fall between 1 and 2°C and between 34·6 and 34·7‰; the 50 per cent boundary does not cover a very much wider range. The water having these characteristics occupies much of the Pacific basin below a few hundred metres in the Antarctic and below 2,000 m. elsewhere. It is designated the Pacific Deep Water. This indicates the great homogeneity of the bulk of the water of the Pacific Ocean. When the 75 per cent boundary is considered a secondary peak is found around the T-S values of 4·25°C and 34·55‰, this water is found across the tropics at depths of 700 to 1,100 m., and is called Tropical Water. A third mode occurs with a temperature of 0·25°C and 34·05‰; this water is found in the Sea of Japan and is one of the very few definitely Pacific deep waters; it fills the Sea of Japan from 400 m. downwards to the bottom, and results from cooling in cold winters and attains such depths because the main Pacific Deep Water cannot enter the Sea of Japan.

Pollak has shown that there is a similar homogeneity in the deep water of the Indian Ocean, again almost one-third of the total volume lies between 0·5 and 2·0°C and 34·7 and 34·8‰; a secondary maximum occurs with a similar density but lower temperature and salinity. This mass of water forms the main deep water of the Indian Ocean; similar T-S relationships are found over a range of latitude of 66°. The Red Sea and Persian Gulf add a small quantity of very saline water, ranging from 38·5 to nearly 44‰. Lack of observational data does not allow seasonal analysis to be made, but present intensive work in this ocean will help to remedy this.

Montgomery's results for the Atlantic include all the adjacent seas, as do those of the analyses already discussed. These adjacent seas show up on the graph as separate entities, as they have very distinctive salinity characteristics, high in the Mediterranean and low in the Black Sea. The finer-scale diagram, on which the 50 per cent line is drawn, shows two maxima; the major one at 2·25°C and 34·95‰ represents the North Atlantic Deep Water, which will be discussed in more detail later, while the other, with T-S values of 0°C and 34·65‰ represents the water found in the south Atlantic and includes the Antarctic Bottom Water; this high value merges into the maximum of the Indian Ocean and that of the Pacific, which have already been given.

It is interesting to compare the relative homogeneity of the three oceans, using the number of fine classes for 50 per cent and 75 per cent of the total observations.

Pacific Ocean	50%	5 classes	75%	20 classes
Indian Ocean		8		33
Atlantic Ocean		11		44
World Ocean		12		43

These figures show that the Pacific is the most homogeneous and the Atlantic the least. The reason for this will become apparent when the formation of the different water masses is discussed. Calculations for the world ocean show that for the coarse-scale class (2°C and 0·4‰) 75 per cent of the entire ocean falls into three classes from 0 to 6°C and 34 to 35‰; this is a small range considering that the total range of the ocean lies between −2 and 36°C and from 0 to 44‰. Most of the ocean water is remarkably homogeneous. Within this general homogeneity, however, a number of separate water masses can be differentiated, and these begin to emerge when the modes for the 50 per cent boundary for the fine-scale diagram (classes include 0·5°C and 0·1‰ groups) are analysed. The density is distributed in such a way that the mean density is greatest in the Atlantic, intermediate in the Indian Ocean and least in the Pacific Ocean, while the world ocean falls between the Pacific and Indian Oceans.

(b) Method of formation and character of the major surface water masses

The water masses are stratified in the oceans according to their density, the densest clearly sinking to the greatest depths. It is only in the high latitudes that conditions are cold enough for deep waters to form. These dense waters occupy most of the ocean basins, but on the surface, floating above the deep water, are the shallow water masses which cover much of the surface of the oceans. The characteristics of these may be mentioned first. Some of the water masses have been given different names by different workers, but the better-known names, as given by Sverdrup *et al.* (1946), will be used. The water masses include the following types:

Surface-water masses: Antarctic Surface Water.
Arctic Surface Water.
North Atlantic Central Water.
South Atlantic Central Water.
Subantarctic Water—all oceans.

Subarctic Pacific Water.
Western North Pacific Central Water.
Eastern North Pacific Central Water.
Pacific Equatorial Water.
Western South Pacific Water.
Eastern South Pacific Water.
Indian Equatorial Water.
Indian Central Water.
Surface and deep water: Antarctic Circumpolar Water—all southern ocean.
Deep-water masses: Antarctic Intermediate Water.
Intermediate Water—North Atlantic.
Intermediate Water—North Pacific.
Mediterranean Water.
North Atlantic Deep and Bottom Water.
Pacific Deep Water.
Arctic Deep Water.
Antarctic Bottom Water.

The distribution of the surface water masses and the sources of the deeper ones are shown on the map, fig. 3–5. The central water masses cover a wide area of all the oceans. In the Atlantic Ocean the two central water masses are defined as those characteristic of the northern and southern part of the low latitudes, respectively. The differences between them reflect the differences of surface temperature and salinity, which have already been mentioned.

1. THE NORTH ATLANTIC CENTRAL WATER. This mass covers a wide area of the northern part of the ocean, but is restricted to shallow depths. Its T-S relationships can be described as an almost straight line connecting the points of the T-S graph with T 8°C and S 35·10‰ and T 19°C and S 36·7‰ (shown in fig. 3–6). This water has been identified at all stations except just south of Cape Farewell in Greenland and at a point south of Iceland, as well as at a station in latitude 6°50′N. Towards the Equator it is replaced by water which has crossed from the South Atlantic. It is remarkably similar on the western and eastern borders of the north Atlantic, to the west of the Bay of Biscay and east of Cape Hatteras.

This widespread body of water must have been formed in the north Atlantic, and it probably attained its characteristic temperature and salinity when it was in contact with the atmosphere. It has been shown that the vertical arrangement of temperature and salinity in this water closely resembles the northward decrease of these factors in the horizontal plane. It is, therefore, thought that this water originated by the sinking of the water along its correct density surface during winter cooling, some lateral and vertical mixing may also have taken place. The thickness of the water mass depends partly upon the currents which are all confined within it on the surface. It is relatively thick on the right-hand side of the currents and thinner on the left of their direction of flow, as it occurs in the Northern Hemisphere, because the rotation

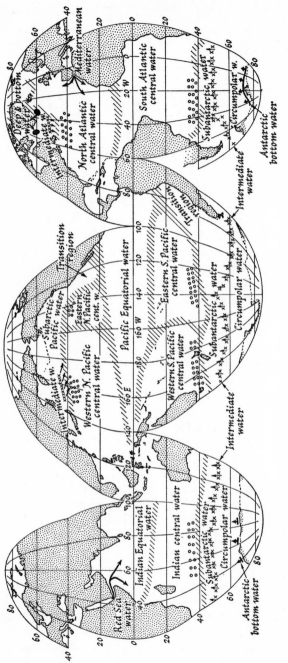

FIG. 3-5. Map to show the distribution of surface-water masses and the source of some of the deep-water masses. The circles indicate regions of Central Water formation, and the regions of Antarctic and Arctic Intermediate Water formation. (After Sverdrup *et al.*) (H. U. Sverdrup. Martin W. Johnson and Richard H. Fleming, *The Oceans: Their Physics, Chemistry and general Biology.* © 1942. Prentice-Hall, Inc, U.S.A. Reprinted by permission.)

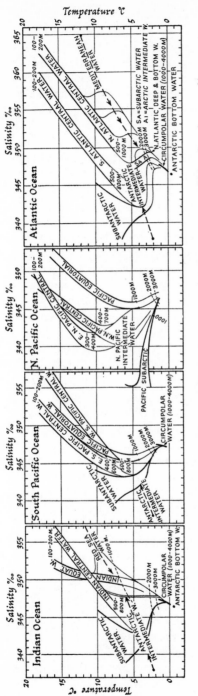

FIG. 3-6. Characteristic temperature-salinity relationships for the principal water masses. (After Sverdrup et al.) (H. U. Sverdrup, Martin W. Johnson and Richard H. Fleming, *The Oceans: Their Physics, Chemistry and general Biology.* © 1942. Prentice-Hall, Inc., U.S.A. Reprinted by permission.)

of the Earth affects it in this way. Its maximum thickness of 900 m. is reached in the Sargasso Sea, but over much of its extent its thickness does not greatly exceed 200 m.

The North Atlantic Central Water mass is formed between latitudes 30 and 40°N, and it is in this zone that the subtropical convergence is found. This is a wide zone in which there is a tendency for currents to converge. A factor which helps to account for this convergence is the deflection to the right of their directions of the wind-driven currents in the Northern Hemisphere. The currents dependent on the trade winds, blowing from the north-east, tend to be deflected to the north-west, where it meets the water influenced by the westerly winds, which is deflected towards the south-east, in the zone north of the trade winds. In the zone of the subtropical convergence there is a rapid increase of density of the surface waters to the north. This zone of convergence, being primarily dependent on the winds, is much more variable with the seasons, than the Antarctic convergence.

ii. SOUTH ATLANTIC CENTRAL WATER. This water also covers a wide area; in general it is rather similar in its T-S relationships to its northern counterpart, but, reflecting the general lowering of temperature and salinity to the south of the Equator, this water mass is cooler and fresher than the northern one. It is defined by a nearly straight T-S curve with values of T 6°C, S 34·5‰ to T 18°C, S 36‰. Again there is a similarity between this vertical range and the horizontal change of temperature and salinity between 30 and 40°S. This is the region of the southern subtropical convergence. Again the water sinks at this convergence and spreads northwards along its correct density surface. The water mass extends from coast to coast in the south Atlantic, and also reaches north of the Equator, because the thermal Equator lies at 5°N. Like its northern counterpart, this water is also shallow, rarely exceeding 600 m. in thickness; again it is in this surface layer that the main currents flow.

To the north and south of the Central Water masses the character of the water on the surface differs considerably from that found in lower latitudes. Considering first the area north of the North Atlantic Central Water, the conditions in what has been termed the Arctic Mediterranean Sea may be mentioned; this area covers the Norwegian Sea north of the Wyville Thomson Ridge. This zone meets the Barents Sea and North Polar Sea. The water flowing into this area from the south is relatively warm and saline compared with the water flowing out, the mean values being 35·3‰ and 32‰ respectively. In this environment the opposite change in the character of the water to that in the Mediterranean takes place; excessive precipitation, runoff and ice melting all help to cool the water and reduce its salinity.

In the North Polar Sea there are three water masses: iii. THE ARCTIC SURFACE WATER, the Atlantic Water and the Arctic Deep Water are found in that order in depth. The main character of the Surface Water is its low salinity, particularly near the mouths of the large Siberian rivers, where it is very low; to the north of Spitzbergen it attains 32 to 33‰. On the north Siberian shelf the salinity is 29·67‰ in May, its maximum value, but as ice continues to melt during the summer a layer of almost fresh, cold water overlies the more saline water. This cold, fresh water rests on top of water of Atlantic origin; the salinity of the latter is 35·1‰ and it has a temperature of 3–4°C, being found at depths between 75 and 400 m.

iv. SUBANTARCTIC WATER. To the south of the subtropical convergence in the South Atlantic, the Subantarctic Water is found at the surface; it lies between this convergence and the Antarctic convergence at about 52 to 53°S. This water mass is transitional between the Central Water to the north and the Circumpolar Water to the south. It is only developed to a very minor degree in the North Atlantic. The Subantarctic Water has a relatively low salinity and it seems that mixing and vertical circulation play a part in its formation. It can be traced all round the Antarctic continent, having very similar characteristics in all the southern oceans.

The Pacific is much larger than the Atlantic, and its Central Water masses are correspondingly diverse, falling into two classes in each hemisphere, while in addition there is a large area of Equatorial Water. In the NORTH PACIFIC OCEAN the SUBARCTIC WATER MASS (v) is much better developed than in the Atlantic; it is one of the important surface masses of the ocean. Its average temperature in latitude 50°N is between 2 and 4°C, and it has a low salinity of about 32‰ at the surface, increasing to about 34‰ at depths of a few hundred metres. As it is traced eastwards towards the coast of California, excess evaporation and heating raise its salinity and temperature, forming a transitional water mass.

vi. THE CENTRAL WATERS OF THE PACIFIC. These form a western and eastern type, each of which has a rather similar range to its Atlantic counterpart, but with a lower salinity. The western type is more extensive than the eastern. At a temperature of 16°C the salinity in the different waters indicates the variation of salinity as follows:

North Atlantic	36·12‰
West N. Pacific	34·67
East N. Pacific	34·62
South Atlantic	35·64
West S. Pacific	35·55
East S. Pacific	35·08
Indian Ocean	35·62

This shows that the lowest values for salinity in the central masses are found in the North Pacific. These figures can be correlated with the distribution of surface characteristics, as already discussed.

The PACIFIC OCEAN differs from the Atlantic in having a wide zone of vii. EQUATORIAL WATER, separating the Central Water masses to north and south. This water is found at the surface in a broad tongue pointing to the west, covering the zone from 20°N to 20°S in the eastern part of the ocean, and tapering to a width of only a degree or two north of the equator off New Guinea. This is a remarkably uniform water mass, the T-S curve is almost straight ranging from T 15°C, S 35·15‰, to T 8°C, S 34·6‰. At a depth of 800 m. the temperature is 5·5°C. The equatorial current system takes place within this water mass.

To the south of this wide belt of Equatorial Water lies the South Central Water masses, which can again be divided into an eastern and western type. Unlike the northern part of the ocean, these two waters cover roughly similar areas of the southern part of the ocean. The Western Central Water mass is practically identical with that of the Indian Ocean Central Water, here the T-S relationship again forms a nearly straight line with the values ranging from T 15°C, S 35·5‰ to T 8°C, S 34·6‰. In the eastern South Pacific Central Water the temperature lies between 10 and 18°C, and the salinity is 0·5‰ lower than in the west. These central water masses form in about the same way as those in the Atlantic, at the subtropical convergences.

To the south of the Central Water masses in the south Pacific lies a broad belt of Subantarctic Water. This is continuous with a similar belt in the Atlantic and Indian Oceans. It lies to the south of 40°S and in its upper layers has a salinity of 34·2 to 34·4‰, with a temperature between 4 and 8°C. Like its northern counterpart, this water extends Equatorward up the Pacific coast of South America, where its temperature and salinity are similarly increased by heating and excess evaporation. In this transitional form it reaches a little north of 20°S.

Tracing it westwards from the Pacific, it can be followed into the Indian Ocean, where it is found between latitudes of about 40°S and 50°S, between the Subtropical and Subantarctic Convergences. Its character is very similar to the same water mass in the other oceans.

To the north lies the viii. INDIAN CENTRAL WATER on the surface. Its character has already been mentioned in connexion with its similarity to the Western South Pacific Central Water. This water seems very uniform throughout the considerable width of the Indian Ocean, from observations made off Port Elizabeth in South Africa, off south-west Australia and north-west of Madagascar. There is, however, a rapid change at the surface at the southern boundary of this water mass near the convergence. The water is formed by sinking at this convergence, as its vertical characteristics, to a depth of 800 m., resemble closely the horizontal variation at the convergence. Its northern limit is less clearly defined, partly owing to lack of observations, but partly because it grades into ix. the INDIAN EQUATORIAL WATER, which occupies the upper layers of the Indian Ocean, north of about 10°S.

There is reasonable homogeneity in this Equatorial Water mass, the points on the T-S graph fall on an almost straight line from T 4°C, S 34·9‰ to T 17°C, S 35·25‰. One of the differences between these two last water masses is the higher surface temperature in the Equatorial Water compared with the Central Water. In the northern Indian Ocean the water is slightly modified at depth by the addition of very saline water from the Red Sea, where evaporation greatly exceeds runoff from the land and precipitation; this is shown by the very high salinities and temperatures, which are T 21·5 −22°C, S 40·5 to 41‰ at a depth of 750 m. On the whole the Indian Equatorial Water covers a much smaller range of salinity over the same temperature range than does the Central Water.

The water masses which have been discussed so far are those which form at and which remain fairly near the surface of the ocean, owing to their relatively high temperature, compared with the waters beneath them. Their density is such that they are unable to sink to the depths of the ocean. However, in a few special circumstances deep-water masses of great density which can sink to the bottom of the ocean are formed. Because of this formation of deep-water masses in some areas and their subsequent movement, there must be upwelling in other areas to maintain the balance. Although this is probably widely distributed throughout the oceans on a small scale, it is also concentrated in position to give rise to a definite water mass. This upwelling water gives rise to the only major near-surface water mass which has not yet been mentioned. The upwelling water does not, however, quite reach the surface, but is overlaid by a shallow layer of colder water, called x. ANTARCTIC SURFACE WATER. It is found between the Antarctic Convergence and the Antarctic Continent and is a layer of cold water lying above more saline, warmer water. The surface water is in a shallow layer which is moving north over a south-moving deeper, warmer layer: in the Atlantic and Indian Oceans it is only 60 to 80 m. deep in the divergence zone between the easterly and westerly surface currents, although it reaches down to 150 m. in the east Pacific. Its depth increases towards the convergence and the continent, reaching 300 m. towards the north and 400 m. to the south. In winter the layer is homogeneous, with a temperature between −1·8 and −1·9°C in the south, rising to between 1°C and 0°C in the north. In summer the surface warms up to a maximum of 3·5°C in the north. The salinity is greatest in winter, varying in the

o.–H

south from 34 to 34·5‰; in summer it may be less than 33‰. The upper layers thus change markedly with the seasons (Deacon, 1937).

xi. THE CIRCUMPOLAR WATER MASS. This water mass is found in a belt encircling the Antarctic Continent in high southern latitudes. It lies between the Antarctic Convergence at about 52 to 53°S and the Antarctic shoreline. This water is found a short distance below the surface, having a temperature maximum at a depth of 500 to 600 m. Its temperature is normally above 0·5°C and its salinity slightly above 34·7‰. Its salinity maximum varies from a depth of 700 to 1,300 m. The water is very uniform all around the southern ocean. It is also very similar in depth, slowly decreasing in temperature and salinity downwards. Throughout most of the body of this water the temperature does not often exceed 0 to 2°C, while below 800 m. the differences of salinity fall within a range of 0·1‰. It is partly because of this uniformity with depth that this water can move upwards towards the surface, where the Antarctic Divergence is found between 60 and 70°S. In the south Atlantic at depths between 1,000 and 4,000 m. the salinity is a little above 34·7‰, increasing rapidly east of 20°E, where it mixes with saline water from the north Atlantic; this relatively high salinity can be traced into the Indian Ocean, giving a value of 34·76‰ south of Australia at 140°E. However, in the Pacific the salinity is again decreased due to the admixture of Pacific Deep Water, which has a low salinity.

The temperature behaves in a similar way, decreasing at first, when the water is traced into the Atlantic from the west, but it increases at about 10°E and lies above 2·5°C between 60 and 120°E; this is also due to admixture of fairly warm Atlantic and Indian Ocean Water. The cooler Deep Pacific Water causes a fall of temperature as the water is traced into the Pacific.

The Circumpolar Water mass incorporates parts of several different types of water which come together and mix in high southern latitudes and which slowly tend to move towards the surface, thus accounting for the homogeneity with depth. Evidence supporting this pattern of movement can be derived from the oxygen studies of this water and its environment. These show that this water cannot travel around the Antarctic Continent without renewal. The water which enters the Atlantic from the west has an oxygen content of 3·7 ml./l. at about 1,200 m. The amount tends to increase eastwards, to 4·8 ml./l. east of the South Antilles arc. There is then a slow decrease at most depths eastwards. The Antarctic Circumpolar Water has a rather higher oxygen content than the deep water farther north, which suggests mixing with more aerated waters, nearer their sources at the surface. The Antarctic Bottom Water is one of these, as this has a high oxygen content above 4·6 ml./l. The Circumpolar Water is an interesting one, as it is the only water mass which is not formed by sinking, being the result of subsurface mixing and subsequent rising. The water masses which are dense enough to sink to greater depths must now be mentioned.

(c) Deeper-water masses

These water masses can be divided into two main classes: (1) the intermediate waters, and (2) the deep and bottom waters. The former are not as dense as the latter and, therefore, only sink to intermediate depths. These waters are, however, formed in fairly high latitudes in all oceans, in varying amounts, and are of differing importance. The best known of the intermediate water masses is the i. ANTARCTIC INTERMEDIATE WATER, which is formed near or just north of the Antarctic Convergence. This area of convergence is one in which there is a rapid increase of surface temperature away from the Antarctic Continent, at about 50°S, varying from between 1 and 3°C in winter to 4–6°C in summer. There is evidence to suggest (Wyrtki, 1961) that the convergence is sometimes a zone of light divergence when west winds are strong, although it is a zone of convergence during light west winds; hence Wyrtki suggests calling in the Antarctic Polar Front and not the Antarctic Convergence.

The convergence is situated entirely in the west wind zone where the deep warm water climbs towards the surface southwards, while lighter, colder Antarctic surface water sinks northwards above it. Its position according to Deacon (1937 and 1959) depends on the volume of northward flowing Antarctic Bottom Water. The position of the convergence, shown in fig. 3–7, is plotted from surface observations of temperature, but it can be seen that this agrees closely with the temperature change at 2,500 m., shown in the figure. These values suggest a steep slope above the bottom water in this zone, and the change is sharpest where the greatest volume of bottom flow is indicated in the Atlantic. The greater volume of bottom water in the Atlantic, which weakens towards the east, may help to explain the more northerly position, by about 10° latitude, of the position of the convergence in the Atlantic.

Another line of argument relates the convergence to the surface conditions of current and wind. The meridional gradient of atmospheric pressure is greatest at the convergence, which leads to a convergence of surface-water transport in this zone. However, it can be argued that it is the influence of the surface temperature which causes the greater atmospheric pressure gradient. This in turn could be due to the amount of bottom water moving north, which is greatest in the favourable geographical conditions for the formation of this bottom water in the Weddell Sea in the Atlantic.

This convergence seems to be remarkably stationary, both seasonally and for longer periods; but if its position were related to the surface wind it would be expected to change seasonally. Thus it seems that its cause is not closely dependent on the winds. It does, however, exert a strong influence on the climate near it. For example, in South Georgia

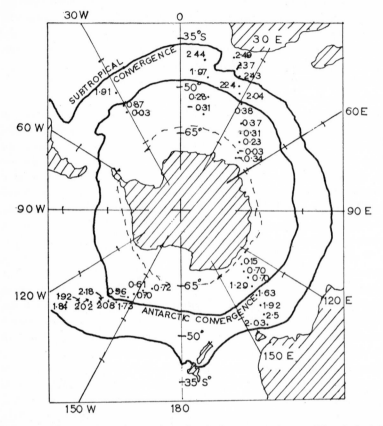

FIG. 3–7. Map to show the southern hemisphere convergences. The dashed line indicates the boundary between the easterly and westerly drifts around the Antarctic continent. The figures give the temperature in degrees centigrade at a depth of 2,500 m. (After Deacon.)

in latitude 54°S, which is in nearly the same latitude as Staten Island, off Tierra del Fuego, 54° 50′ S, the climate is very much colder. The latter is north of the convergence, while the former is south of it. Staten Island is clothed with luxuriant vegetation, while South Georgia is much more barren. The tree-line of Tierra del Fuego is as low as the snow-line of South Georgia. The position of the Antarctic convergence also affects the marine life of the areas on either side of it.

It is to the north of this zone of convergence that water sinks to form the Antarctic Intermediate Water, which has a temperature between 2·2 and 7°C and a low salinity of 34·1 to 34·6‰, which gives it a density of sigma$_t$=27. Its essential character, by which its movements can be traced as it sinks and spreads northwards, is its low salinity. In the south Atlantic it is found below the Central Water, and can be recognized by its low salinity at a depth of about 800 m. It is better developed on the western side of the ocean in the south. It has also been traced in the north Atlantic, just north of the Equator, where its density is still about 24·4; it does, however, show evidence of mixing with waters of roughly the same density. At this position is also found some evidence of the corresponding water mass of the north Atlantic.

ii. This is the NORTH ATLANTIC INTERMEDIATE WATER, which is only formed in small quantities, but which is found there with a salinity of about 34·88‰ and a temperature of 3·5°C. This water does not spread as far as its southern counterpart. In the Pacific Ocean, on the other hand, at moderate northern latitudes a large body of iii. PACIFIC INTERMEDIATE WATER is formed, this is not quite the same as the Antarctic Intermediate Water, as it does not form in such high latitudes, nor does it have the high oxygen content which characterizes the Antarctic Intermediate Water and North Atlantic Intermediate Water. The Pacific type is formed about latitude 40°N, and is found below the central waters of the north Pacific, being characterized by a salinity minimum. It is found at depths of 600 to 800 m. in the north-western part of the ocean, but nearer the Equator in the eastern Pacific it divides, one layer being at 200 m. and the other at 900 m. At these intermediate depths of less than 1,000 m. there is a pronounced oxygen minimum in the north Pacific; the low oxygen values are found 400 to 500 m. below the salinity minimum, and it is particularly low off the American coast at depths less than 1,000 m. This low-oxygen water sometimes upwells almost to the surface, where the oxygen value may be less than 0·1 ml./l. This suggests very slow circulation in this area at this depth.

Before dealing with the waters which fill the deepest ocean levels, the very characteristic iv. MEDITERRANEAN WATER should be discussed. This water, because of its very special quality, can be traced for very great distances. The reason for its peculiar characteristics has already been mentioned, but figures of its quantity and details of its temperature and salinity are of interest. This water mass is one of the denser ones, owing to its very high salinity. As it leaves the Straits of Gibraltar it has a salinity of over 37‰ and a temperature of 13°C. These figures indicate that intense mixing takes place in the Straits, as these values are considerably modified from those characteristic of the deep water of the Mediterranean itself.

The Mediterranean Sea can be divided into four basins, each of which has its own characteristic type of deep water, while there is also a recognizable surface layer, intermediate layer and a transition layer. The intermediate layer is lacking where the deep water is formed, but where it is present it has a salinity maximum and is composed of the surface water of the eastern Mediterranean, flowing westwards beneath the fresher inflowing Atlantic water. Its salinity is obtained in the eastern part of the sea, where the excess of evaporation over runoff and rainfall reaches a maximum. This high salinity, despite its high temperature, enables the water to sink below the surface water. The transition layer between 600 and 1,500 m. links the intermediate and deep waters; it is a zone in which the temperature falls off more rapidly than the salinity.

The deep waters are formed in the northern part of the sea, where cold winter winds, such as the Mistral in south France and the Bora, at the head of the Adriatic, lower the surface temperature sufficiently in winter for the water density to be increased enough for it to reach the deep basins. It is probably only in extra cold seasons that the temperature is lowered sufficiently for bottom water to form at such densities that it can sink to the bottom. The oxygen content and the amount of inflow and outflow through the Straits of Gibraltar indicate that this renewal takes place at such a rate that on the average the whole water of the Mediterranean is renewed every seventy-five years. The oxygen decreases from east to west in the intermediate water, which confirms its westward travel. The minimum oxygen values are found in the transitional zone of the eastern Mediterranean, and values in the deep water suggest that deep water forms most readily in the basin west of Corsica and Sardinia. The character of the deep water in the four basins reflects the external circumstances which form this very distinctive, saline water:

Basin		Temperature °C	Salinity ‰
Algiers-Provencal	} West	13·00	38·39
Tyrrhenian		13·10	38·44
Ionian	} East	13·57	38·65
Levantine		13·62	38·66

It can be seen that the farther east the basin the warmer and saltier the water is, the greatest difference being between the two western and two eastern basins, owing to the shallow straits between them south-west of Sicily.

The Mediterranean Sea is particularly important, because of the considerable density of this saline water produced there. It, therefore, takes part in the deep-water circulation of the Atlantic and can be readily recognized by its high salinity, which can be traced as far as the southern tip of Africa at least. The amount of water which enters the Atlantic from the Mediterranean has been estimated as 1,750,000 m.³/sec. This is quite an appreciable quantity of the total deep-water formation of the North Atlantic Ocean; estimates of this proportion vary between one-third and one-tenth of the whole. Thus the Mediterranean plays a greater part in the general oceanic circulation than other adjacent seas. In the Atlantic it mixes with waters whose densities lie between sigma$_t$ 27·5 and 27·7, which is below the Antarctic Intermediate Water. Its density is nearest to that of the North Atlantic Deep Water, with which it largely mixes.

v. THE NORTH ATLANTIC DEEP AND BOTTOM WATER is so called because in the North Atlantic it occupies the bottom of the ocean basin, being the densest water here, while in the South Atlantic it is found as deep water above the even denser Antarctic Bottom Water. The water mass is formed in the North Atlantic in the region on either side of Cape Farewell, South Greenland, where the warm, saline waters of the North Atlantic Drift come into contact with the cold currents moving down from the Arctic Ocean on either side of Greenland, the Labrador Current to the west and the East Greenland Current to the east. This water which mixes at the surface is cooled in winter to such an extent that its density is increased, allowing it to descend to depths greater than 1,000 m. Its sigma$_t$ value reaches a maximum of 27·88, which is rather greater than that of the Mediterranean water at its most dense. Its temperature lies between 2·8 and 3·3°C and its salinity is in the range 34·9 to 34·96‰.

It is interesting to note that a corresponding deep water is not formed in the north Pacific, owing to the absence here of cold currents flowing out of the North Polar Sea, as a result of the very narrow and shallow Bering Straits. This has important repercussions on the general circulation of the oceans. It has been estimated that on the average North Atlantic Deep and Bottom Water forms at the rate of about 2 million m.³/sec. on either side of Greenland. More recent views (Stommel), however, suggest that the amount of deep water forming in this area may be as much as 20 million m.³/sec., while Wyrtki suggests 10 million m.³/sec. as a possible figure. Whatever the exact amount formed, it is generally agreed that this source, with the Mediterranean Water, amounts to one of the most important sources of deep-water formation in the whole world ocean.

The rate of formation of the deep and bottom water is, however, only an average. It only forms in winter, as it is only at this season that the water is cooled enough for its density to increase sufficiently for it to sink to the greatest depths. Interesting observations on its formation at sufficient density to sink to the bottom of the north Atlantic have been

discussed by Worthington (1954). He has come to the tentative conclusion, by studying its oxygen content, that the water, which at present
fills the deep north Atlantic basin, was formed very long ago. A chart
showing the dissolved oxygen at the 2,500 m. level was prepared from
data available in 1934 and compared with one from more recent data
obtained during 1947–54. The data for the earlier chart were obtained
during surveys of 1921–2 and 1931–3. A comparison of these two charts
shows that during the interval there was a general drop in the level of
oxygen values by 0·3 ml./l. Profiles throughout the ocean show a
systematic drop in the value of the oxygen between 1922 and 1953 at
depths of 1,500 m. to 5,000 m. This loss of oxygen also appears to occur
in the eastern Atlantic off the Mediterranean at the 2,000 m. level,
which is the only one for which earlier values are available. The rate of
oxygen loss suggested by these data is 0·015 ml./l. per annum, although
the experimental error is such that these figures may be misleading.

Assuming this loss has continued at the same rate since the water
was saturated at the surface, the data can be extrapolated backwards in
time, to give the time when the water was formed at the surface. The
result arrived at suggests that the water now found in the deep basins of
the Atlantic may have been formed around the year 1810. It is very
interesting to note that about this period, particularly in the first decade
of the nineteenth century, the weather was abnormally cold. This cold
was the most intense in northern Europe, but also affected the north-
eastern United States. There seems an interesting possibility, therefore,
that the present North Atlantic Deep and Bottom Water was formed
during this cold period, and it is possible that never since has water of
sufficient density been formed to replace it at lower levels. This one
water mass occupies about half the whole Atlantic Ocean and must have
formed by the mixing of water of different origins to form a new and
homogeneous water mass, whose movement can be traced partly because of the very saline Mediterranean water, which mixes with it to
give it a salinity maximum, to the south of the Straits of Gibraltar
mainly.

Water of north Atlantic origin also finds its way into the deep basins
of the north Polar Sea, over the sills between the Atlantic and the
Norwegian Sea and Polar Sea. There is no means whereby water with
the characteristics of the deep polar water could form within the Arctic
Ocean, but this Arctic water is very similar to the deep water of the
Norwegian Sea. Its temperature is −0·85°C and its salinity is 34·93‰;
it therefore probably is derived via the Norwegian Sea from the north
Atlantic.

vi. THE DEEP WATER OF THE PACIFIC may be mentioned briefly. It
has already been shown that there is no source of deep water within the

north Pacific; the water must, therefore, be derived from more distant sources, hence its relatively low oxygen content. In the south Pacific the deep water shows a slow increase of salinity, which remains constant below 2,500 to 3,000 m. A similar zone of constant salinity is found in the lower 1,000 m. of the north Pacific. The oxygen is usually lower in the north Pacific than the south in the deeper layers, which suggests that the northern water masses have travelled farther and longer from their source areas, either in the North Atlantic, Mediterranean or Antarctic areas. This last source of deep water must now be mentioned, as it plays an important part in many ocean basins.

vii. THE ANTARCTIC BOTTOM WATER, the densest of all water masses, is formed mainly in the Weddel Sea area off the Antarctic Continent. This very dense water is formed from the very cold water at the surface, whose density is further increased by an increase of salinity due to freezing. It is formed of an equal mixture of Circumpolar Water and shelf water, the latter has a temperature of $-1 \cdot 9°C$ and a salinity of about $34 \cdot 62‰$, while the former has a temperature of $0 \cdot 5°C$ and a salinity of $34 \cdot 68‰$. The resulting water at a level below 4,000 m. has a temperature of $-0 \cdot 4°C$ and a salinity of $34 \cdot 66‰$, where its density is $27 \cdot 86$; the shelf water, which sinks along the continental slope, has a higher density, of $27 \cdot 89$, but this is slightly decreased as it mixes with the Circumpolar Water, whose density is $27 \cdot 84$.

The freezing of sea water to increase the salinity is an important part of the process of formation of this water mass. Most of the Antarctic Bottom Water is formed in the Weddell Sea, where sufficiently saline water is present between 30°W and 30°E. A small amount of a similar water may form off the Antarctic in the Indian Ocean sector, but there is no evidence that similar bottom water is formed in the Pacific sector of the Antarctic. The amount forming in the Weddell Sea has been estimated by Stommel to be of about the same volume as that forming in the Northern Hemisphere, which is about 20 million m.^{3}/sec., although Wyrtki (1961) gives 10 million m.^{3}/sec. In general this water becomes somewhat warmer and more saline as it is traced eastwards around the Antarctic Continent.

The circulation of the oceans, to be discussed in the next chapter, is clearly influenced by the fact that the areas where deep water is formed are so few and nearly all occur within the Atlantic Ocean. This leads to very interesting differences between the general pattern of deep-water circulation in the two major oceans.

The part played by the freezing of sea water in the formation of the Antarctic Bottom Water has been mentioned, but ice formation in the sea has other aspects of great interest, which should be commented upon.

4. ICE IN THE OCEAN

Ice in the sea is of importance in several respects; the danger to shipping of floating ice-bergs has led to the initiation of a complex system of ice-berg warning in the seas around Newfoundland, where they are particularly menacing on account of the frequency of fogs, while the formation sea-ice is a limiting factor in the use of many northern ports. The distribution of sea-ice is closely related to climatological processes.

Ice in the sea is broadly divisible into two types; there are the ice-bergs, originating on the land, and the sea-ice, or pack-ice, which forms directly by the freezing of sea water. It is the ice-bergs which are the major menace to shipping, as they can survive to reach fairly low latitudes at times, while the pack-ice causes the freezing up of harbours in winter.

(a) Ice-bergs

There are two distinct types of ice-bergs, which are characteristic of the Northern and Southern Hemispheres respectively. The northern bergs are derived largely from calving glaciers, while the larger flat ice-bergs of the south originate by calving of large blocks from the ice-shelves around parts of the Antarctic continent. The smaller number of true glacier bergs in the Antarctic is due partly to the slow movement of Antarctic glaciers compared with those in Greenland, where ice-berg formation is most active. The ice-bergs characteristic of the Northern Hemisphere are generally much smaller and more irregular than those of the Antarctic, being calved from crevassed, fast-flowing glaciers, which break up into fairly small pieces. Many of the Antarctic bergs are usually composed more of *firn* than ice; they are often very large and flat-topped, and being less dense, float higher in the water. Bergs up to 60 miles in length have been observed, but they are mostly much smaller, being often less than 4 miles and usually about $\frac{1}{4}$ mile long and 30 to 40 m. high.

Calving of Antarctic ice-bergs is very irregular and some years produce many more than others; for example, 1832, 1854, 1893, 1897 and 1922 produced very abundant bergs. In the last decade of the nineteenth century so many ice-bergs were formed that shipping between South America and Africa and Australia had to use a more northerly route. The distribution of ice-bergs in the ocean is of considerable importance and reflects in part the source of ice and also the current pattern in which they move. The ice-bergs of the Southern Hemisphere are all produced around Antarctica. The ice-bergs, however, drift much farther north than the pack-ice, reaching a limit of about 35°S in the Atlantic, 45°S in the Indian Ocean and 50°S in the Pacific;

the cold Falkland Current helps to account for their more northerly extent in the Atlantic. Where the ice-bergs float in the pack-ice, they sometimes move at a considerable speed through it, as their greater draught makes them respond to ocean currents, while the pack-ice is influenced more by the wind. This can be dangerous to ships held in the pack-ice, and which are lying in the ice-berg's path.

In the Northern Hemisphere the sources of ice-bergs are numerous; Greenland, Franz Josef Land and Novaya Zemlya are the main sources, but the origin of the ice-bergs is localized along these coasts. In Greenland bergs are most numerous off the north-west and south-east coasts. From both sources the bergs drift south in the Labrador and East Greenland Currents respectively, where they merge in the 'Gateway of Ice-bergs', east of the Grand Banks between 43 and 47°N. It is in this zone that the International Ice-Patrol has operated since the loss of the S.S. *Titanic* in 1912. The southerly extent of the ice-bergs varies greatly from year to year; for example, the ice-patrol sighted over 1,300 ice-bergs in 1929, but only eleven in 1924. Between 1900 and 1953 an average of 407 ice-bergs reached 48°N, although the number was very variable. In years rich in ice-bergs they penetrate at times as far as 30°N, when they drift east towards the Azores or even the British coasts. Most of the Greenland ice-bergs last less than two years, a berg decreasing from 50 million cu. ft. in the Davis Strait to only 6 to 8 million cu. ft. at the Grand Banks. The main ice-berg season lasts in the Grand Banks area from mid-March to mid-July, with the maximum number arriving in May; for the rest of the year there are very few ice-bergs in this area.

The ice-islands of the Arctic Sea are also derived from the land initially; their smooth surface contrasts strongly with the chaotic pack-ice in which they occur. Their dimensions reach up to $17\frac{1}{2}$ by 7 km. approximately. They originate from the thick ice-shelves off North Greenland and Ellesmere Island, and as they slowly drift with the pack-ice they melt from below and are built up from above by snow precipitation, owing to their greater elevation above the surrounding pack. The currents of the Arctic basin take them on an anticlockwise circuit of the ocean, during which they may drift over the Pole. This long slow journey gives plenty of time for the original ice to melt away from the bottom, so that the ice-island finally consists entirely of *firn*. Their movement gives useful evidence of the currents in the Arctic Ocean; they always are found within the pack-ice, which forms directly from the freezing of sea water.

(b) Sea-ice or pack-ice

Sea-ice occurs in a number of forms according to its age and place of origin. The temperature at which water in the sea freezes depends on the salinity, at 35‰ the freezing-point is −1·9°C, the maximum density being reached at a temperature of −3·6°C. As ice first freezes it has little solidity, because the ice crystals are separated by a concentrated salt solution. Ice first forms on the surface as a sheet and then thickens downwards. It grows most readily in sheltered bays and where the water is not so saline, as off Siberia. This may be called bay-ice, land-ice or shore-ice. It may extend out for 270 miles from the Siberian coast, and it is widespread amongst the islands off Northern Canada.

The salinity of newly formed sea-ice may be about 4–5‰; salinity decreases downwards as growth slows as the ice thickens. It is diluted on the surface by snowfall and draining downward of salt concentrate, and hence falls off with age. The salinity of the ice is higher when the temperature is lower, as freezing is more rapid, and the dense salt concentrate cannot penetrate so quickly down through the ice. Thus at a temperature of −16°C the salinity is 5·64‰, but if the temperature is as low as −40°C the salinity is 10·16‰. However, when the ice is raised above sea-level as it thickens, the salt drains out to a great extent. The thickness to which sea-ice grows varies between 1·5 and 5 m. in one winter, and subsequently it grows both by freezing below and snowfall above. The age of sea-ice does not exceed five to six years, according to the observations of Nansen in the Arctic Ocean; its rate of growth slows down rapidly with time, due to the low conduction qualities of ice. As the sea-ice is moved by currents and the wind, it breaks up into floes, which may be subsequently driven together to form a very irregular, hummocky surface; while the general thickness of the sea-ice rarely exceeds 9 m., pressure ridges may be built up to 20 to 30 m. high, although the higher values are rare, and occasional clear lanes also occur. It is the pressure in the pack-ice which has caused the loss of many ships; for example, the crushing of the *Endurance* in 1914 in the Weddell Sea, when under the command of Shackleton.

Drift-ice has been estimated to cover over 6 per cent of the total area of the oceans; in the Antarctic both ice-bergs and sea-ice are found, but in the Arctic the sea-ice is by far the most important with regard to area covered. In the Davis Strait—Baffin Bay area, where ice-bergs are most numerous, they only amount to 2 per cent of the total drift-ice. In the Antarctic the sea-ice is associated with the area of the east wind belt, which extends to about 65°S, but there are various 'bays' in the pack-ice. Due to warmer currents, the ice extends farther north in the south Atlantic and Indian Oceans than in the Pacific. The mean total area occupied by sea-ice is about 22,610,000 sq. km., but this varies greatly with the seasons, being at a maximum from July to October in the Southern Hemisphere.

The northern sea-ice varies much in extent from season to season and throughout the year. Where the warm waters of the North Atlantic Drift reach the north-east Atlantic the sea-ice limit is farthest north; north-west of Spitzbergen it reaches latitude 81°N, and north of Jan Mayen it is in latitude 72 to 75°N. Sea-ice forms on the whole of the wide continental shelf off Siberia in winter, partly on account of the low salinity, which makes winter shipping along this coast difficult. The whole of the centre of the Arctic Basin, about 5 million sq. km., is covered by old pack-ice, which covers about 70 per cent of the whole basin; the total ice-covered area is 8·7 million sq. km. or 75 per cent of the whole north Polar basin.

The ice drifts across the basin, in response to the winds, at a direction measured as 30° to the right of the wind according to Nansen; the ice drifts at a rate of 1·4 per cent of the wind speed at an angle of 15° to it in winter, when it is tightly packed, but when open leads occur in summer the figures are 2·4 per cent and 40° on the north Siberian shelf. The time taken to drift across the entire Arctic Ocean is about four to five years, as shown by the movement of driftwood from the Siberian rivers to Spitzbergen, Jan Mayen and Greenland. The pack-ice enters the Atlantic via east Greenland and east Canada, where cold currents flow to the south.

The extent of the sea-ice influences the air pressure and cyclone tracks, the latter tending to swing Equatorwards in years of heavy ice. The pack-ice makes it difficult to approach the coast of east Greenland, north of 77°N and from Cape Farewell to 70°N, in between coastal lanes and more open pack-ice make approach possible in most summer seasons. The total amount of ice leaving the Polar Basin has been estimated at 12,700 cu. km. between Greenland and Spitzbergen, 5,000 by Baffin Bay and 2,000 between Bear Island and Franz Josef Land each year. This amount of ice must play an important part in the formation of the deep water mass of the north Atlantic. It has been calculated that 32 million cu. km. in the Southern Hemisphere and 7 million in the Northern melt each year. This greatly changing area of ice cover has a considerable effect of the climate of the Earth, and is in turn influenced by it. There is thus a very close correspondence between the processes affecting the atmosphere and the ocean surface which strongly affect each other.

REFERENCES

Böhnecke, G., Temperatur, Salzgehalt and Dichte an der Oberfläche des Atlantischen Ozeans. Deutsche Atlantische Exped. Meteor 1925–1927. *Wiss. Erg.* Bd. **5**, 62 pp., 1938.

Charlesworth, J. K., *The Quaternary Era*, chapter VIII, 177–208. Arnold, London, 1957.

Cochrane, J. D., The frequency distribution of surface-water characteristics in the Pacific Ocean. *Deep Sea Res.* **4**, 45–53, 1956.

Cochrane, J. D., The frequency distribution of water characteristics in the Pacific Ocean. *Deep Sea Res.* 5, 111–27, 1958.

Cox, R. A., and Smith, N. D., The specific heat of sea water. *Proc. Soc. A.*, 252, 51–62, 1959.

Cox, R. A., The Chemistry of sea water. *New Scientist* 6, 518–21, 1959.

Deacon, G. E. R., The hydrology of the Southern Ocean. *Discovery Reports* 15, 1–124, 1937.

Deacon, G. E. R., The Antarctic Ocean. *Sci. Prog.* 47, 647–60, 1959.

Defant, A., *Physical Oceanography*, Vol. I. Pergamon Press, 1961.

Dietrich, G., and Kalle, K., *Allgemeine Meereskunde*. Berlin, 1957.

Helland-Hansen, B., Nogen hydrografiske metoder, *Skand. Naturforsker möte*, Oslo, 1916.

Kuenen, P. H., *Realms of Water*, 1955.

Montgomery, R. B., Water characteristics of the Atlantic Ocean and of the world ocean. *Deep Sea Res.* 5, 134–48, 1958.

Mosby, H., Verdunstung und Strahlung auf dem Meere. *Ann. d. Hydrog. u. Mar. Meterol.* 64, 281–6, 1936.

Pollak, M. J., Frequency distribution of potential temperature and salinities in the Indian Ocean. *Deep Sea Res.* 5, 128–33, 1958.

Schott, G., *Geographie des Indischen und Stillen Ozeans*. Hamburg, 1935.

Sverdrup, H. U., Johnson, M. W., and Fleming, R. H., *The Oceans*. Prentice-Hall, New York, 1946.

Worthington, L. V., A preliminary note on the time scale in the North Atlantic circulation. *Deep Sea Res.* 1, 244–51, 1954.

Wyrtki, K., The thermohaline circulation in relation to the general circulation in the oceans. *Deep-Sea Res.* 8, 39–64, 1961.

CHAPTER 4

THE CIRCULATION OF THE OCEANS

INTRODUCTION

THE circulation of the oceans is an important aspect of oceanography from the geographical point of view; it helps to distribute heat received in low latitudes to certain areas in higher ones, with all this implies with regard to climatic modifications. The distribution of the fertile areas of the ocean depend to a considerable extent on the oceanic circulation, which brings nutrients to the surface in some areas, while in the early days of sailing ships the major ocean currents were of great significance and areas of calm were avoided.

The oceanic circulation depends fundamentally on two factors: the wind stress is very important in its influence on the surface water, while the distribution of density is both partly caused by and partly causes the movement of the water. In the upper wind-driven layers a balance is achieved between the wind stress, Coriolis force and the pressure field. The Coriolis force arises through relative motion on a rotating earth and is proportional to the relative velocity and the sine of the latitude. It acts at right-angles to the velocity, to the right in the Northern Hemisphere and to the left in the Southern Hemisphere. The wind stress may be balanced by the Coriolis force only, without pressure gradients arising. A strong wind stress leads to a strong Coriolis force. Although the wind plays a very important part in the surface current pattern, at least in some areas it has been suggested that the thermohaline density factors cause the surface gradients; these in turn may influence the wind field to some extent. The two main factors are, therefore, very closely linked and the circulation of the ocean represents the balance between these two forces, although the wind stress is the most important.

1. CAUSES AND CHARACTER OF THE OCEAN CURRENTS

No part of the water of the oceans is completely stationary and it is by means of the oceanic circulation that waters of different temperatures and salinities are distributed throughout the ocean basins. Because of the differences of density in the sea water, resulting from variations in temperature and salinity, it cannot remain immobile, but is forced to move in sympathy with these density variations. The major elements of the oceanic circulation can be explained by the drag of the wind on the sea surface and the distribution of density in the ocean. The major directions of flow can be calculated from the observed temperatures and salinities, and observations show that these calculated movements bear reasonably close resemblance to the actual currents. The upper layers are much influenced by the frictional and inertial forces due to the stress of the wind, while one of the fundamental causes of the deep-water movements is the distribution of mass within the ocean. The flow is related to the distribution of mass, while it in turn affects the distri-bution of mass, which leads to a continuous circulation.

From the close relationship between the general pattern of the surface circulation and that of the planetary wind system it can be seen that the winds exert an important influence on the surface oceanic circulation. The wind provides the energy to maintain the system of circulation. Surface winds can only affect directly the uppermost layers of water to a depth of about 100 m., the bulk of the deep-water circulation, and in-deed some of the surface movement, is the result of density differences, although the wind has a widespread indirect effect at all depths.

The wind exerts a frictional drag on the water surface, which results in shearing stresses, particularly when the motion is turbulent. At low wind velocities, when the flow may be laminar, the stress is much lower, although Phillips (1957) in his views on wave generation considers that there is no minimum wind velocity for disturbing the sea surface. The stability of the air exerts some effect on the disturbance of the sea sur-face and should also be taken into account, although this effect is not yet clearly understood. The stress of the wind causes an upslope in the direction of flow, parallel to the wind direction, in shallow constricted areas, where transverse currents cannot operate. The slope is shown to depend on the depth and the square of the wind force from observations in shallow seas, such as the Baltic.

The wind in the open ocean piles up the light surface water, for example on the western side of the ocean in the trade-wind belts. The effect extends to 150 m. in the Atlantic and 300 m. in the Pacific. The trade winds, therefore, actually blow uphill, as the isobaric surfaces slope at $3 \cdot 7 \times 10^{-8}$ in the Atlantic and $4 \cdot 5 \times 10^{-8}$ in the Pacific. The equatorial counter-currents flow downslope in the region of calms be-tween them to compensate, the lighter water being on the right in the Northern Hemisphere. In this instance the distribution of mass is main-tained by the current.

Where the water is homogeneous and no piling up takes place and no stress is exerted on the bottom, transport is to the right of the wind direction in the Northern Hemisphere and to the left in the Southern

Hemisphere. This possibility was first considered by Nansen in observing that the *Fram*, drifting in the Arctic pack-ice, was moving 20 to 40° to the right of the wind direction. The theoretical angle, as calculated by Ekman in 1905, for simplified conditions of great depth and constant velocity, is 45° to the right in the Northern Hemisphere, the flow decreasing and swinging farther to the right with increasing depth, giving the Ekman spiral. This value of 45° is independent of latitude, but more recent analyses suggest a smaller angle. The direction of current flow in relation to the wind probably requires more refinements. In shallow water observations also show the same angle between the current and the wind at the surface. However, observations made by recording the drift of plastic envelopes on the surface in the Atlantic, west of Britain, do not confirm the theoretical results. These observations showed that the surface water drifts parallel to the gradient wind, determined by isobar spacing, at 2·2 per cent of its velocity. There is reason to suppose that the surface wind was about parallel to the gradient wind; these results, therefore, do not show agreement with the theory. The current velocity would be 3·3 per cent of the surface wind speed, assuming this to be two-thirds of the gradient wind. The deviation of the current from the wind direction might occur in rather deeper layers than those in which the envelopes floated (Hughes, 1956).

In the open ocean the total transport of water is determined by the wind stress on the water surface, which is related to the square of the wind velocity, divided by a factor dependent on the Earth's rotation, and takes place perpendicularly to the wind direction, regardless of depth. This leads to a change in the distribution of mass, which in turn sets up currents. A wind blowing nearly parallel to a shore on its right in the Northern Hemisphere will cause transport of water towards the coast and the surface will slope up in this direction, with lighter water converging in this area (see fig. 4–1). This is compensated by a relative current in the direction of the wind parallel to the shore. If the coast is on the left of the wind, upwelling will take place, as the transport will tend to be offshore, to the right of the wind direction. This upwelling brings up water from depths of about 200 to 300 m. only.

The differences in the distribution of mass of density are also important to the circulation; these are brought about by a number of factors which must be considered as the fundamental causes of the deep oceanic circulation. The most effective external processes are those associated with the heating and cooling of the surface waters, with which are associated the changes of temperature and salinity, so important to an explanation of the movement. The distribution of temperature and salinity is also influenced by the surface winds blowing over the ocean. These winds cause considerable transport of water and, both in

O.–I

this way and by altering the distribution of temperature and salinity, affect the general circulation. The convergence and divergence due to wind patterns also exerts an important effect on the subsequent movement of the ocean waters.

The ocean circulation can be broadly divided into that which takes place in the shallow surface layer, within the upper water masses; this is sometimes called the Ekman layer, and is about 100 m. deep. Beneath

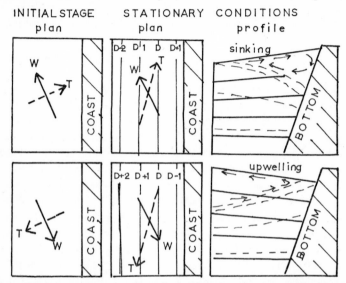

Fig. 4–1. Diagram to show the effect of wind blowing along a coast in the northern hemisphere. W refers to the direction of the wind, and T to the direction of water transport. D, D 1 etc. are contours on the sea surface. (After Sverdrup *et al.*) (H. U. Sverdrup, Martin W. Johnson and Richard H. Fleming, *The Oceans: Their Physics, Chemistry and general Biology.* © 1942. Prentice Hall, Inc., U.S.A. Reprinted by permission.)

this layer the deep-water circulation moves the deeper water masses. Clearly the two are intimately connected; if there is a surface flow across the Equator from one hemisphere to the other, there must be a compensating deeper water flow in the opposite direction. Where water sinks at one point it must be compensated by an equivalent rise elsewhere, with horizontal movement between at the appropriate depth. Before considering the actual currents, the basic concepts of flow in relation to mass may be mentioned. The technique of observing deep-water flow, which has recently been devised, and used to test the newer theories, may then be considered.

From a study of the distribution of density or mass, derived from the observations of temperature and salinity, it is possible to work out mean current velocities, sea surface slope and the total transport of water, to a reasonable degree of accuracy, if certain basic assumptions are made.

The factors which have to be taken into account are the force of gravity, the force due to the pressure gradients and the deflecting force due to the rotation of the earth, and the forces of friction and inertia. The conditions applicable to the Northern Hemisphere will be discussed, those in the Southern Hemisphere being the exact reverse, owing to the opposite effect of the Earth's rotation. In dealing with the ocean flow the friction effects can, in general, be omitted away from the sea surface, bottom and continental boundaries, as can the inertia terms. Time dependent terms are also neglected as well as the vertical term of the deflection force.

From the simplified hydrodynamic equations it is found that the horizontal components in the east and north direction are dependent on the balance between the force due to the rotation of the Earth and the pressure gradient force, which itself depends on the lateral variation of total pressure or mass. The equation of motion in the ocean is equivalent to the geostrophic equation in the atmosphere, used for the evaluation of the geostrophic wind. The velocities can be expressed either in terms of the pressure gradient or by the inclination of an isobaric surface. The flow is directed along the isobars, because of the balance between the force due to the gradient and that due to the rotation of the Earth.

If the pressure field in the oceans is known the approximate currents can be deduced from it. This pressure field can be expressed in terms of the contours, showing isobars drawn by reference to a 'level surface'. This surface is not as easy to observe in the ocean as on land, where sea-level may be taken as the datum. It is defined as the surface everywhere normal to the acceleration of gravity, where the gravity potential is constant. The currents flow parallel to the contours in such a way that the surface rises to the right of the observer in the Northern Hemisphere. This slope of the sea surface can be calculated, although there is no means of actually measuring it. For example, in the Gulf Stream, where the surface current flows at 150 cm./sec. in latitude 35°N, the slope up to the right would be 1·5 cm. in 1 km. From observations of temperature and salinity it is possible to calculate the field of mass in the ocean, using the density worked out from these observations. This can be demonstrated by means of a chart showing anomalies of density. A line joining points of equal density is called an 'isopycnal' and a chart on which these are shown gives the contours of the depth of a particular density.

The stability of the oceans depends on the stratification with depth; this is normally stable, density increasing downwards. Lateral mixing, however, can take place, and this seems to occur along the sigma$_t$ surfaces. Sigma$_t$ refers to the density of sea water at atmospheric pressure and the temperature at which it was collected. It is convenient from the point of view of using the anomalies of density that the standard pressure values in decibars, from which these differ, can be regarded as values of geometrical depth, without introducing any great errors, there being only 1 to 2 per cent difference between these values. The field of pressure, found by calculating the density variations, may be modified by the piling up or removal of mass due to external causes, in which case other factors are brought in, and the flow does not depend entirely on the density distribution. The two factors of general density distribution and piling up of water give respectively the internal and the slope pressure fields.

If the water is stratified into two differing densities, with the denser layer to the left of the other, the two waters moving at different velocities, the boundary between them must slope. The water masses are so arranged in this instance that the boundary between them slopes down to the right, while the lighter water lies on the right-hand side of the current in the Northern Hemisphere, with its surface sloping up in this direction.

One of the difficulties of calculating ocean movements from the data giving the form of the isobaric surfaces is the lack of sufficiently detailed observations of temperature and salinity at all depths in enough places to draw accurate isobars. Near the surface conditions change rapidly, but in the deep ocean conditions are stable enough to allow observations taken at long time intervals to be used, even covering different years. It has been shown that the isotherms and isohalines (lines of equal salinity) are often parallel at different levels; their direction, therefore, coincides with that of the relative isobars or contour lines on an isobaric surface (isopycnals). This suggests strongly that the main oceanic circulation is related intimately to the pressure field or the internal distribution of mass. It appears that slope currents are largely determined by the distribution of mass. However, where stationary conditions do not exist, there is also evidence that some currents are not determined altogether by the distribution of mass.

To calculate absolute current velocities it is necessary to know the level at which there is no movement, or the velocity is zero. Various methods of arriving at a value for the level of no motion have been adopted by different oceanographers. Such a surface need not coincide with an isobaric surface. Stommel has shown that the layer of no horizontal flow may well be that in which the vertical movement is at a maximum. Where detailed observations are available it has been shown that computed currents often conform closely to the observed ones, specially where the currents are strong, for example in the Straits of Florida. That such calculations are sufficiently accurate to be of practical value is shown by the use made of these methods of computation in the preparation of forecasts of ice-berg movement off the Grand Banks of Newfoundland. Ocean-current velocities here are estimated from the observed temperatures and salinities above the 1,000-decibars surface, or a depth of nearly 1,000 m. It is assumed that the flow follows the contour lines, and from this the drift of the ice-bergs is forecast, with results that justify the continuation of the method (Carruthers, 1956).

It is also possible to calculate the mass transport under these assumptions, from the temperature and salinity observations. Again the depth of no motion must be known, and where questions of continuity arise this may not be at the bottom. It can often be assumed, for example, that in one cross-section the amount of water flowing in one direction must be compensated at depth by an equal amount flowing in the opposite direction. It is frequently found that the surface of no motion follows the isothermal and isohaline surfaces. It is found to slope from about 1,450 m. off South America to about 1,200 m. off South Africa, across the south Atlantic, according to the calculations.

The general pattern of surface ocean currents is well known; in the Northern Hemisphere there is a general system of anti-clockwise circulation around the Atlantic and north Pacific. In the Southern Hemisphere the currents in general move clockwise in a similar manner. There is, however, one very striking feature of the arrangement of the surface currents, which also probably applies to the deep-water circulation; this is the strong asymmetry of the systems. In nearly all the ocean basins the currents are so arranged that there is a very strong and concentrated flow on the western side of the ocean, whilst on the east the currents are much more diffuse. This also applies to the deep-water circulation according to the theoretical analysis of Stommel (1958b), and in the limited areas where they have been checked by observations his views have been confirmed.

Various possible causes of this asymmetry have been suggested, and both Munk's theory (1950) of the wind-driven circulation and Stommel's analysis require such a strong western boundary current. One of the main causes of this phenomenon is the fact that the Earth's rotational effect, the Coriolis parameter, varies with latitude. A wind-stress system may be considered with westerlies in mid-latitudes and trades in low latitudes; a clockwise water circulation will be set up in the ocean in the Northern Hemisphere as a result of this system. It may be considered that a clockwise (negative) spin or vorticity has been imparted to the water. If there were only pressure gradients apart from the wind-stress there would be dissipation and the system would accelerate. Therefore, suppose there is friction at the side of the ocean; this acts in a direction opposite to the current and results in a positive vorticity tendency which balances the wind stress vorticity. This does not, however, lead to asymmetry, so the effect of the variation of the Coriolis force with latitude may be considered. Suppose a column of water is moving from low to high latitudes, its total spin, the spin relative to the Earth and the spin of the Earth about the axis of the column, will tend to remain constant in the absence of dissipation. Consequently as the anticlockwise (positive) spin of the Earth about the axis of the column increases towards higher latitudes, the relative motion of the water gains a counteracting clockwise, negative vorticity and vice versa when moving south. This will lead to increased velocity in a boundary current on the west, but not on the east side of the ocean.

Stommel has shown how the balance of vorticities is achieved in an asymmetrical system, leading to a steady state, which does not apply to a symmetrical system. Assuming both the Coriolis and wind-stress vorticity tendency to be -1 on the west side of a symmetrical system, and the friction force to be $+0.1$, the north-flowing current on the west side would have a vorticity tendency of -1.9. On the east, where the Coriolis vorticity tendency is $+1$, it would partially cancel to give $+0.1$; on the west side a steady state is impossible. In a very asymmetrical system, on the other hand, the frictional force would be increased on the west, as a result of faster flow, to ten times the wind-stress vorticity, giving $+10$, for instance. The Coriolis vorticity tendency would also be greater, at about -9, with a negative wind-stress vorticity of -1, the total vorticity tendency would cancel to zero and a steady state is possible. It would also cancel to zero on the east, where the smaller frictional vorticity tendency of 0.1 and smaller Coriolis vorticity tendency of 0.9 would balance the negative wind-stress vorticity of -1. This argument only applies to the viscous theories of the ocean currents, but it does illustrate how a strong boundary current could preserve a state of zero vorticity tendency, which would result in a steady state. Therefore, the main cause of the western boundary currents is the variation of the Coriolis force with latitude, which increases away from the Equator with the sine of the latitude, according to the analyses of Stommel, Munk, Morgan and others. This is not the only factor involved, because, although it varies in the same way in the Northern and Southern Hemisphere, the currents differ, being considerably stronger in the north. This could be due to a difference in the vertical structure of the ocean.

Summarizing, it may be pointed out that the surface currents of the ocean are due to the direct effect of the wind on the sea surface and to the variations in the distribution of mass due to the differences of temperature and salinity. The wind stress, when a steady state is reached, causes a redistribution of mass as a result of wind transport of water, such that the flow balances the mass distribution. At times, however, the water may be piled up by the wind and slope currents are formed. These are not fundamentally important in the circulation, but the variation of the Coriolis force with latitude is very important, as it probably explains the asymmetry of the surface current pattern.

2. *THE SURFACE CURRENTS*

(a) The currents of North Atlantic Ocean

i. NORTH EQUATORIAL CURRENT. The North Equatorial current is primarily dependent on the trade winds (see fig. 4–2). It is a shallow current moving westwards slowly, within the uppermost 200 m. The current covers a wide belt, reaching from about 10°N to nearly 30°N. North of 20°N it is more variable, but south of this it moves at an average speed of 15 to 17 nautical miles/day. The water in the current is derived from the south-easterly currents flowing off the coasts of north-west Africa. These coastal currents, having the shore on their left, are characterized by relatively cold and dense water near the coast. Offshore winds also initiate some upwelling of cooler water from moderate depths. On reaching longitude 60°W the current divides into two branches, one of which flows into the Caribbean Sea, and eventually re-enters the Atlantic from the Gulf of Mexico via the Straits of Florida. The other branch joins the first again by a much more direct route north of the West Indies at about 8°N.

ii. EQUATORIAL COUNTER-CURRENT AND SOUTH EQUATORIAL CURRENT. The trade winds of the Southern Hemisphere also generate a westerly flowing current, the South Equatorial Current, which is stronger and more uniform than its northern counterpart. Its velocity in June and July exceeds 20 nautical miles/day. Between the two currents, in the zone of equatorial calms, where little stress is exerted by the wind, the Equatorial Counter-current flows to the east. It is strongest in the summer months. The Equatorial Counter-current is a downslope current between two upsloping ones; it also is confined to the shallow upper layer, above the major discontinuity at the base of the light surface water. The thickness of this light water increases from east to west, where its respective thickness is 40 and 140 m. As the counter-current is flowing fairly fast in the opposite direction to the currents on either side, it is influenced considerably by friction. The trade winds, in maintaining the slope, provide the energy to compensate for the loss by friction. Lateral friction is developed which acts at right-angles to the wind stress; this is important and results in some mixing of the waters of the different currents and sets up a transverse circulation as well.

In this connexion it is important to remember that the thermal Equator is north of the geographical Equator. For this reason the South

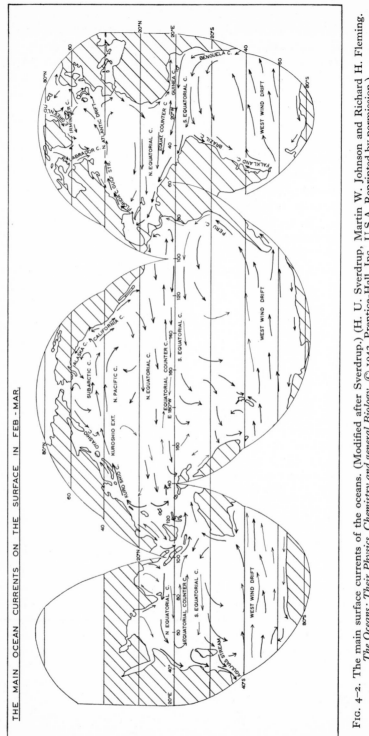

THE MAIN OCEAN CURRENTS ON THE SURFACE IN FEB - MAR.

FIG. 4-2. The main surface currents of the oceans. (Modified after Sverdrup.) (H. U. Sverdrup, Martin W. Johnson and Richard H. Fleming. *The Oceans: Their Physics, Chemistry and general Biology*. © 1942. Prentice-Hall, Inc., U.S.A. Reprinted by permission.)

Equatorial Current at most seasons extends north of the geographical Equator into the Northern Hemisphere, while the Counter-current lies entirely within the Northern Hemisphere. This means that the rotation of the Earth, which acts symmetrically about the geographical Equator, does not influence these currents in a symmetrical fashion. As a result of the Earth's rotational force, lateral mixing and frictional forces, a secondary flow at right-angles to the main east-west direction is set up. Also as a result of the fairly rapid flow of the water, the discontinuity between the surface water and the denser subsurface layer must slope. This slope is down to the right of the direction of flow in the Northern Hemisphere and to the left in the Southern Hemisphere, while the secondary flows are directed to the right of the current in the Northern Hemisphere and the left in the south. The sea surface slopes in the opposite direction to the discontinuity, but at a smaller gradient.

The result of superimposing these forces on the current pattern is shown diagrammatically in fig. 4–3. Where the transverse currents are

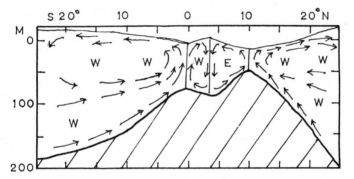

FIG. 4–3. Vertical circulation giving convergences and divergences in the Equatorial Atlantic. W and E refer to the direction of the main currents. The discontinuity above the Intermediate Water is shown, while the latter is supposed at rest. (After Sverdrup *et al.*) (H. U. Sverdrup, Martin W. Johnson and Richard H. Fleming, *The Oceans: Their Physics, Chemistry and general Biology.* © 1942. Prenctie-Hall, Inc., U.S.A. Reprinted by permission.)

flowing towards each other convergences are set up, and where they separate divergences occur. The North Equatorial Current, lying entirely in the Northern Hemisphere, has a northerly directed subsidiary current, and its surface slopes up to the north and the discontinuity beneath it slopes down to the north as the main current is flowing west. The Counter-current flows east, south of the North Equatorial Current; its subsidiary flow is, therefore, to the south, as its position is entirely within the Northern Hemisphere. Between these two currents is a zone of divergence at about 10°N. The part of the South Equatorial Current which lies in the Northern Hemisphere is affected in the same way as the North Equatorial Current, as it flows west. Therefore, between the

Equatorial Counter-current and the South Equatorial Current there is a zone of convergence, where the southerly flow of the former meets the northerly flow of the latter. This is situated in about 4°N, and the discontinuity surface sinks down to this point from either side. The whole system is shallow, varying between 50 and 100 m. in depth. The South Equatorial Current, lying partly in the Northern Hemisphere, is influenced at its northern edge to flow to the north, while south of the Equator the secondary flow is to the south. There is, as a result, a zone of divergence at the Equator, with the discontinuity sloping down in both directions from this point, while the surface slope is upwards to north and south. This divergence at the Equator is specially noticeable in summer, when it is indicated by a tongue of colder water, upwelling from shallow depths below.

The fact that a considerable quantity of water crosses the Equator from the Southern Hemisphere to the Northern on the surface in the South Equatorial Current is of considerable importance. The amount which crosses to the north has been calculated to be about 6 million cu. m./sec. This amount of warm surface water moving to the north may have helped to displace the thermal Equator northwards. The South Equatorial Current, which covers approximately the zone between 20°S and about 4°N, on reaching the east coast of Brazil divides at Cape Sao Roque, part flowing north-westwards towards the Caribbean, where it joins the North Equatorial Current, and part flowing south as the Brazil Current, which flows fairly fast along the South American coast. The Equatorial Counter-current, at the eastern side of the ocean, merges into the east-flowing Guinea Current, which flows with a considerable velocity along the African coast, where this runs east–west just north of the Equator.

iii. THE GULF STREAM SYSTEM. The waters driven westwards by the trade winds, forming the Equatorial Currents, provide the greater elevation on the western side of the Atlantic, which raises the sea-level in the Gulf of Mexico and helps to cause the Gulf Stream System. This very important current can be divided into three parts: the southerly part, the Florida Current, extends from the Straits of Florida to Cape Hatteras; the Gulf Stream proper extends from there northwards to the east of the Grand Banks in longitude 45°W; thereafter the current is more diffuse and tends to branch, and in this area it has been called the North Atlantic Drift.

The character of the Gulf Stream has sometimes been misinterpreted; it is not a stream of warm water flowing through the ocean, but, as Stommel (1958a) has pointed out, it is a narrow ribbon of fast-flowing water which acts as the boundary between two very different types of water. It prevents the warm water of the Sargasso Sea on the right of its flow from overflowing the colder, denser water on its left or inshore side. At the surface there is a very rapid fall of temperature between the zone of maximum flow, which runs along the edge of the continental slope, and the coastal water; this difference is at a maximum in winter, when the Gulf Stream water, in its southern section, is nearly 20°C, while the coastal water is only 14°C. This sharp change in surface temperature was noted by early travellers. It was commented upon in 1609 by Lescarbot (Stommel, 1958a, p. 2). In a vertical section the Gulf Stream can be divided into three layers; the surface layer is a few metres thick and varies greatly in temperature with the seasons, below this is a layer in which the temperature falls off rapidly with depth and which is called the main thermocline, under this is a layer of great thickness of cold water below 1,500 m. Rapid movement is restricted to the surface layers. There is probably a slow sinking from the surface to intermediate levels in the north, with a slow upward mixing with surface water in lower latitudes from 20–45°N. Specially in winter, a surface transference of water to the north must exist to keep the circulation going.

The total transport of the Gulf Stream System off Chesapeake Bay, which was estimated as 82×10^6 m.³/sec. in April 1932, also includes some water which circulates to the south-east of the Stream, but which is not properly the North Equatorial Current. This value may be too high; Munk's theoretical analysis gives half the amount, calculated from the density observations. The reason for the high value could be due to taking the depth of no motion at the bottom, instead of at 1,500–2,000 m., below which observations show southerly flow (Charnock 1960), Swallow and Worthington (1961).

The width of the Gulf Stream is narrow compared with the currents which feed it, because of the westward intensification already discussed. It forms a band stretching from the continental slope off Cape Hatteras to 50°W longitude, south of the Grand Banks. On either side of the main stream there are distinctive water types, the slope water on the west and the Sargasso water on the east. The submarine relief influences the position of the current; it flows along the Blake Plateau at about 800 m. depth to 33°N, but beyond this it flows through an area where the depth is 4,000 to 5,000 m. and where its position is not determined by the relief of the sea floor, because the movement below 1,500 m. is not great. Sea mounts, recently discovered in this area, may have some influence on its course. Observations suggest that the water carried northwards increases in volume in this direction. Wüst has calculated that 26 million m.³/sec. passes east through the Straits of Florida as the Florida Current; this is much less than the amount moving north-east farther north. The additional water is partly derived from the Antilles Current, which supplies about 12 million m.³/sec., and the Sargasso water on its right side supplies most of the remainder, which makes up the total given above.

The limits of the Gulf Stream can be defined in different ways. There are the obvious surface features, such as the colour change and the lines of Sargassum weed, but these may not coincide with the inner edge or western side of the current as defined by the pressure gradient between the warm, saline water to the south-east and the colder, fresher water to the north-west. On this basis the limits of the Gulf Stream can be defined as the points where the pressure gradient becomes zero. This may not coincide with the surface change in temperature and can only be located if there are detailed observations of temperature and salinity at depth. The surface phenomena are associated with shear zones at the edge of the 'warm core'. This is defined as that part of the Gulf Stream in which the water is warmer than that at the same depth to the east; it is usually at 300 to 400 m. depth, with the maximum temperature anomalies at about 100 m. There can be abrupt changes in surface temperature, colour and other features at the left edge of the warm core.

The actual speed and position of the main current varies as shown by the detailed observations of Worthington (1954b). He has indicated that the current is very narrow and has a high velocity; where the flow is fastest it moves at over 100 miles/day. The flow at high velocity is confined to a narrow band about 40 nautical miles wide, which reaches a speed of 250 cm./sec.; a counter-current flows at 50 cm./sec. approximately in the opposite direction. The positions of the high temperature and high velocity do not always coincide. In the main thermocline the 10°C isotherm drops from 200 to 900 m. across the stream in less than 70 miles (fig. 4–4a). The position of this zone of rapid temperature

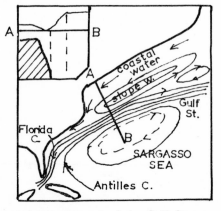

FIG. 4–4a. The approximate transport of the Gulf Stream system is indicated; each full line corresponds to a transport of 10 million m.³/sec. The slope of the water surface across the stream is shown. (After Sverdrup *et al.*) (H. U. Sverdrup, Martin W. Johnson and Richard H. Fleming, *The Oceans: Their Physics, Chemistry and general Biology.* © 1942. Prentice-Hall, Inc., U.S.A. Reprinted by permission.)

change can be recognized fairly readily and many observations of its position at varying times have shown that the Gulf Stream develops large eddies or meanders. Fugilister and Worthington (1951) have shown that two of these meanders moved eastward about 11 nautical miles/day, while their amplitude doubled in a fortnight. Their wave length may be about 200 km. The movement of these eddies can be traced by an air-borne radiation thermometer. As the Gulf Stream merges into the North Atlantic Drift the meanders intensify and break up into detached eddies at times, in about 40°N latitude.

Another point of interest in connexion with the Gulf Stream is the variation of sea-level along the east coast of the United States, deduced by precise levelling. This has shown that sea-level slopes up to the north from zero in Florida to 6 cm. at Norfolk, Virginia, 1,000 km. along the coast, to 20 cm. at Atlantic City, New Jersey, 1,400 km. along the coast. It is 28 cm. higher at Boston, Mass. 2,000 km. up the coast and 35 cm. at Halifax, Nova Scotia, 2,600 km. to the north. This causes a current flowing downslope to the south along the coast and continental shelf. The reason for this is in some doubt, but it may be related to the piling up of water in the north-western north Atlantic, resulting from the south-west wind and oceanographical distribution of mass. According to Iselin (1940), the variation in level noted on the tide gauges of the east coast of the U.S.A. is associated with the changing volume of the

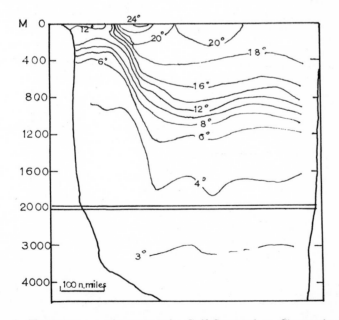

Fig. 4–4b. Temperature section across the Gulf Stream from Chesapeake Bay to Bermuda, 11–18 February 1932. (After Stommel (Iselin).)

water carried by the Gulf Stream. This evidence suggests a weakening of the Gulf Stream since 1934.

Other differences of sea-level are associated more directly with the Florida Current. As the current flows through the Straits of Florida its energy is derived from the difference in level of 19 cm. which exists between the Gulf of Mexico and the Atlantic, as measured by precise levelling across the peninsula. The average amount of water passing through the Straits of Florida has already been given as 26 million m.³/sec., but this varies with the seasons, and fluctuation can take place very fast. Because the speed of flow of the Florida Current is considerable and it is confined within the straits between Florida and Cuba in one area, it illustrates the character of the sloping surface which develops as a result of the rotation of the Earth. The surface gradient is such that it slopes up to the south towards the coast of Cuba, while the lower interface of the current slopes down to the south. The maximum slope across the stream occurs in July, when the flow is greatest, while at the same time there is a maximum downslope from west to east on the coast of Florida. The highest velocity, which exceeds 150 cm.-sec., is found nearer the coast of Florida, the speed falling off rapidly with depth. Considerable fluctuations in the amount of water carried by the Florida Current have been observed, and these can be linked with changes in the major atmospheric circulation in the North Atlantic, particularly in the break-down of the sub-tropical Azores high-pressure cell, although the relationship is not direct.

Large fluctuations in the transport of water by the Gulf Stream farther north have also been reported. The well-defined July maximum and November minimum in the speed of the surface current of the Florida area continues to a position south of Cape Hatteras, but to the north-east of the Cape the maximum flow occurs earlier in May and the minimum in October; the variation amounts to about 15 million m.³/sec. and is shown in fig. 4–4c. South-west of the Grand Banks the

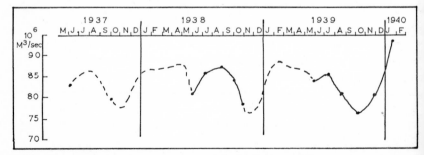

FIG. 4–4c. Gulf Stream transport determined by hydrographic stations. (After Stommel (Iselin).)

maximum is in March and the minimum in November. It might be supposed that the transport of the Gulf Stream would increase in winter due to the increase in wind strength, which would reduce the diameter of the current curve and thereby interrupt or decrease the north-eastern discharge of water, while the southerly movement of the winds should cause the Gulf Stream to be farther offshore in winter, north of Cape Hatteras. However, the Caribbean and Straits of Florida influence the circulation in such a way that this does not occur. In summer the flow is increased by the water moving directly into the Gulf Stream and by-passing the Straits of Florida, as a result of the northerly movement of the wind belts.

In considering the constancy of the Gulf Stream System it is worth noting the relative energy available in the kinetic energy of the wind-stress currents and the potential energy of the warm mass of Sargasso water. Stommel has worked out that the potential energy stored in the warm core of the Sargasso water, over and above that which would exist if the thermocline were level, is very great. It would be sufficient to keep the current system going for 1,700 days in the absence of the driving force of the wind. Thus the current system is to a considerable extent independent of the fluctuations of the weather. The density field in mid-latitude ocean areas does respond to variations in the wind-stress, but for variations within the period of a week and a year the response does not reach equilibrium. The main thermocline in the North Atlantic is influenced by the movement of the main high-pressure centre, but is not entirely adjusted to it. Fluctuations of less than one week cannot produce any changes. The Gulf Stream carries an enormous amount of water northwards, amounting to thirty-three times all the water flowing in all rivers and glaciers on land, while the amount of salt carried north is 1,210,000 tons/sec. (Defant, 1961, Vol. 1, p. 641). A considerable amount of heat is carried north by the northerly extension of the Gulf Stream, the North Atlantic Drift.

The North Atlantic Drift differs from the Gulf Stream in that it is not a narrow band of fast-flowing water, but consists of several broader bands or variable filaments of current. This form can be traced as far as 65°W, into the zone where the westerly concentration decreases and is no longer strongly marked. Farther east the water transport branches, part being carried to the east and south-east to form the Canaries Current, while the rest passes north-eastwards and northwards into the northern north Atlantic and Polar Ocean. The surface water is influenced by the west wind drift, but beneath this there are the eddies and frag-mentary remnants of the Gulf Stream. In this zone of the decay of the Gulf Stream the surface conditions of the now slowly moving water are considerably altered by the climate. In the subpolar regions of this northern part of the system thermohaline processes become important. ⌡ The central part of the north Atlantic Ocean contains a mass of warm water covering the uppermost 700 m. This water drifts slowly to the south-west as a result of the trade winds and the rotation of the Earth. Carruthers has reported interesting evidence of the currents in the Sargasso Sea area, shown by the drift of the *Fanny Wolston*, which was abandoned in October 1891 and drifted for three years; until February 1893 the wreck zigzagged in the Sargasso Sea area, until it got into the Gulf Stream, in which it drifted north-east till October 1894, finally sinking in 38°N after travelling 7,560 nautical miles. The Gulf Stream system forms the edge of this mass of slow-moving water, and the rapid flow of the Gulf Stream takes place in the boundary zone of this water mass and forms an effective barrier, preventing this warm water flowing over the colder, denser water of the northern parts of the ocean. The Gulf Stream is not, therefore, a river of warm water flowing through the ocean, but a limit to the northern spread of warm water. Its essential role is not carrying warm water towards the north-west European coast but preventing the northward extension of this warm water. It is not possible to relate warming of the European climate to increased transport of the Gulf Stream, and Iselin (1940) has suggested that increased transport by the Gulf Stream may, in fact, be associated with cooler conditions in Europe. This is based on the argument that a deepening of the thermocline in the Sargasso Sea might be associated with a radial shrinkage of the current system, when the transport is increased. This would lead to a southern retreat of the warm surface water in the North Atlantic. There is little evidence that this does, in fact, happen, although the tide-gauge data for the east coast of America supports it. There is a suggestion that the warming of the Norwegian Sea by about 2°C and the decrease of about 50 m. in the 10°C isotherm throughout the Sargasso Sea would cause a slowing down of the north Atlantic circulation. This would decrease the transport of the Gulf Stream at the same time as the climate of northern Europe is ameliorating. Although no definite conclusions can be arrived at, it is significant that the annual variations in flow are greater than the year-to-year mean variation in the transport of the Gulf Stream; such seasonal changes could be used to evaluate the probable effect of a longer term change.

The more diffuse currents of the north Atlantic Ocean do carry warmer water into Arctic latitudes; some of this water flows west, south of Iceland, as the Irminger Current. This water eventually comes into contact with the cold-water current flowing south-west along the east coast of Greenland. The zone in which the two waters meet is the place of origin of the North Atlantic Deep and Bottom Water. Some of the

Gulf Stream water penetrates west and north of Iceland towards the Norwegian Sea, while the more easterly branch also flows into this sea along its eastern boundary, off the west coast of Norway. Some of this water penetrates as far as the Polar Ocean, in which its character is changed, by cooling and excessive runoff and precipitation, to become the relatively fresh and cold East Greenland Current, flowing out of the Polar Ocean along the east coast of Greenland. The greater effectiveness of the North Atlantic Drift in warming the northern land of Europe, compared with the Kuroshio, its Pacific counterpart, is partly due to its shorter route of 5,000 km., compared with 8,000 km. in the Pacific, and the favourable arrangement of the land masses, which allow greater penetration. The addition of warm Mediterranean water at depth also helps to reduce downwards conduction of heat.

The southern branch of the North Atlantic Drift also changes its character in part, some of this water enters the Mediterranean as relatively less saline water, to emerge below the surface as the very distinctive warm, saline Mediterranean Water, while the rest continues to the south to join again into the circulation as the North Equatorial Current, completing the circular motion. This current, flowing south along the coast of Africa, is associated with upwelling particularly from January to May, when temperatures along the coast may show an anomaly of -7 to $-10°C$, between the Canaries and Cape Verde.

(b) The currents of the south Atlantic Ocean

i. BENGUELA CURRENT. This current flowing north moves close to the coast of Africa, it is particularly strongly developed between the Cape of Good Hope and latitude 17 to 18°S. Because it is in the Southern Hemisphere, the denser water lies on the right, close inshore. The coldness of the offshore water is also increased as a result of the upwelling of water caused by the offshore winds. This takes place from moderate depths of 200 to 300 m. and gives rise to a belt of cool, relatively fresh water up to a distance of 200 km. offshore, reaching to the edge of the continental shelf. This upwelling of water is important, as it brings nutrients towards the surface, which makes it a region of high-fertility.

It has been estimated that the Benguela Current carries about 16 million m.³/sec. to the north. As this water moves north beyond 20°S it gradually flows away from the coast to form the northern part of the South Equatorial Current. It helps to produce the tongue of cooler water which extends along the Equator, and which is reinforced as a result of the divergence there. The Benguela Current carries more water to the north than the opposing southwards-flowing current, which carries equatorial water south along the coast of Brazil, and which is known as the Brazil Current.

O.–K

ii. BRAZIL CURRENT. This current is fed by the southernmost part of the South Equatorial Current. As a result of the loss of 6 million m.³/sec. to the Northern Hemisphere, there is only 10 million m³./sec. left. to flow south along the coast of Brazil. This current is warmer than the surrounding water, as it is flowing away from the Equator. It flows south to about 30°S, where it meets the cold Falkland Current, flowing north up the South American coast from the Southern Ocean. The Brazil Current transports only one-tenth of the amount of water carried by the Gulf Stream. This may be due to the greater wind-stress in the north Atlantic, resulting from the shorter distance between the trade winds and westerlies, which is 60 per cent less in the Northern than the Southern Hemisphere. This again depends on the northerly position of the climatic Equator, relative to the geographical one, resulting from the distribution of land and sea. According to Munk (1950), the permanent currents are related to the rotational component of the wind-stress field over the ocean, hence the vector difference between the trades and westerlies is of great importance, and is called the wind-stress curl.

The Falkland Current brings water of lower temperature and salinity into contact with the warmer water coming from the Equator. Together these waters turn east to flow across the south Atlantic as the West Wind Drift. This completes the anticlockwise circulation of the south Atlantic Ocean. An important point to bear in mind with regard to the surface circulation of the south Atlantic Ocean is the loss on the surface of 6 million m.³/sec. to the Northern Hemisphere, which is also due to the northward displacement of the climatic Equator in part.

(c) The currents of the Southern or Antarctic Ocean

The flow of water in the southern ocean, which is continuous round the Antarctic Continent, results from both the wind drift and the distribution of mass. The water of greatest density is found near the Antarctic land. The isobaric surfaces, therefore, slope up to the north, this results in a current directed from west to east, because the denser water lies to the right of the direction of flow in the Southern Hemisphere. The slopes are not great and the velocities of the currents are low, being about 15 cm./sec. around 50°S and 4·4 cm./sec. near latitude 60°S on the surface. Deacon (1960) has shown that drifting material travels eastwards round the Antarctic at about 8 miles/day, taking three or four years to complete the circuit. There is a relatively sharp bend of the isobaric surfaces in the position of the Antarctic convergence, where a wedge of lighter water is found above a denser layer. The general west-to-east flow of water around the Antarctic continues all round the continent, although in places its direction is affected by submarine ridges. It has been estimated that between 80 and 100 million m.³/sec. is transported by this current (Stommel, 1957). The effect of the submarine ridges is to bend the current to the north as it approaches the ridge and to the south again as it passes across it. Five such deflections of the current are indicated. The southern extension of South America constrains the drift into an abnormally narrow zone, but on passing into the Atlantic the current bends north to form the Falkland current, which has already been mentioned. It is probably only in this region that there is much flow uphill across the isobaric contours; elsewhere the lines bounding the zones of equal flow also indicate the direction of the current. Thus in the region of South America the current is not purely zonal, but has a considerable meridional component. This southern part of the West Wind Drift may be called the Circumpolar Current.

Close to the Antarctic shore the direction of the current may be reversed owing, to the effect of the prevailing winds, which are easterly in this zone. Between 40 and 60°S the strong winds are westerly in direction and, therefore, reinforce the currents due to the distribution of mass. Between the two wind systems there must be a zone of divergence. The transport of water due to the prevailing westerly wind will have a component towards the north, which must be compensated by a southwards flow at a greater depth, resulting in the climb of water towards the surface. This has an important effect on the fertility of this part of the ocean.

(d) The currents of the Indian Ocean

The west-to-east current of the southern Atlantic continues on into the southern Indian Ocean, while there is an anticlockwise circulation in the Southern Hemisphere similar to that in the south Atlantic. The seasonal variations in the northern Indian Ocean cause a complete reversal of the currents, while there are also significant seasonal changes in the pattern of the southern Indian Ocean. The west-to-east current in the southern summer bends northwards before reaching Australia, where it is reinforced by a current flowing to the west along the south coast of Australia. In the southern winter this current flows eastwards along the coast. The South Equatorial Current flows to the west, north of 20°S, flowing faster in the southern winter, when it is augmented by water flowing west along the north coast of Australia. In the southern summer this flow is reversed. On reaching the coast of Africa the water bends south to form the strong Agulhas Stream.

South of 30°S the Agulhas Current forms a well-defined narrow flow extending less than 100 km. from the shore. The coldest water lies nearest to the shore and the surface slopes up away from the coast at a gradient of 29 cm. in about 110 km. This is what would be expected in the Southern Hemisphere. This current mainly turns east on reaching the southern tip of Africa, although some of the water may flow west into the Atlantic and strong vortices develop. The current is caused by the piling up of water on the coast of Africa and is a typical gradient current.

In the northern part of the ocean the currents reflect closely the seasonal changes in the wind direction as the monsoon develops. The North Equatorial Current is well developed in February and March, when the north-west monsoon is blowing. An Equatorial Counter-current is also strongly developed, with its axis at 7°S. When the south-west monsoon develops in August and September the North Equatorial Current is replaced by the Monsoon Current, which flows towards the east. At this season the water flowing along the coast of Africa moves northwards from latitude 10°S and some of this crosses the Equator. At this season the Equatorial Counter-current is also lacking. These movements take place above the tropical discontinuity in the uppermost layers.

Data are lacking to establish accurately the amount of water moving in these different currents, but Dietrich has suggested that the transport by the Aghulhas Stream amounts to rather more than 20 million m.³/sec. The surface currents of the Indian Ocean do show that in the upper layers of this ocean the transport by the wind is an important factor, as the direction of flow changes in sympathy with the variations in the wind direction of the monsoon climate.

(e) The currents of the Pacific Ocean

i. THE SOUTH PACIFIC. Information concerning the currents of the south Pacific is limited, but it appears that the usual anticlockwise circulation probably exists, but that the width of the ocean is such that there may be two gyres. That on the eastern side of the ocean is better developed than the western one. The latter appears to be very variable with the seasons; the changes in direction off Australia with the seasons have already been mentioned.

The current which flows north up the coast of Chile and Peru is, however, better known, as its vagaries have an important influence on certain aspects of the life of the area. It is called the Peru or Humboldt Current. The water of this current is derived from the subantarctic water which flows eastwards across the south Pacific. The volume transported seems to be about 10 to 15 million m.³/sec. The current extends to about 900 km. from the shore and flows north along it until just south of the Equator, where it turns west. The part of the current close to the shore is greatly influenced by upwelling, as a result of the prevailing offshore winds. The upwelling water is thought by Gunther (1936) to come from depths between 40 and 360 m., the average being 133 m. It is restricted to certain regions, four of which occur between 3 and 33°S. This leads to zones of alternating cold and warmer water offshore. Beneath the northward surface current a counter-current flows to the south about 400 m. This is formed of Pacific Equatorial Water, which is less saline than the surface water off Peru, but more saline than that off Chile to the south.

The southward extension of warm, relatively fresh water is associated with the Peru Current; this varies from season to season. This incursion of warm water along the coast has very serious consequences on the life of the area, particularly the guano birds, which play an important part in the economy of the coastal zone. Their normal source of food, which is derived from the highly fertile upwelling water of the cooler Peru Current, is not available, and they die of starvation in large numbers or migrate. During periods when the warm water extends south along the coast there is liable to be heavy rain on the usually dry coast, as the winds change from southerly to northerly. This incursion of warmer water is known as 'El Nino' and its disastrous consequences occur about every seven years, for example 1911, 1918, 1925, 1932, 1939 and 1941. Particularly severe periods occurred in 1891, 1925 and 1953. The main food of the guano birds are the anchovies, which die or migrate during the periods of 'El Nino'. It is thought that the anchovies either move south into cooler waters, or further offshore, where the temperature is also lower.

There are various possible ways in which the water can be warmed: firstly, warm water may extend southwards along the coast; secondly, warm water may come close inshore from out to sea when upwelling is not active; thirdly, solar radiation, in the absence of upwelling, may cause local warming. Another problem is to establish whether the disastrous consequences are due to warming of the water only, or to a decrease in the nutrient supply, warming only being a secondary feature. The warming of the coastal waters extends at times as far south as Pisco Bay, in latitude 13°45'S, although this may be due more to warming as a result of lack of upwelling, than to the extension of 'El Nino' this far south. The observed warming of Pisco Bay can be accounted for by the solar radiation, particularly as the salinity tends to increase rather than decrease, which it would do if the warming were due to an incursion of warmer, less saline water from the north. The actual surface temperature may be about 20 to 21°C in both normal and abnormal years, but the downward gradient varies. In abnormal years the 14°C isotherm is about 50 m. below its level in normal conditions. In a normal year repeated upwelling prevents any warming at depth and the average temperature down to about 50 m. is about 14·5°C as against an average of 18°C in 1941, an abnormal year.

The biological effects of abnormal conditions are of two types; the first leads to the disappearance of the anchovies, which results in the death by starvation or migration of the guano birds. This could be due either to excess warming or to the absence of upwelling water. The second possibility is the appearance of 'red water'. This leads to large-scale mortality of fish and has usually been associated with the incursion of 'El Nino'. The term 'red water' refers to the colouring of the water as a result of the excessive numbers of small planktonic organisms. These small phytoplankton grow when the water is extra warm, but other factors on which their abnormal production depends are not clearly known, although it has been suggested that fresher water is sometimes present. The development of red water does not necessarily depend on the incursion of water from elsewhere, the usual upwelling water of the Peru Current, if warmed at the surface, may give rise to red water (Sears, 1954).

There is still much to be learned about the problems associated with abnormal conditions along this coast, where they play an important part in the life and economy of the coastal region.

ii. THE EQUATORIAL CURRENTS OF THE PACIFIC OCEAN. Work during the last decade has thrown interesting light on the water movements of the equatorial Pacific; particularly interesting is the discovery of the Cromwell Current, which was not suspected till fairly recently. The main current system of the Pacific is in general similar to that of the equatorial Atlantic, there being a South Equatorial Current flowing astride the Equator, which is separated from the west-flowing North Equatorial Current by an Equatorial Counter-current flowing east. This latter current is much more strongly developed than its Atlantic counterpart. Defant (1961) shows that this current, unlike that in the Atlantic, is due entirely to the wind-stress system. The Cromwell Current, called originally the Pacific Equatorial Undercurrent by Cromwell, who first found it, also flows to the east a short distance below the surface. It was discovered in 1951, while fishing for tuna, when it was found that the long-line fishing-gear drifted to the east below the surface, where the surface current flowed west. The speed of flow of the Equatorial Counter-current is considerable, flowing at up to 100 cm./sec. (2 knots) on the surface during the northern summer, when it lies farther north of the Equator. It has been estimated to carry about 25 million m.³/sec. eastwards, an amount which probably increases towards the east. A similar system of transverse circulation is set up as a result of lateral friction and the rotation of the Earth as that described in the Atlantic. As in the Atlantic, zones of divergence and convergence are found between the west- and east-flowing currents and at the Equator.

The Cromwell Current is a thin ribbon of swiftly flowing water, moving east beneath the South Equatorial Current at the Equator. Where direct current observations have been made on the Equator at longitude 140°W the velocity of the current was found to be 125–150 cm./sec. at a depth of 100 m. The rate of flow fell off with depth to 10 cm./sec. at a depth of 350 m. The change of direction took place at a depth of 20 m. at the Equator and the current extended 2° either side of the Equator. The velocity gradient above the maximum was greater than that below it, changes of velocity of 150 cm./sec. taking place over a depth range of 70 m. The current seems to be nearly symmetrical about the Equator and is in the form of a thin ribbon; taking the 25 cm./sec. line as the boundary, it is 0·2 km. thick and 300 km. wide, as shown in fig. 4–5. The amount of water transported is very great, amounting to an average of 39 million m.³/sec. The steadiness of the current was marked, specially compared with the observed changes in the Counter-current, flowing east 500 miles north of it. The Cromwell Current was traced eastwards to 92°W, near the Galapagos Islands, but it has not been found east of 89°W. The current generally weakens as it is traced eastwards.

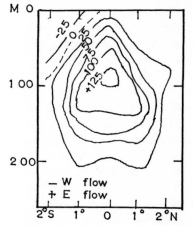

FIG. 4–5. A velocity cross-section in cm./sec. of the Cromwell Current at 140°W on 20–22 April 1958. The total transport was 42 million m.³/sec. (After Knauss.)

At a position 140°W a sharp drop of temperature downwards was recorded; it fell from 25 to 28°C at a depth of 100 m. to between 10 and 12°C at a depth of 300 m., which was at the base of the thermocline. This was better developed on either side of the Equator than at it. The oxygen content was also greater beneath the Equator than the low values found at similar depths of 100 to 300 m. on either side. This is indicative of considerable mixing of water in a vertical sense at the Equator, probably accompanied by some upwelling. The marginal limits of the Cromwell Current to north and south coincide with the limit of the zone of mixing.

Knauss (1960) suggests that the Cromwell Current can be accounted for as a result of the mixing which takes place at the Equator. If there were a simple two-layer structure extending across the Equator, there would be no north-south horizontal pressure gradient and no resulting geostrophic current. If, however, the water at the Equator is mixed, the density structure here is altered with respect to that to north and south, and this will result in the formation of a geostrophic current. Both the pressure gradient and the deflection due to latitude change sign at the Equator, so the resulting current is symmetrical about the Equator. The Cromwell Current, therefore, seems to be in geostrophic balance and results from mixing across the thermocline at the Equator. The current becomes shallower to the east, as the thermocline rises in this direction. In order to account for the Cromwell Current in this way it is necessary to explain the vertical mixing at the Equator to a depth of 300 m.; this could be explained by the wind-induced divergence. This has already been mentioned in connexion with the Atlantic, and Neumann (1960) has suggested that a similar current is found in the Atlantic.

Voorhis (1961) has recently observed an easterly flowing equatorial under-current in the Atlantic. The observations, in longitude 10 to 19°W, suggest a current with a velocity of up to 100 cm./sec., in places along the Equator, at a depth of 105 m., where the surface current was 40 to 60 cm./sec. westwards. Temperature effects were also marked; to the south of the boundary of the current a well-marked thermocline was found at a depth of 50 m., but in the current the temperature decrease was uniform to a depth of 100 m., falling from 28°C to 15°C.

iii. CURRENTS OF THE NORTH PACIFIC. The North Equatorial Current in the Pacific resembles that of the Atlantic in many ways. It runs from east to west, increasing in volume as it flows west. It starts from the west coast of America, where some of the waters of the Counter-current flow north to meet those flowing south in the Californian Current. As it flows to the west, the Central Water masses of the north Pacific add to its volume. It is broad and deep, but not very fast, its velocity mostly being below 20 cm./sec. As it approaches the western part of the ocean it divides, some feeding the Counter-current and some flowing to the north to follow the northern Phillipine Islands and the coast of Formosa.

The Kuroshio Current. This water turns northwards to form the Kuroshio Current, the Pacific equivalent of the Gulf Stream. Like it, it is divisible into three sections: the Kuroshio Current, which forms the southern portion, flowing from Formosa to Riu Kiu and as far as 35° N, close to the coast of Japan; the Kuroshio Extension branches there to form two streams extending to about longitude 160°E; finally the North Pacific Current reaches eastwards to around 150°W, sending various branches off to the south as it progresses in an easterly direction.

The Kuroshio Current is in many respects similar to the Florida Current. According to the work of Japanese oceanographers, the current extends to a depth of 700 m. and attains a speed of flow of 90 cm./sec. on the surface in summer, while in winter the maximum is 61 cm./sec.

at a depth of 150 m. The amount of water carried in this zone reaches 21 million m.³/sec. in winter and 23 in summer, the transport increasing a little towards the north-east. The temperatures of this water are similar to those in the Atlantic, but the salinities are considerably lower, owing to the generally lower values in the Pacific. The current is variable and has shown considerable fluctuation during the period 1919 to 1950; a large cold eddy evolved during 1935–42 off Cape Shiono Misaki, diverting the current 200 km. offshore, but it has since returned to its former position (Stommel, 1958, p. 152).

In latitude 35°N the current branches to form the Kuroshio Extension; one branch turns east, flowing to 160°E, while a smaller amount flows north-east to 40°N, where it also bends eastwards. It still forms a fairly well-defined narrow current. The northern branch mixes with the southerly flowing cold water of the Oyashio Current. This mixture forms the subarctic water of the north Pacific. Most of the North Pacific Current turns south again before it reaches the longitude of the Hawaiian Islands, turning eventually back to the west. In the northern part of the ocean the Aleutian Current flows in a very different type of water, the subarctic water mentioned above. Some of this water flows anticlockwise around the Bering Sea, but some flows east on the southern side of the Aleutian Peninsula and Islands, this amounts to 15 million m.³/sec. It does not by this time resemble in any way the water of the Kuroshio, from which it was originally derived, owing to mixing and to external changes. The Kuroshio Current has less effect on the climate of the North Pacific than the Gulf Stream in the North Atlantic, owing partly to the greater distance it must cover before reaching the eastern shores of the ocean. The Aleutian current also divides, one branch flowing into the Gulf of Alaska and another flowing south along the west coast of Canada and North America.

This latter branch is then known as the *Californian Current*, where it flows south from 48° to 23°N. Its offshore boundary is about 700 km. away from the coast, while its total transport is only about 10 million m.³/sec. It is, therefore, only a sluggish flow to the south, very different from the fast-flowing western currents. Like the Peru Current in the Southern Hemisphere, at some seasons, particularly spring and early summer, offshore winds induce upwelling. In areas of active upwelling this results in lower temperatures in spring than in winter. The regions of upwelling are localized and result in the formation of swirls. The upwelling water does not come from depth greater than 200 m. and ceases towards the autumn.

The total transport of water by the surface currents of the North Pacific is less than that in the Atlantic; the maximum transport of the Kuroshio system is about 65 million m.³/sec., compared with the value of 82 million for the Atlantic. However, both patterns illustrate the strong asymmetry of transport, with the strong currents and transport concentrated on the western side. Clearly the transport of so much water across the surface of the oceans must alter the distribution of surface characteristics of temperature and salinity, and thereby alter the distribution of mass in the upper layers of the ocean. These factors will, therefore, have some influence on the deep-water circulation.

3. DEEP-WATER CIRCULATION

The deep-water movements cannot be spoken of as currents, as they are mostly slow diffusions of water masses through broad zones of the oceans rather than localized zones of flow, although there are some interesting exceptions to this generalization. The development of methods of measuring the rate of flow in deep water is giving much more reliable information concerning flow at depth, which can supplement the deductions made on the basis of temperature and salinity observations, and theoretical analyses of movement. The theoretical analyses of deep-water circulation may first be mentioned briefly and the observations made to confirm them described, before the deep-water circulation in the different oceans is discussed.

(a) Theoretical analysis

The work of Stommel and others has given a reasonable picture of the factors on which the deep-water circulation of the oceans depends. Some of the features predicted by Stommel's theory have subsequently been verified by direct observations. The basis of his analysis is that over most of the ocean the flow is steady and geostrophic, except in narrow bands where other forces such as friction or inertia play an important part. The driving force of the circulation is related to zones of sinking water, themselves related to the surface circulation, derived initially from the wind force, and other external factors. Thus vertical movements are essential to an explanation of the deep-water circulation (Stommel and Arons, 1960, and Stommel, 1958b).

One of the major elements of the circulation as worked out by Stommel is the narrow boundary current on the west side of the ocean, similar to that on the surface. It is based on a small source region of deep water in high latitudes, compensated by a slow upward movement at mid-depths in other areas. There are only two important source regions of deep cold water, on which the oceanic circulation depends; these are situated in the north Atlantic, where the North Atlantic Deep and Bottom Water forms, and in the Weddell Sea, where most of the Antarctic Bottom Water originates.

The theoretical model deduced by Stommel is idealized, but it does, nevertheless, bear a striking resemblance to conditions as they are known. Assuming an idealized Earth, which corresponds approximately to the actual conditions, it can be shown that there must be a strongly localized current flowing southwards at depth on the western side of the Atlantic Ocean. There is also a general upward movement over the whole ocean at mid-depths. The necessity for this strong localized boundary current results from the incomplete geostrophic balance between the pressure gradient forces and the forces due to the Earth's rotation. In order to compensate for this state a strong current, in which other forces, frictional and inertial, are important, is invoked. Such a current would compensate for the net transfer of water in the opposite direction at other depths.

Stommel's analysis is based on a model of the ocean in two layers. The upward movement at mid-depths would lead to divergence, which would be associated with poleward flow. This must be compensated by Equatorward flow in a concentrated stream. This is the opposite of the effect which gives rise to the strongly concentrated western boundary current at the surface. This has been shown to be the result of convergence in the upper layers, due to the variation of the Coriolis parameter with latitude. In this way a circulation is set up in the north Atlantic in the lower layer of water; a strong boundary current would be expected to flow south on the western edge, while a more diffuse northerly flow would be expected towards the east. This northerly flow is fed by an eastern flow from the southerly boundary current. The southward flow of the boundary current continues in part across the Equator to about latitude of 35°S, where it meets a northerly flow from the other source of deep water in the Weddell Sea. From there the hypothesis suggests that the water turns eastwards, to produce a great zonal flow, which continues all round the Antarctic Continent. It is suggested that it has a slight southerly component which brings it eventually to the region south of the southern tip of South America. From this position the current again becomes concentrated on the western side of the ocean, flowing north-east to join the northerly flow from the Weddell Sea source in about 35°S (see fig. 4–6).

In the Pacific Ocean Stommel's theory suggests that there is also a western boundary current. Here, however, unlike the Atlantic, it is directed to the north to a point about 30°N, where it may meet a southerly directed boundary current. This difference is due to the lack of a source of deep water in the Pacific; the main source for the deep-water circulation in this area is the west-to-east-moving water, which reaches the Pacific to the south of New Zealand. The theoretical circulation of the Indian Ocean is similar to that in the south Pacific; a concentrated northward movement on the west side is balanced by a more diffuse circulation to the east and south in the central low latitudes and east respectively, thus completing a clockwise gyre. In the north Pacific the direction of movement, apart from the northerly directed boundary current between 0° and 35°N, on the west side of the ocean, is in the form of an anticlockwise circulation as in the North Atlantic.

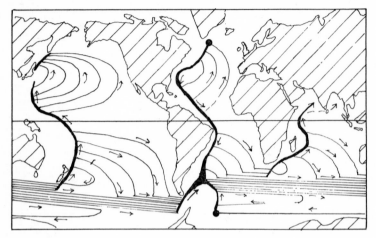

FIG. 4–6. Deep-water circulation, showing two source regions in the north and south Atlantic respectively. (After Stommel.)

Stommel and Arons (1960) have also attempted to estimate the possible volume of water taking part in these movements. They suggest that 20 million m.³/sec. move south from the northern source in the western boundary current of the North Atlantic. This assumes a level of no motion at 1,500 m. The Weddell Sea source is estimated to produce another 20 million m.³/sec. The two deep-water sources together thus produce about 40 million m.³/sec. This sinking is compensated for by a similar upward flux, which is spread throughout the ocean at mid-depths. This is estimated to amount to about 1 million m.³/sec. for each area of 7·5 million sq. km., rising across the 3,000 m. level. The amount of water assumed to be moving south across the Equator in the Atlantic Ocean is 16 million m.³/sec, while 2 million move north in the Indian Ocean and 10 million in the Pacific across the Equator. Other amounts of flow are shown diagrammatically in fig. 4–7.

The essential cause of this suggested abyssal circulation lies in the character and mechanism of the main thermocline, which divides the two layers of water. This is the result of heating at the surface and the effects of wind-stress; it demands the upward flux of water from mid-depths. The position of the main sources of deep water is a climatological and geographical accident, which could change, given different circumstances, without affecting the basic theory of the circulation. On the more traditional concept of oceanic circulation winter cooling is fundamental to the formation of deep water, and a reduction in this, due to increased warmth in high latitudes, would lead to a reduction in the intensity of the deep oceanic circulation. Stommel, however, maintains

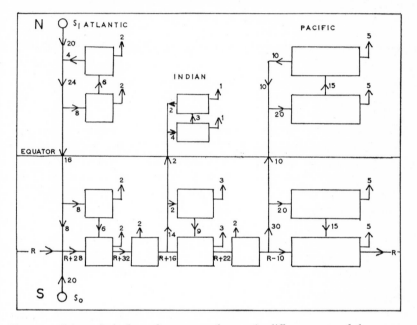

FIG. 4–7. Schematic budget of transport of water in different parts of the oceans. R refers to the volume of water which is continuously moving around the southern ocean. The figures refer to million m.^{3}/sec. (After Stommel and Arons.)

that warming of the polar regions by 1 to 2 °C would not slow down the abyssal circulation, although it might alter the source regions and change the boundary currents. The thermocline affects the vertical component of velocity at mid-depth. An estimate of the speed of this upward movement gives an average of 4×10^{-5} cm./sec., occurring at a depth of about 1,000 m. at its maximum. Assuming an average depth of 3,000 m. below the thermocline, the renewal of deep water would take place on the average every 200 years. This value, of course, does not take local variations into account, and it is based on certain assumptions, which may not be justified. The result is uncertain and other methods of calculation give very different values; various values for the replacement time of the deep water vary from 1,800 to 300 years, while estimates of the total flux taking part in the abyssal circulation varies between 15 and

90 million m.³/sec. respectively. The total flux of the abyssal circulation is assumed to be two to three times that of the western boundary current of the Atlantic Ocean.

Another approach to the problem of the time scale of oceanic circulation is that of Broecker *et al.* (1960) on the natural radio-carbon of the Atlantic Ocean. They have studied the C^{14}/C^{12} ratio, which gives some evidence of the residence period of the various water masses. This ratio changes from low to high values in the surface waters from the Antarctic northwards to the north Atlantic. The lowest values are found in the Antarctic Bottom Water. Assuming a steady state of oceanic circulation the results are as follows: (*a*) Antarctic water masses appear to have a shorter residence time than those originating in high latitudes in the north Atlantic. (*b*) Except for the surface North Atlantic Central Water and for a wedge between 1,200 and 2,400 m. depth, the waters of the western north Atlantic seem to be at least 600 years old. (*c*) Those of the eastern north Atlantic, below 4,000 m., seem to be older; at least 900 years is suggested. (*d*) Water of Antarctic origin has a shorter residence time of 350 years. (*e*) The residence time of Pacific deep water appears to be only fairly slightly longer than that of the Atlantic, not exceeding 30 per cent. These results could be considerably in error if the ocean is not in a steady state, although there is some evidence that it probably is. If the ocean were subject to discontinuous mixing, at intervals of tens to hundreds of years, the results would not apply, but they probably give an upper limit to the residence times.

(b) Observations

A technique of observing the actual speed of flow at different depths has been developed by Swallow at the National Institute of Oceanography. The movement of a float, whose density is such that it will remain at a predetermined depth, is followed from a ship above, which is not directly attached to the float. It is followed by means of pulses emitted from it and received in the ship above. Thus the movement of the float is independent of the ship and its movement relative to the ship can be followed. It is necessary to fix the position of the ship accurately, which can best be done in areas not far distant from the shore, where positioning aids are available. Measurements of the currents can be carried out over several days or weeks, during which time the floats can be followed. So far observations have been made in the western Atlantic, where they were made to ascertain whether the deep southerly boundary current does, in fact, exist, and in the eastern Atlantic, where theory suggests that the movements are probably more sluggish.

Measurements were made as a joint project between the National Institute of Oceanography and the Woods Hole Oceanographic Institute, in the area around 33°N and between longitude 75½ and 76°W (Swallow and Worthington, 1957 and 1961). Nine floats were followed, three of them at 2,500 m. depth and four at 2,800 m. The former moved south and south-west at 2·6 to 9·5 cm./sec., while the deeper ones moved at speeds of 9·7 to 17·4 cm./sec. Another method used by Laughton showed a southward movement of 5 cm./sec. at a depth of 3,200 m., only 50 cm. above the bottom. This result was obtained by underwater photography of the deflection of a ball suspended on a string. Hydrographic data suggested that the level of no motion in this area must lie around a depth of 1,500 to 2,000 m. These observations confirm in a very satisfactory way the presence of deep south-flowing water beneath the Gulf Stream in the western Atlantic Ocean.

Since these and other early experiments were made various improvements in technique have been introduced and further observations have been carried out in the eastern Atlantic (Swallow, 1957). The early method of determining the depth of the floats left an ambiguity of ∓ 200–300 m., but improved methods now allow fixing to be accurate to ∓ 30 m., while the work can now be carried out in rougher conditions. The second series of measurements were made to the north of Scotland and in the area between 30 and 40°N and 10 to 20°W off the Straits of Gibraltar. The currents in the Faroe-Shetland channel were calculated from hydrographic data and observed directly at the same time, and although the values differed, the currents flowed in the same direction. The results off the Straits of Gibraltar also agreed fairly well with the expected values, deduced from hydrographic observations.

A longer series of observations has since been carried out to the west of Spain, in latitude 41°W (Swallow and Hamon, 1960). This is near the edge of the Iberian abyssal plain. The floats used were modified so that they could be followed for longer periods, some of which extended over a period of twelve weeks. The position of the buoys was fixed by reference to small sea mounts on the bottom, as other navigational aids were not available in this area. An attempt was made to locate the level of no movement by observing the variation of the current with depth. Five floats were used between a depth of 1,500 and 4,500 m. The floats all moved in nearly the same direction of about 143° true, but they varied in speed. There was no uniform decrease of velocity with depth, nor was there a depth of no horizontal motion. As the floats were followed over a considerable period, it was possible to establish that the movement was variable. Two floats only 25 km. apart moved with speeds differing by a factor of 5. One float, followed for a total period of forty-eight days, moved at 1·2 cm./sec. for the first six days in a direction 156°; it then remained stationary for a period of twenty-two days, after which it moved at 1 cm./sec. in a direction at right-angles to its previous movement; the float was at nearly 3,000 m. depth. The movements recorded can be compared with hydrographic data obtained at the same time, but there is little agreement between the observed currents and the geostrophic currents relative to 4,500 m. as calculated. It seems that short-term fluctuations in deep-water movements, when the velocities are between 1 and 5 cm./sec. are such that it is difficult to compare them with steady state models. The details of the recorded movements are shown on fig. 4–8.

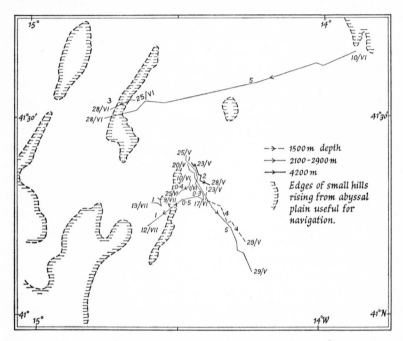

FIG. 4–8. Movement of floats in the eastern Atlantic Ocean. Observed depth of floats in metres:

1	2,760∓110.		6	2,430∓130.
2	2,120∓ 50		7	1,560∓ 50.
3	2,460∓ 50.		11	4,240∓160
5	2,590∓ 70.		D	2,940∓ 70.

(After Swallow.)

(c) The deep-water circulation of the oceans

i. THE ATLANTIC OCEAN. So far direct observations have not been sufficiently numerous or prolonged to give a clear picture of the oceanic circulation in depth. The circulation must be deduced more indirectly from observations of temperature and salinity at depth, in relation to theoretical concepts. From this point of view the Atlantic Ocean is easier to consider than the other oceans, as it contains very distinctive water masses, which can be followed by means of their characteristics of temperature and salinity, and has a much better coverage of data. It has already been pointed out that it is only in the Atlantic Ocean that there are sources of deep water, and it is these distinctive water masses which can be traced as they move away from the source areas into the ocean. Another factor of significance is that in the Atlantic Ocean there is a transference of water across the Equator on the surface, which has been estimated as 6 million m.^{3}/sec. This must be compensated by a return flow at depth, as the north Atlantic is not in free communication with the rest of the world ocean. Stommel (1960) has, however, suggested that the compensation for the sinking of water at either end of the Atlantic is widely distributed throughout the whole oceanic area.

The general pattern of oceanic movement at depth in the Atlantic Ocean is based on the interdigitation of distinctive water masses, formed in high latitudes, each lying above the other in order of their density. This pattern can readily be appreciated by examining a vertical section showing the variations of temperature and salinity, running north–south the length of the ocean.

These sections, fig. 4–9, show that a tongue of low-temperature, low-salinity water extends northwards from the Antarctic coast, reaching across the Equator as far as 35°N. The salinity of this water is below 34·9‰, while temperatures below 2°C extend almost as far north on the bottom to 20°N. Above this is a tongue characterized by its high temperature, but particularly by its high salinity, which stretches southwards. Salinities above 34·9‰ extend in a broad wedge as far as 40°S, reaching through a considerable depth of water. The high salinity of this tongue of water is partly due to the very saline Mediterranean water, whose density as it flows out through the bottom of the Straits of Gibraltar is such that it mixes with the North Atlantic Deep Water, giving this its high salinity by which it can be recognized and traced right through the Atlantic Ocean and into the Indian Ocean. This water is also warmer than that below it; in the Southern Hemisphere it forms a sandwich between two layers of fresher water.

The uppermost of these layers consists of the fresh, cool Antarctic Intermediate Water. This has a salinity minimum of less than 34·4‰ extending nearly to 10°S; although mixing reduces this minimum northwards, the water mass can be traced far into the Northern Hemisphere, and the water extends through the thermocline into the surface layer. Above this water mass there are the shallow water masses of the surface. The whole of the deep-water circulation of the Atlantic takes place within these major water masses, with the exception of the Antarctic Circumpolar Water, which will be discussed in connexion with the Antarctic circulation.

O.–L

The distribution of oxygen also gives useful information concerning the water movements of the Atlantic Ocean. The oxygen content of the Atlantic waters is much greater than that of the other oceans, and within the Atlantic there is in general a diminution of oxygen between the north

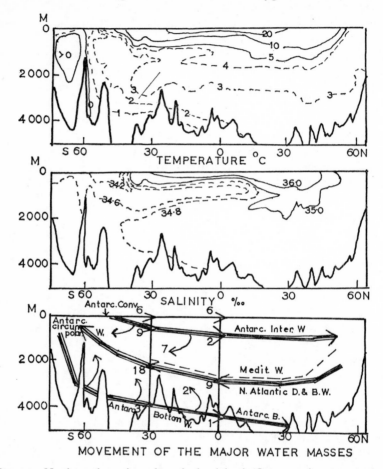

FIG. 4-9. North–south sections through the Atlantic Ocean to show temperature, salinity and the movement of the major water masses. The figures give volume in million m.³/sec. (Partly after Sverdrup *et al.*) (H. U. Sverdrup, Martin W. Johnson and Richard H. Fleming, *The Oceans: Their Physics, Chemistry and general Biology.* © 1942. Prentice-Hall, Inc., U.S.A. Reprinted by permission.)

and south, particularly in the North Atlantic Deep and Bottom Water and Mediterranean Water. Another zone of relatively high oxygen content is found in the deeper layers of the south Atlantic, within the Antarctic Bottom Water. The minimum is found above 1,000 m. just north of the Equator.

These figures suggest a circulation consisting of two elements: firstly there is a movement in the southern hemisphere to the north at the bottom and relatively near the top, with a compensating southerly movement between as shown in fig. 4–10. There is also a movement

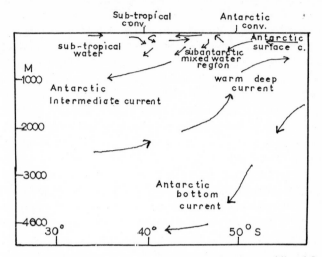

FIG. 4–10. Vertical circulation in the southern ocean, showing meridional flow, which is superimposed on a general west to east zonal flow. (After Deacon.)

across the Equator at the surface and reverse movement at depth. The amount of these transfers can be generalized from considerations of continuity as in the following table (Sverdrup, Johnson, and Fleming, p. 629).

Latitude	Water Mass	Current	Transport in million m.³/sec.	
			North	South
30°S		Benguela	16	
	Upper water	Brazil		10
		Central part		
		of gyre	7	7
	Inter. water		9	
	Deep water			18
	Bottom water		3	
0°	Upper water		6	
	Inter. water		2	
	Deep water			9
	Bottom water		1	

These figures may be compared with the theoretical estimate of Stommel and Arons (1960), in which they suggest that 16 million m.³/sec. move south at depth, being concentrated on the western side of the ocean. It is presumed that the compensating flow takes place at higher levels, partly on the surface and partly in the much shallower intermediate water. These figures suggest a more vigorous circulation across the Equator than that derived from hydrographic data and considerations such as the constancy of salt content in both hemispheres. The former figures are derived from the work of Wüst.

ii. THE SOUTHERN OCEAN. As the southwards-moving water progresses it is increasingly diluted, by mixing with surrounding waters, so that it gradually loses its high salinity and eventually rises to the surface to form the Antarctic Circumpolar Water mass. In this form it continues to move eastwards into the Indian and Pacific Oceans. This surface flow, according to Stommel and Arons, also continues at greater depth, where they suggest that the Antarctic Bottom Water, moving northwards, is partly deflected to the east. The water character and oxygen content also indicate an eastward flow of deep water around the southern continent, derived from both northern and southern sources of deep water. If the estimate of Stommel and Arons of 20 million m.^{3}/sec. for the original amount of the deep southern source, the Antarctic Bottom Water, is correct, a large proportion of this remains to travel eastwards, if only 3 million is moving north, as suggested in the table. This eastward movement continues right around the Earth, in the only zone in which continuous movement in a zonal direction is possible. The water is, however, deflected north after passing through Drake Passage, south of South America, because the island arc in this area effectively prevents deep water from moving east in this zone. The total amount of this water circulating around the southern continent varies, as it diverges in part into the other oceans or is replenished by water flowing into it on the eastern side of the oceans. Stommel and Arons do not attempt to estimate the amount which is continuously circling this zone. The major loss from this circulation is into the western Pacific, where they show a concentrated flow along the west side, off New Zealand.

iii. THE PACIFIC OCEAN. The deep circulation of the Pacific is dominated by this deep boundary current which flows north as far as the southern part of Japan in theory. From a study of the temperature and salinity distribution it is possible to trace the movement of waters in the Pacific, and it is clear from the much lower oxygen content that there is no source of deep and bottom water in this ocean. The different surface characters and distribution of land and sea determine the absence of suitable conditions, in which water can be rendered dense enough to sink to the deeper layers of the ocean. This applies particulary to the northern part of the ocean, which must be fed, therefore, indirectly via the Southern Hemisphere. There is as a result an even lower oxygen content in the northern than the south Pacific Ocean. Values in excess of 3·0 ml./l. are found throughout the southern Pacific, but only in the lowest layers is this value exceeded in the north Pacific.

The bulk of the deep Pacific waters are much more homogeneous than those of the Atlantic and there is no evidence of the layered structure so typical of the Atlantic. There is in general a decrease of temperature with depth, the value being less than 2°C below 2,000 m. There is a general decrease of salinity with depth to a level of 1,000 m., the water of the upper layers being less saline than 34·6‰, while below 2,000 m. the salinity is only slightly above 34·6‰, except in the south, where it rises to 34·7‰ and slightly above. This homogeneity suggests a very slow circulation, which is also confirmed by the very low oxygen values. The water which fills the deeper part of the Pacific Ocean must have originally been at the surface in either the north Atlantic or the Weddell Sea region. The latter water has followed the shorter path to the south Pacific, where its low temperature makes it recognizable, and where the oxygen content is greater. The rest of the Pacific water probably left the surface in the north Atlantic or the Mediterranean, although in its journey to the Pacific it has been very thoroughly diluted, partly by the water sinking all round the Antarctic at the Antarctic Convergence, to form the Antarctic Intermediate water, and partly by the Antarctic Bottom Water. The layer of salinity minimum at the upper level reveals the influence of the former water mass (Antarctic Intermediate Water). The exchange between the two hemispheres in the Pacific probably takes place in a northerly direction in the west and the reverse sense on the east, where, however, the flow is probably very sluggish, although on the west it seems to be concentrated as a boundary current. The exchange between the hemispheres was thought at one time to be very slight in the Pacific, but Stommel's theory suggests that it is more marked than originally thought, at least on the west, which is compensated by upwards flux at mid-depths.

iv. THE INDIAN OCEAN. The Indian Ocean, like the Pacific, has no source of deep water within it; this would not be expected in the northern part of the ocean, on account of the low latitude of the northern boundary. Temperature and salinity observations do, however, suggest a similar exchange in the southern Indian Ocean as that already described in the south Atlantic. There is a northward extension of bottom water and intermediate water, with a return flow at deeper levels. The former water masses are the Antarctic Bottom Water and the Antarctic Intermediate Water respectively. Stommel and Arons suggest that this circulation is based on a northward-flowing boundary current on the west, with more diffuse southerly flow on the east. The extremely saline Red Sea Water helps to give a salinity maximum to the southward-moving deep water, which has a salinity maximum at a depth of 3,000 m. This Red Sea Water probably penetrates eventually as far as the Antarctic. There is thus a slight transfer north across the Equator in the Indian

Ocean, which is estimated as 2 million m.³/sec. by Stommel in the deeper layers.

v. GENERAL CONCLUSIONS. Although there is still considerable uncertainty of the exact nature of the deep-water circulation in the oceans and the relationship between this and the surface currents, it does appear that the deep circulation of the Atlantic is more vigorous than that of the other oceans, because only in this ocean is deep water formed to any important extent. The formation of this deep water depends partly on the nature of the surface currents; for example, the Gulf Stream and North Atlantic Drift help to determine the position of warm saline water in the north Atlantic, but it is the cooling of this water which plays the most important part in the formation of the North Atlantic Deep and Bottom Water. External influences of heating and cooling are also important; for example in the formation of the Mediterranean Water, due to excessive evaporation.

As Wyrtki (1961) has pointed out, the wind alone cannot account for the deep-water circulation of the oceans. The thermohaline effects are important; four processes operate, (a) the heating of the surface layer and poleward flow at the surface, (b) sinking of the heaviest water in the highest latitudes, (c) spreading of water towards the Equator in the deep layers, and (d) ascending deep water through the thermocline into the surface layer. The poleward flow at the surface takes place in the western boundary current. In low latitudes the upward velocity of water through the discontinuity layer is between 2 and 5×10^{-5} cm./sec., giving the total contribution of the thermohaline circulation as between 3 and 10 million m.³/sec., which is added to the surface circulation. In considering the deep western boundary currents, friction and inertia impose a limiting width which has been computed as about 100 km.; elsewhere the movements are very slow and affected by large-scale horizontal turbulence.

The thermohaline circulation, in the absence of wind, has been calculated by Wyrtki, who finds that it would be much less strong than the actual circulation, indicating that the wind effect is dominant. His theoretical model shows that the main features of thermohaline origin are the strong thermocline and ascending water associated with it in low latitudes, and the sinking of deep water in high latitudes. Features due to the wind circulation are the Subtropical Convergence, the Antarctic Convergence (Antarctic Polar Front), the ascending deep water in high latitudes, the sinking of the Antarctic Intermediate Water and, of course, the surface circulation. The wind-induced divergences and convergences are essential to drive the deep circulation.

REFERENCES

Broecker, W. S., Gerard, R., Ewing, M., and Heezen, B. C., Natural radio-carbon in the Atlantic Ocean. *Journ. Geophys. Res.* **65**, 2903–31, 1960.

Carruthers, J. N., 'Bottle Post' and other drifts. *Journ. Inst. Navig.* **9**, 261–81, 1956.

Charnock, H., Ocean currents. *Science Prog.* **48**, 257–70, 1960.

Deacon, G. E. R., The southern cold temperate zone. *Proc. Roy. Soc. B.* **152**, 441–7, 1960.

Defant, A., *Physical Oceanography*, Vol. I. Pergamon Press, 1961.

Dietrich, G., and Kalle, K., *Allgemeine Mereskunde.* Berlin, Borntraeger, 1957.

Ekman, V. W., On the influence of the Earth's rotation on ocean currents. *Arkiv f. Matem. Astr. and Fysik.*, Stockholm 2 **11**, 53 pp., 1905.

Fugilister, F. C., and Worthington, L. V., Some results of a multiple ship survey of the Gulf Stream. *Tellus* **3**, 1–14, 1951.

Gunther, E. R., A report on oceanographical investigations in the Peru coastal current. *Discovery Reports* **13**, 107–276, 1936.

Hughes, P., A determination of the relation between wind and sea-surface drift. *Quart. Journ. Roy. Met. Soc.* **82**, 494–502, 1956.

Iselin, C. O'D., Preliminary report on long-term variation in the transport of the Gulf Stream System. *Pap. Phys. Oceanogr. & Meteor.* **8**, 1, 40 pp., 1940.

Knauss, J. A., Measurements of the Cromwell Current. *Deep-Sea Res.* **6**, 265–86, 1960.

Lawford, A. L., and Veley, V. F. C., Change in the relationship between wind and surface water movement at higher wind speeds. *Trans. Am. Geophy. Un.* **37**, 691–3, 1956.

Morgan, G. W., On the wind-driven ocean circulation. *Tellus* **8**, 301–20, 1956.

Munk, W. H., On the wind-driven ocean circulation. *Journ. Meteor.* **7**, 79–93, 1950.

Neumann, G., Evidence for an equatorial undercurrent in the Atlantic. *Deep-Sea Res.* **6**, 328–34, 1960.

Phillips, O. M., On the generation of waves by turbulent wind. *Journ. Fluid Mech.* **2**, 417–45, 1957.

Sears, M., Notes on the Peruvian coastal current, I: An introduction to the ecology of Pisco Bay. *Deep-Sea Res.* **1**, 141–69, 1954.

Rossby, C. G., A comparison of current patterns in the atmosphere and in the ocean basins. *U.G.G.I.* **9**, Ass. of Met. Bruselles, 1951.

Stommel, H., A survey of ocean current theory. *Deep-Sea Res.* **4**, 149–84, 1957.

Stommel, H., *The Gulf Stream.* Univ. of California Press, 1958a.

Stommel, H., The abyssal circulation. *Deep-Sea Res.* **5**, 80–82, 1958b.

Stommel, H., and Arons, A. B., On the abyssal circulation of the world ocean, II: An idealised model of the circulation pattern and amplitude in oceanic basins. *Deep-Sea Res.* **6**, 217–33, 1960.

Sverdrup, H. U., and Munk, W. H., *Wind, Sea and Swell—theory of relationships in forecasting.* H.O. Pub. 601, U.S. Navy Dept., 1947.

Sverdrup, H. U., Johnson, M. W., and Fleming, R. H., *The Oceans.* Prentice-Hall, New York, 1946.

Swallow, J. C., Some further deep current measurements using neutrally-buoyant floats. *Deep-Sea Res.* **4**, 93–104, 1957.

Swallow, J. C., and Worthington, L. V., Measurements of deep currents in the western N. Atlantic. *Nature* **179**, 1183–4, 1957.

Swallow, J. C., and Worthington, L. V., An observation of a deep counter-current in the western north Atlantic. *Deep-Sea Res.* **8**, 1–19, 1961.

Swallow, J. C., and Hamon, B. V., Some measurements of deep currents in the eastern north Atlantic. *Deep-Sea Res.* **6**, 155–68, 1960.

Voorhis, A. D., Observations in the equatorial Atlantic Ocean. *Nature* **191**, 157–8, 1961.
Worthington, L. V., A preliminary note on the time scale in the north Atlantic circulation. *Deep-Sea Res.* **1**, 244–51, 1954a.
Worthington, L. V., Three detailed cross-sections of the Gulf Stream. *Tellus* **6**, 116–23, 1954b.
Wyrtki, K., The thermohaline circulation in relation to the general circulation in the oceans. *Deep-Sea Res.* **8**, 39–64, 1961.

CHAPTER 5

THE TIDE

INTRODUCTION

THE MOON rarely plays an important part in the affairs of the Earth, but in its influence on the tidal phenomena of the oceans and seas it is of fundamental importance. It is well known that the gravitational attraction of the Earth, Moon and Sun for each other is the basic cause of the tides in the oceans. The movements of these bodies are complex, but regular and well known, which enables the tides to be predicted with with some assurance. Nevertheless, other factors are also involved which are not so well understood; the response of the oceans to the tide-producing forces has, in the past, given rise to a number of different theories to account for the observed tidal phenomena, while unusual meteorological conditions can cause considerable differences between the predicted and actual tidal conditions. Of particular significance in this respect are the occasional tidal surges to which some fairly enclosed bodies of water, such as the North Sea, are liable.

The range and character of the tide varies greatly from place to place, and, in order to understand these variations, it is necessary to consider the response of the waters to the tide-producing forces. In some areas the special conditions give rise to abnormal tidal features, such as the double high waters of Southampton Water on the south coast of England and the solar tides found on some Pacific Islands. Other features of interest are the tidal bores characteristic of some tidal rivers. These fairly isolated phenomena show that special conditions must obtain if they are to develop. It is, therefore, of interest to analyse the factors on which these tidal phenomena depend. Tidal currents are also significant from several points of view; they influence the movement of material on the sea floor, and also affect waves and coastal shipping. Some fish also react to the tide in their biological cycle, and in others their movement, reflected in the fishing industry, is to a certain extent governed by the Moon, and through it the tide.

1. *TIDE-PRODUCING FORCES*

The work of Sir Isaac Newton on gravity made possible the analysis of the tide-producing forces, in terms of the gravitational attraction of the Sun and Moon on the Earth. He developed the theory of the equilibrium tide, which would occur on an ideal Earth, completely covered with water and ignoring the effects of inertia. The equilibrium tide is of value in giving a picture of the tide-producing forces; the response of the oceans to these forces is, however, an entirely different problem.

The gravitational attraction of two particles for one another is proportional to their masses and varies with the square of the distance between them. Thus the attractive force is proportional to the product of their masses divided by their distance apart squared, mm'/r^2. The force is exerted in a straight line between the two bodies. The attractive force of the Moon can, therefore, be expressed in terms of the mass of the Moon and the Earth and the distance between them. It is balanced by the centrifugal force, which acts everywhere parallel to the line of centres at a constant rate. However, not all points on the Earth are at an equal distance from the Moon; the nearer ones will be attracted by gravity to a greater degree than the farther. It is this difference in the attractive force on the different parts of the surface of the Earth which gives the relative attractive force, which is the most important in tidal matters. The differential tidal force, as it is called, is the difference in the attractive force at any point and that in the centre of the Earth. It is only this differential force which has any tide-raising capacity.

Taking four points on the Earth, two in line with the Moon's direction at opposite ends of a diameter, and two at right-angles to the first, they may be called respectively U U' V V', as shown in fig. 5–1. The attractive force at U, nearest the Moon, will be greatest, while that at U' on the far side will be least. The respective values are 0·000,003,493g, and 0·000,003,268g, where g is the force of gravity, while at the centre of the Earth the value is in between. These forces are all directed towards the Moon, but if the differential force in relation to the Earth is considered, it is clear that the outer edge is pulled least far towards the Moon, and the inner edge farthest. This creates the bulge under the Moon and that on the opposite side of the Earth, and thus accounts for the semi-diurnal character of the tide in many areas. The differential forces are, therefore, directed away from the centre of the Earth at U and U'. In the plane V V', at right angles to U U', the differential force is zero, as all the points along this circle are equidistant from the Moon; however, there is a slight compressional force towards the centre of the Earth, resulting in a force directed towards the centre. The differential forces at these points are all at right-angles to the surface of the Earth. The tidal force only alters the value of gravity slightly, and it plays no part in the generation of the tides; it is, therefore, necessary to consider the forces at other points on the surface of the Earth.

Taking a point x on the Earth's surface, the different forces there can be subdivided into two parts: that acting parallel to that at V and that parallel to U. The resultant of these two forces is almost parallel to the surface of the Earth. This force has the power to move particles over the surface, towards the line of centres of the two bodies. This is called the 'tractive force', and on it depends all the tidal movements. It is, therefore, necessary to consider it more closely and to analyse it into its component parts. This tractive force is directed everywhere from $V V'$ towards $U U'$, the force being zero at U and U' and on the great circle through V and V' at right-angles to U and U'. This force can be expressed in terms of the mass of the Earth and Moon and the radius of the Earth, e, and their distance apart, r, and the latitude, C, by the

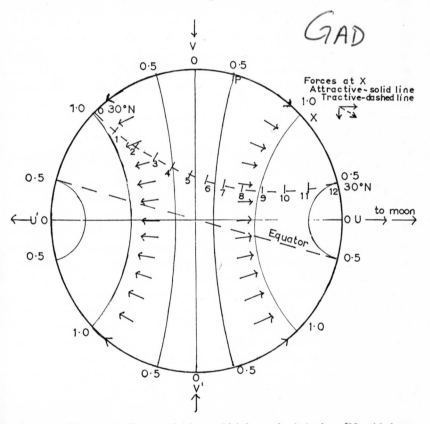

FIG. 5–1. Diagram to illustrate the lunar tidal forces for latitude 30°N, with lunar declination of 15°N. The arrows at $V V' U U'$ and X show the attractive forces, while the figures on the circumference of the circle indicate the relative strength of the tractive forces, whose direction is indicated by the arrows within the circle. The direction and strength at each hour on the 30°N latitude can be obtained. (Modified from Doodson and Warburg, A.M.T.) [By permission of the Controller of H.M. Stationery Office.]

formula $\dfrac{3}{2} g \dfrac{M}{E} \dfrac{e^3}{r^3} \sin 2C$; the maximum value of this force is

0·000,000,084 g, half-way between U and V. It is important to note that the cube of the distance of the two bodies comes into the formula. This means that although the mass of the Sun is much greater than that of the Moon, the fact that the Moon is much nearer more than compensates for its smaller mass. Thus the tractive force of the Sun is only 0·46 times that of the Moon. Working out the formula gives a value of 35 ft./hour after one hour for the speed of the tractive force, the maximum velocity in a normal twelve-hour cycle would be about 70 ft./hour.

By plotting the intensity of the tractive forces on a stereographic projection, on which angles are shown correctly, it is possible to show graphically how these forces vary throughout the tidal cycle at different latitudes. If it is assumed that the Moon is overhead at the Equator, the forces will be symmetrical, as the Moon revolves round the Earth. There will be two maxima and two minima each lunar day, the direction of the force being everywhere towards U or U' in the line towards the Moon. The Moon is not, however, always overhead at the Equator. When it is overhead at some other latitude, which can be up to 28°35', as the angle of the Moon's orbit is set at an angle of 5°8' to that of the Earth round the Sun, which itself varies through 23°27', the forces are no longer symmetrical twice daily. As soon as the Moon's declination is no longer zero, which means that it is overhead north or south of the Equator, the curve showing the variation of the tractive forces throughout the lunar day becomes asymmetrical and varies with latitude.

It can most easily be understood by reference to an example. Taking latitude 30°N, with a lunar declination of 15°N, the method of analysis can be demonstrated graphically, as illustrated in fig. 5–2. Using the stereographic projection, on which the varying direction of the tractive force can be determined, it is possible to construct a diagram showing the changes in direction and strength of the tractive force hour by hour. This complex curve shows that the force at hour 0 is directed southwards at its maximum value. It then swings towards south-west and between hours 5 and 6 becomes zero, followed by a slight north-easterly component, finishing up at hour 12 due south again, but half the value it had at hour 0. The second half of the day is a mirror image of the first part.

This complex curve can be simplified by splitting it into its component parts; this is initially done on the basis of the northerly and easterly components. These curves are still asymmetrical, but further analysis can divide them into their diurnal and semi-diurnal parts, each of which forms a smooth sine curve, showing that the complex curve is made up of components of these periods. Thus the north component of

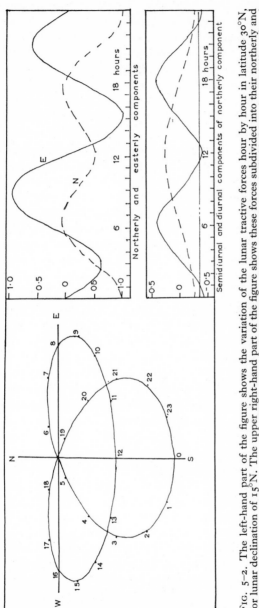
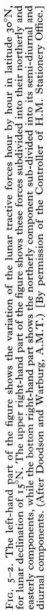

Fig. 5–2. The left-hand part of the figure shows the variation of the lunar tractive forces hour by hour in latitude 30°N, for lunar declination of 15°N. The upper right-hand part of the figure shows these forces subdivided into their northerly and easterly components, while the bottom right-hand part shows the northerly component sub-divided into its semi-diurnal and diurnal components. (After Doodson and Warburg, A.M.T.) [By permission of the Controller of H.M. Stationery Office.]

the curve under consideration can be split into one diurnal portion, which has a maximum at hour 12 and a minimum at hour 0, and the semi-diurnal curve, with two maxima at hours 6 and 18. In this way all the variations can be treated to give their relevant semi-diurnal and diurnal components.

From this analysis it is possible to determine the influence of the declination of the Moon on the tractive force and its variation with latitude. It has already been shown that the tides are symmetrical when the declination is zero; this means that the diurnal portion of the curve is missing. The diurnal part of the lunar tide-producing force is almost proportional to the declination of the Moon. The semi-diurnal portion, on the other hand, diminishes in range at times of high declination. The solar tide-producing forces are similar, but of smaller magnitude and slightly different period, as the lunar day is fifty minutes longer than the solar one.

The tractive tide-producing forces set tidal streams in motion, which can be analysed in a similar way to the tractive forces. This method of reducing a complex curve to its simple harmonic components, in the form of sine curves, is a useful technique in tidal analysis and is called harmonic analysis. It is the basis of some methods of tidal prediction, because the complex movements of the heavenly bodies, on which the tractive forces depend, can be similarly simplified. The tide-producing forces can be used to work out the equilibrium tide; it is assumed that there are no land masses and that inertia does not play a part. This is clearly unrealistic, but all the same the tide as it exists must in some measure respond to the forces in a way related to the equilibrium tide. Before considering the response of the oceans to the tractive forces, it is necessary to consider the types of wave motion in the oceans, associated with the tidal forces and their streams.

2. TYPES OF WAVE MOTION IN TIDAL THEORY

(a) Progressive wave

A wave propagated in a channel of infinite length will have certain properties; it is known by the term 'progressive wave'. Where the wave is long compared with the depth of water the streams will extend uniformly from the top to the bottom of the water; this applies to waves of tidal length, where only two crests occur around the whole circumference of the Earth. The length of the progressive wave is defined as the distance between two adjacent crests, and its period as the time it takes to move one wave length. The velocity of travel of the wave form, not of the water in the wave, is dependent on the depth of the water; this applies to waves of tidal length, which are very long compared with the depth of the ocean. Thus the wave velocity, c, equals the square root of the depth, d, times the force of gravity, or $c=\sqrt{gd}$. The variation in the height of the wave is assumed to be small compared with the depth of the water, which is true over the ocean, and is only inapplicable when the waves are in very shallow coastal waters. The rate of propagation of the wave is not dependent on the period or length, but only on the depth. In this respect waves of tidal length differ fundamentally from the short period, wind-generated waves to be considered in chapter 6.

The rates of travel of the wave form can readily be given in terms of the depth from the formula $c=\sqrt{gd}$; the following values give some examples:

Depth in fathoms	Wave velocity in knots
50	58·17
100	82·27
200	117·34
500	183·95
1,000	260·15
2,000	367·90

The actual movement of the water is, however, very much slower than that of the wave form. For example, in a depth of 100 fathoms the wave form moves at about 82 knots, while the water is only moving at 1·4 knots, assuming an amplitude of the wave of 10 ft. The amplitude is defined as the elevation of the wave above the mean level. This is derived from the relationship $u/c=y/d$, where u is the rate of the stream, c is the wave velocity, y is the elevation of the wave crest above the mean level, and d is the mean depth. This speed of 1·4 knots is only achieved at the crest and trough of the wave, when the stream is at its maximum. In a progressive wave this current flows in the direction of wave propagation at the crest of the wave and in the opposite direction at the trough, in between it becomes zero and changes sign when the mean level is reached. Thus the essential characteristics of a progressive wave are the dependence of the velocity on the depth and the fact that the current flows in the direction of wave propagation and is at its maximum at the crest, while at the mean water level there is no current; at the trough the speed is also at its maximum, but flows in the reverse direction.

(b) Stationary wave or standing oscillation

There is a second type of wave which is very important to tidal analysis; this is the stationary wave or standing oscillation. The progressive wave must necessarily be somewhat theoretical, as it was assumed that it moved in a channel of infinite length. This is clearly not possible on the Earth, with the exception of the narrow belt of continuous water around the Antarctic continent. The stationary wave, on the other hand, can be thought of as developing in a basin of finite dimensions.

If a rectangular basin is tilted and then set down horizontally again, the water within it will rock to and fro with an oscillatory motion, but will not leave the basin, hence the term standing oscillation. The movement of the water in the basin can be divided into four stages; first, the surface has its maximum slope, with high water at one end of the basin and low at the other; second, the surface becomes flat as the water flows from the high to the low end and the streams are at their maximum; third, the streams cease as the elevations reach their maximum at the opposite ends this time; finally the surface is again flat, but the streams reach their maximum in the opposite direction. This type of wave motion differs from the first, in that now the streams do not coincide with the maximum elevations.

The period of the standing oscillation can be related to the dimensions of the basin. This fact is very important in considering the response of the oceans to the tide-producing forces. The length of the basin may be taken as L, the breadth as b, and the mean depth as d, with the period of the oscillation, that is the time between two successive high waters at the same end of the basin, as T. The rate of the stream is u and the elevation above the mean surface as y. It can be shown that the breadth of the basin does not affect the period of the oscillation nor does the amplitude of the wave. The period $T=\dfrac{2L}{\sqrt{gd}}$ this means that the period depends only on the dimensions of the basin, in terms of its length and depth. Each basin, therefore, has its own natural period of oscillation which depends on these dimensions. If this natural period of oscillation is the same as that of the period of the tide-producing forces, the basin will respond actively to the appropriate tidal period, and a state of resonance will be set up.

The formula giving the period of oscillation also shows an interesting connexion between this type of wave and the progressive wave. It is apparent that the period of the standing oscillation is such that it equals that of a progressive wave with a length equal to twice the length of the basin, as the square root of gd comes into both equations. The connexion between the two types of waves becomes apparent when the reflection of a progressive wave is considered.

Fig. 5–3 shows what would happen if a vertical barrier were placed in the path of a progressive wave in such a way that all its energy were reflected to form a second wave of equal size, travelling in the opposite direction to the first wave. In the first diagram the two crests coincide, which added together give the maximum elevations, the streams on the other hand are flowing in the opposite directions and therefore cancel out. In the third diagram the stage is reached when the advancing crest coincides with the retreating trough, the elevations cancel out to give a flat surface, but the streams are now flowing in the same direction and

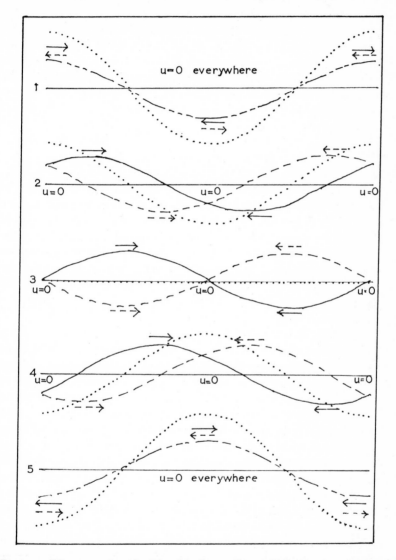

FIG. 5–3. Diagram to show the formation of a standing oscillation by the reflection of a progressive wave. The dotted curve is the sum of the full curve and the dashed curve, the former being the progressive wave moving to the right and the latter that moving to the left. (After Doodson and Warburg, A.M.T.) [By permission of the Controller of H.M. Stationery Office.]

O.–M

reinforce each other to give the maximum currents. In this way it is apparent that a reflected progressive wave has all the characteristics of the standing oscillation. It is seen that the streams are always zero at intervals of half a wave length, while the elevations are always nil at the intermediate points. It would thus be possible to place barriers every half wave length without disturbing the motion. This gives the simple oscillating system already described, where there is a line across the middle of the basin along which the elevations do not change; this is called the nodal line of the system. It also demonstrates that an oscillating system can have more than one nodal line; several can be present at intervals of half the length of the original progressive wave.

3. *THE EFFECT OF THE ROTATION OF THE EARTH— AMPHIDROMIC SYSTEMS*

The importance of the rotation of the Earth in the oceanic current systems has already been discussed, and it also plays a very important part in tidal phenomena. Water which is moving on the Earth is subject to the deflecting Coriolis force, the deflection being to the right in the Northern Hemisphere. When a particle of water is moving the effect of the rotation of the Earth can either produce an acceleration to the right of its path, or create a slope up to the right in the Northern Hemisphere. The adjustment could also be a combination of these two effects.

The modification of a standing oscillation, by the gyroscopic forces of the Earth's rotation, gives rise to the amphidromic system. When the streams are flowing at the maximum velocity a gradient transverse to them will be set up, causing subsidiary elevations. These will set up currents which carry the water across the basin to build up the necessary elevation on the opposite side, as the main current reverses. The diagram, fig. 5–4, shows how these subsidiary elevations and streams transform the simple swing of the standing oscillation in the North Sea into a movement round three points in the North Sea basin. These are called amphidromic points, because the tidal elevations and streams appear to move round the points, where there is no change of elevation. The movement is in an anticlockwise direction in the Northern Hemisphere and the reverse in the Southern. It is interesting to note that when the elevations and streams are combined the maximum currents now occur at high water and that they flow in the direction of progress of the wave round the basin at high water. These are characteristics of a progressive wave; the result of adding the effect of the rotation of the Earth to a simple standing oscillation is to produce an amphidromic system, which has the characteristics of a progressive wave move anti-clockwise around a point.

The co-tidal lines, which join points where high water occurs simultaneously, radiate from the amphidromic point and the tidal range increases away from this point in the centre. The tidal streams associated with the system are rotatory in character, moving in an anticlockwise sense. Towards the edges of the basin, however, the pattern becomes modified and the currents are more nearly rectilinear, flowing in opposite directions at the flood and ebb of the tide, with only weak currents between.

The rotation of the Earth also affects a progressive wave. If this is moving along a narrow channel, the Earth's rotation will lead to the

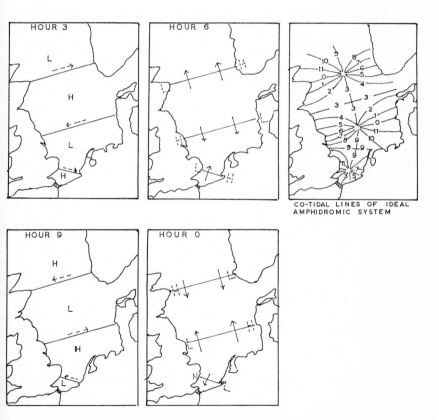

CO-TIDAL LINES OF IDEAL
AMPHIDROMIC SYSTEM

FIG. 5–4. Diagrams to illustrate the amphidromic system in the North Sea. The full letters and arrows refer to the primary standing wave oscillation, and the dashed ones refer to the gyroscopic modification. The top right diagram shows the co-tidal lines of the ideal amphidromic system. (Modified from Doodson and Warburg, A.M.T.) [By permission of the Controller of H.M. Stationery Office.]

development of a surface sloping up to the right in the Northern Hemisphere. If the channel runs east-west, as is approximately true of the English Channel, this will have the effect of increasing the range on the south coast of the channel. The tidal current flows east at high water, causing an elevation on the south side and a depression on the north side. At low water the stream will be flowing west, if the wave is advancing towards the east; the level will then be higher on the north and lower on the south. These two factors together account for the low range on the north coast and the high one on the south. This type of tidal modification is known as a Kelvin Wave and is found in the English Channel, where the tidal range on the coast of southern England is much smaller than that on the north French coast. This type of wave is found in situations in which much of the energy of a progressive wave is lost, preventing the formation of a true amphidromic system by reflection of the progressive wave.

Amphidromic systems are fundamental to the modern analysis of tidal phenomena in the oceans, and their adjacent seas and gulfs. But before considering their application to the actual oceans, the earlier ideas concerning the oceanic tide may be mentioned, as these show how the development of the idea of the amphidromic system, as described, follows the development of theories of tidal motion in the oceans.

4. THE RESPONSE OF THE OCEANS TO THE TIDE-PRODUCING FORCES

(a) Early ideas of oceanic tides

The earliest ideas concerning the tide in the oceans were not very realistic, such as the equilibirum theory, because they did not take into account the distribution of land and sea. However the work of Laplace, done as long ago as 1776, is worthy of mention. He took into account the rotation of the Earth and inertia, working out his solution for a globe completely covered by water of a constant depth. It was nearly 100 years before Lord Kelvin justified the mathematics of Laplace in 1875. The data were worked out for four different depths of 7,260 ft., 14,520 ft., 29,040 ft., and 58,080 ft. The results showed that for depths greater than 29,040 ft. the tide progressively approached the equilibrium value as the depth increased, but for a value a little less than 29,040 ft. the tide became infinitely large, while at lesser depths it was inverted in relation to the equilibrium tide; thus under the Moon it would be low water rather than high water. This has an interesting application to the consideration of the movement of a progressive wave of tidal length around the Earth in different latitudes. At the Equator the circumference is such that the tidal wave would have to travel at 871 miles/hour to get round the Earth in the time available. A free wave can only travel at this rate if the water were 67,200 ft. deep. This is much greater than the depth of the oceans and suggests that inverted tides near the Equator would become direct as the circumference gets smaller in higher latitudes.

This idea led to one of the earliest theories of the tide in the actual ocean. This progressive wave theory suggested that the tide-producing forces generated forced tidal waves, which travelled round the southern ocean at a speed determined by the tide-producing forces and the latitude; this wave set up free progressive waves, which travelled up the other oceans according to their depth. There were some observations in favour of this theory, such as the progressively later time of high water northwards along the coast of South America, but there are even more serious points against it. The most important of these is the fact that such free waves would be reflected from the northern edges of the oceanic gulfs, to form standing oscillations. Another point is that even the Atlantic Ocean is quite large enough to generate its own tidal oscillations. If the sea were three miles deep, it would only need to be 900 miles long to support an oscillation of twelve hours period. A depth of 15,840 ft. is not at all uncommon.

The next important theory is Harris's standing oscillation theory, which is based on a system of stationary waves. He stressed the importance of resonance in his explanation of the tides, suggesting that where the natural period of oscillation of a water body coincided with one of the periods of the tide-producing forces the ocean would respond to that period. Harris produced a chart on which he divided the ocean into a series of rectangular areas, of suitable dimensions to support oscillation of a particular period. This type of analysis could explain a number of tidal anomalies, by considering the position of a place in relation to the nodal line of an oscillating system. Thus if the tide were very small, the place should be near the nodal line, but if it were large it should be far from it. One of the weaknesses of Harris's theory, which was put forward towards the end of the last century, was his assumption that two neighbouring oscillating areas did not react with one another, and his omission of the effect of the rotation of the Earth. However, his emphasis on the importance of resonance was a great step forward and paved the way for the modern ideas.

Most modern co-tidal charts are based on a series of amphidromic systems. An early one of this type was prepared for the North Atlantic by Sterneck in 1920 and is very similar to that of Dietrich in 1944. The chart of Sterneck, shown in fig. 5–5, has three amphidromic points: one between Scotland and Iceland, one in the centre of the North Atlantic, about half-way between Ireland and Newfoundland, while the third is situated just south of the eastern end of the West Indies. These charts show the semi-diurnal co-tidal lines; others are needed for the diurnal component, which because of its longer period does not necessarily react in the same way as the semi-diurnal one. Another more recent

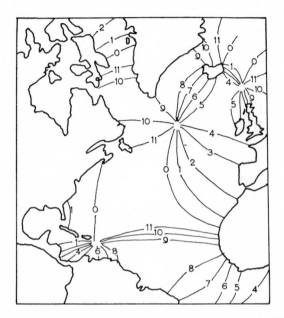

FIG. 5–5. Co-tidal lines in the Atlantic Ocean after Sterneck (1920). (After Doodson and Warburg, A.M.T.)

approach has been to work out the tidal pattern in oceans bounded by different meridians and of varying depths. Such patterns are often complex, but they are mostly based on some pattern of amphidromic systems. Although they differ very considerably from the actual oceans, they do suggest that these are of suitable dimensions to support amphidromic systems of varying periods according to their dimensions.

(b) Types of oceanic tide

There is an infinite variety in the forms of the tide curves in different areas, due to the great number of possible combinations of the many variables. The essential features of the tidal pattern in different areas can be divided into three main groups. Firstly the synodic tides, such as those around Britain, where the diurnal inequality is small, but the fortnightly cycle of spring and neap tides is dominant; the latter feature is due to the relative position of the Sun and Moon. Secondly, the declinational type of tide in which the diurnal element is marked and changes in value over the spring-tide period, as in parts of Borneo. Thirdly, the anomalistic tide, dependent to some extent on the varying distance of the Moon, as in the Bay of Fundy.

The tides of the Atlantic are dominated by the semi-diurnal lunar-pattern, with two high waters occurring each twenty-four lunar hours. This suggests that the size of the Atlantic is more suited to react with the semi-diurnal tide-producing forces. In the Pacific, on the other hand, the tide is often mixed, having one high high and another low high each lunar day, which indicates that the Pacific is large enough to respond to the diurnal tide-producing forces.

The second type of tide is well seen in the Pacific, and Victoria in British Columbia illustrates it clearly. This curve is mainly diurnal, but the period of low water is shorter than that of high water. However, at neap tide this is reversed to show a double low water. This tide is also influenced to some extent by the Sun, and can be described as a mixed tide. The occurrence of diurnal tides in the Atlantic is limited to those bays where the conditions are such that resonance with tidal forces of this period can take place, as, for example, in Chaleur Bay and North-umberland Strait. The former has a marked inequality of high water and the latter of low water. This asymmetry is also well developed on the coast of California, while some areas in the western Pacific have diurnal tides only, or a mixture of semi-diurnal and diurnal during the fort-nightly cycle of neap and spring tides. Examples of some of these types are shown in fig. 5–6.

Purely diurnal tides are not common, but do occur in parts of Viet-nam (see Do-Son in fig. 5–6) and in the northern half of the Gulf of Mexico. The tides of southern California show an interesting variation with the seasons. The spring and neap cycles at full and new Moon and half Moon respectively are clearly shown, as well as the diurnal in-equality. This cycle is associated with regular movements of sand on the beaches, specially during the summer, which the Grunion, *Lereuthes tenuis*, take advantage of in their spawning habits. Eggs are deposited on the beach in such a position that they are covered by sand during the spring-tide stage, and are uncovered again at the next neap tides, when the eggs are just ready to hatch, after being protected in the sand during the incubation period of fourteen days. There is also a longer-term seasonal change, whereby the diurnal range is considerably less at the equinox than it is at the solstices. The maximum range is only 8·7 ft. and the mean range 3·7 ft.

This tide may be compared with that on the north coast of Borneo, which also shows the influence of the diurnal tide-producing force. The maximum range is still small, being just over 6 ft., but the tide is diurnal for a period of a week around spring tide, when its range is greatest; during the neap-tide period the range is smaller and the pattern is semidiurnal. There is also an increased range here during the solstices.

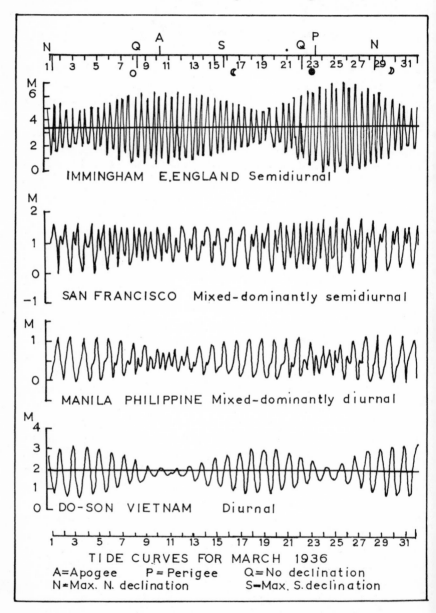

Fig. 5–6. Representative types of tidal curves. (After Dietrich.)

The tide in some areas is more influenced by the solar forces than the lunar ones. Tahiti, for example, has high tide at the same time each day, instead of being fifty minutes later each day. This can be explained if an amphidromic point of the lunar tide-producing forces were situated near the island. These forces would, therefore, be reduced in effectiveness sufficiently for the smaller solar tide to become conspicuous, although the total range is not large.

Apart from the types of tide already mentioned, there are also the variations due to the distance of the Moon and other factors related to the movement of the Moon and Sun. The variations due to the position of the Sun and Moon relative to each other, giving the fortnightly succession of spring and neap tides, when the Sun and Moon are working together or opposing each other respectively, have already been commented upon. The various elements of which any complex tide curve is compounded can be analysed by the procedure of harmonic analysis, whereby the curve is split up into its smooth harmonic parts. When the major constituents have been isolated there are left various longer-term effects, which can be related to the rather complex movements of the Sun, Moon, and Earth. The distance of the Moon from the Earth varies, from its closest approach at perigee to its farthest at apogee, in a monthly cycle.

The tides of the Bay of Fundy respond to this factor in such a way that the spring tides at perigee are considerably greater in range than those at apogee. This type of tide is called an anomalistic tide. The perigee spring range is 50·5 ft., while the apogee spring range is 40·18 ft., the difference being over 10 ft. There are also longer-term effects related to the repetition time of certain specific relationships in the orbits of the Earth and Moon, one of which has a period of about eighteen years.

The range of the tide over large stretches of the coasts of the world is fairly small, while it is probably even smaller in the open ocean, although it cannot easily be measured here. Oceanic islands, however, rarely have large tidal ranges. The areas where the tidal range exceeds 20 ft. are restricted to the more enclosed seas; for example, around parts of the coast of Britain. The only section of the coast of Africa to have this range is near Zanzibar on the east coast. A few isolated areas with this range are found in the Gulf of Cambay and the Hoogly delta region of India, near Rangoon, and the west side of the Malay Peninsula. There are also small areas on the south coast of Borneo, the west side of the Straits of Formosa, the western part of the north coast of Australia, and the southern tip of South America. In North America ranges over 20 ft. are found in the inner end of the Gulf of California, parts of the Gulf of Alaska, Ungava Bay in Quebec Province, and the Bay of Fundy on the Atlantic coast. Ranges over 10 ft. are rather more widespread, but by far the larger proportion of the coasts of the world have ranges under this value. Nearly all large tidal ranges are found in gulfs and bays, and these frequently have interesting tidal phenomena; they are, therefore, worthy of consideration.

(c) Tides in gulfs and seas

A rectangular gulf is about the nearest approach to the theoretical rectangular basin in which the character of an amphidromic system and standing oscillation can be examined. In considering the response of a gulf to the tide-producing forces it is necessary to know its dimensions, particularly its length and depth, as these two factors determine its natural period of oscillation as already mentioned. If this natural period of oscillation is nearly equal to that of one or other of the tidal periods the gulf will respond to the tide-producing forces and the range of the tide will be considerable. There is, therefore, a critical length of each gulf in relation to its depth, which will enable it to support a standing oscillation.

The position of the node of the standing oscillation in relation to the mouth of the gulf will depend on its length relative to its depth. There is thus a critical length for each depth which will support a standing oscillation in such a way that the nodal line will run through the mouth of the gulf. In such conditions there will be no change of level at the mouth and the range will increase to a maximum near the head of the gulf. If the gulf is shorter than this critical length, it will be high water throughout the gulf at the same time, but there will be a small tidal range at the mouth. If, however, the gulf is longer than the critical length, it will be high water at the head of the gulf while it is low water at the mouth, with a nodal line in between. The final possibility is that the gulf is twice the critical length; the nodal line will then occur in the centre of the gulf and the range will be as great at the mouth as it is at the head, it being high water at one end while it is low at the other. Under these conditions there will be no streams across the mouth of the gulf, and, in fact, if a barrier were placed here it could still respond to the tide-producing forces, in the same way as the theoretical basin. Where the gulf is of the critical length, the energy for the tidal rise and fall in the gulf is derived from the open ocean outside, and although the level does not change at the mouth, when the surface is flat at mid-tide, the currents would be at their maximum.

The critical lengths for different depths may be given both for the gulf and the enclosed sea. The formula giving the critical length of the gulf is $L = \frac{1}{4} T \sqrt{gd}$. It is apparent that the figures given in the table are likely to occur in nature, but those for the gulf are more common than those for the enclosed sea, thus it is probable that in many gulfs it will be high tide throughout the gulf at the same time, and strong tidal currents may be expected across the mouth of gulfs in many instances.

Critical length of gulf in nautical miles		
Depth, fathoms	Period, 12 hours	Period, 24 hours
50	175	349
100	247	494
200	349	698
500	552	1,104
1,000	780	1,561
2,000	1,104	2,207

Critical length for enclosed sea in nautical miles		
Depth, fathoms	Period, 12 hours	Period, 24 hours
50	349	698
100	494	987
200	698	1,396
500	1,104	2,207
1,000	1,561	3,122
2,000	2,207	4,415

So far the tide in a gulf has been considered as a simple standing oscillation, but it is clear that it will be affected by the rotation of the Earth to a greater or lesser degree, to have the characteristics of an amphidromic system. Gulfs in nature also have not the symmetrical form of the ideal theoretical gulf, and other factors, such as friction, will also modify the ideal results. Nevertheless, there is reason to believe that the actual tides in gulfs are associated with the type of movement suggested. One or two examples will illustrate the actual tides of gulfs in different areas.

The Bay of Fundy, which has the greatest tidal range anywhere, illustrates the importance of resonance. The bay averages 225 ft. in depth; its critical length is 160 miles, which agrees closely with its measured length of 162 miles. The natural period of oscillation of the bay is about 6·29 hours, which almost exactly fulfils the conditions for resonance to occur; it reacts, therefore, to the semi-diurnal tidal force. The range of the tide increases towards the head of the bay, as would be expected from the theory, although this effect is increased by the shallowing water, and by the narrowing and bifurcation of the bay towards its head, where the spring tidal range exceeds 50 ft. The rotation of the Earth increases the range on the southern side of the bay. According to theory the time of high water occurs almost simultaneously throughout the bay, being only twenty-four minutes later at the bifurcation than the mouth of the bay.

Long Island Sound at the eastern entrance to New York Harbour also illustrates this relationship. Again the tide is high at nearly the same time throughout the basin and the range increases from $2\frac{1}{2}$ ft. to $7\frac{1}{2}$ ft., from the mouth towards the head, while over the same distance the streams decrease from $3\frac{1}{2}$ knots to almost negligible velocities. The dimensions of the harbour are mean depth 66 ft. and length 80 miles. The critical length for this depth would be $82\frac{1}{2}$ miles; it is, therefore, nearly correct.

The English Channel, on the other hand, demonstrates a gulf where the dimensions are more nearly those given for an enclosed sea. The mean depth is about 36 fathoms (216 ft.) and the channel approximates to 300 miles in length; this is the length required for the type of oscillation which has a nodal line across the centre, and high tide occurs in the east at Dover when it is low tide off Cornwall. This is nearly true of the actual tide. It is worth examining the tides around the coast of Britain in rather more detail, as they illustrate the application of tidal theory to actual seas.

(d) Tides around the British Isles

The English Channel has already been mentioned in connexion with the characteristics of a Kelvin Wave, and its dimensions have been shown to be such that it can react to the tide-producing forces of semi-diurnal period, in such a way that a nodal line would lie across it centrally, in the absence of the rotation of the Earth. This nodal line would run near the Isle of Wight, but other forces, such as friction, prevent the formation of a true amphidromic system. The amphidromic point in this instance is said to be degenerate, as it lies inland, although the tendency for an amphidromic system to form is apparent from the convergence of the cotidal lines towards the coast in this vicinity; this indicates that there is a degenerate amphidromic system. It is partly this fact that accounts for the interesting double tides which are characteristic of this area around the Isle of Wight.

Shallow-water tides. The double tides which are found around the Isle of Wight can be explained, at least partially, in terms of shallow-water effects. It is relatively easy to appreciate the influence of shallow water on a progressive wave, but more difficult to apply these principles to amphidromic systems. The speed of a progressive wave depends upon the depth of water, and when this becomes shallow the crest, which is in deeper water, moves faster than the trough, which is in shallower water. The smooth sine curve of the wave form thus becomes distorted; the rising tide is more rapid than the ebbing tide, as the crest is accelerated and the trough retarded. This asymmetrical curve can be resolved into its regular components in the same way as the complex curve of tidal forces resulting from the lunar declination. When it is analysed in this way the residual curve is found to have two crests to one in the original curve, as shown in fig. 5–7; this curve is called the quarter-diurnal tide. It is also irregular and can be further split up to give a symmetrical quarter-diurnal tide and the remainder, which has three crests and is called the sixth-diurnal tide; this process can be continued indefinitely. When these curves are added together they never give a double low water or high water, as their crests and troughs never coincide; they merely give the distorted curve, characteristic of a progressive wave in shallow water.

It is not clearly known how shallow water affects a standing wave, but it is reasonable to assume that the effect is somewhat similar. It can easily be shown that if the crests or troughs of the semi-diurnal and quarter-diurnal tides coincide, and these are of a specific range relationship, the two curves added together will give a double high or low water. When the two crests coincide the phase relationship is said to be 0°, and this will lead to the development of double low water if the amplitude relationship is correct. If a trough of the quarter-diurnal tide coincides with the crest of the semi-diurnal tide, the phase relationship is 180° and double high water will tend to result (see fig. 5–7).

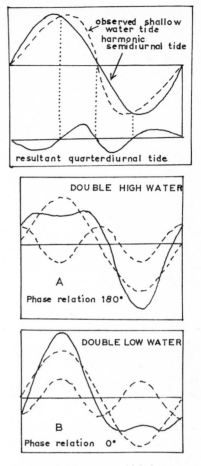

FIG. 5–7. Shallow-water tidal phenomena. (After Doodson and Warburg, A.M.T.) [By permission of the Controller of H.M. Stationery Office.]

The amplitude ratio which is required to produce a double effect is that four times the quarter-diurnal tide must exceed the semi-diurnal tide, or nine times the sixth-diurnal tide must exceed the semi-diurnal tide. These conditions are most likely to be fulfilled where the range of the semi-diurnal tide is diminished, as near a degenerate amphidromic point, which is close to the shore, where the water is shallow. This condition is fulfilled in the area around the Isle of Wight.

Examples of the applications of these principles to actual instances in this area will show how they apply. At Portland the phase relationship is —002°; this is very nearly 0° and shows that the crests of the two wave types must nearly coincide; this would suggest the probability of double low water. The amplitudes are such that the semi-diurnal tide has an amplitude of 2·07 ft., while the quarter-diurnal tide is 0·41 ft. Four times 0·41 is not quite equal to 2·07, but it is near enough to produce a long stand at low water, while the higher species of tide produce the double effect. Freshwater, with a phase relationship between the two tides of 176°, is well situated to have a double low water. The respective amplitudes of the semi-diurnal and quarter-diurnal tides are 2·02 and 0·53, which is suitable to produce a double high water by the simplest means, as 4×0·53 is more than 2·02.

The case of Southampton, which is so important from the point of view of shipping, is less easy to explain (Macmillan, 1949). The tides here are such that there is a very long stand at high water, which at some phases of the tidal cycle becomes a double high water. The tide here and in other areas where tidal currents can flow in from two directions is affected by the hydraulic gradients set up as a result of different levels at either end of a strait. Thus at the eastern entrance to the Solent the tide has a range of 13 ft. at spring tide, while at the western end the area of double high water, already referred to at Freshwater, is situated, and the range is only half. This sets up hydraulic gradients, which naturally complicate the analysis of the tide.

An example of the analysis of the Southampton tide shows that the phase relationship of the semi-diurnal and quarter-diurnal tide is not suitable to the generation of double high water, as it is —279°. This is neither representative of the progressive wave or standing oscillation, but somewhere between the two. The amplitude relationship is also not satisfied to produce a simple double high water, as the semi-diurnal amplitude is 4·46 ft. and the quarter-diurnal one is 0·82 ft. When the sixth-diurnal tide is taken into account it will account for a long stand at high water, but it requires the eighth- and tenth-diurnal tides to produce the double effect. This indicates that many complex phenomena are concerned with the double tidal effect at Southampton.

In general it can be said that double tidal features will occur (*a*) where the phase relationship between the semi-diurnal and quarter-diurnal shallow water tides is suitable, and (*b*) when the amplitude relationship of these tides is favourable. Double tides also occur on the other side of the English Channel at Le Havre and Honfleur, but these may be caused by a different process, as the range of the semi-diurnal tide is considerable in this area. The reason for the double tides in this area is related to the reflection of the tide from the Straits of Dover. The tidal current first flows eastwards to produce a preliminary high water, while at times the subsequent westerly stream produces a second high water. This westerly flowing stream, affected by the rotation of the Earth, has an upgradient on the English side of the Channel and may help to produce the long stand of high water at Southampton, while shallow-water effects produce the double tide.

The North Sea. The development of a multi-nodal amphidromic system is well illustrated in the North Sea. The dimensions of the sea are such that, in the absence of the rotation of the Earth, there would be three nodal lines, as shown in fig. 5–4. These would extend roughly east–west across the sea; the most northerly of them would run from the south-west coast of Norway to Rattray Head in Scotland, the central one would run from central Denmark to the east coast of England near Flamborough Head, while the southern one would lie between south Holland and East Anglia. The pattern of tidal streams, when the surface is flat, and the position of high tide and low tide at the different hours are indicated in fig. 5–4. Areas of high and low water would alternate as shown. The energy to keep this tidal motion going would be derived from the tide in the Atlantic Ocean to the north. As a first approximation it may be assumed that there is a barrier across the Straits of Dover.

The effect of the rotation of the Earth on this system of standing oscillations converts them into three amphidromic systems. Subsidiary slopes are set up across the nodal lines by the development of gradients sloping up to the right when the streams reach their maximum. These subsidiary slopes are reversed six lunar hours later. When the co-tidal lines are drawn for this system it is seen that there are three inter-connecting systems in each of which the tide revolves anticlockwise round a central amphidromic point. The three systems are related in such a way that the tide moves continuously south down the coast of Scotland and England and northwards along the continental coast.

If the barrier of the Straits of Dover is now removed and the effect of friction on the tidal energy is considered, this rather ideal tidal pattern can be related to the actual tidal chart, shown in fig. 5–8. The energy to maintain this tidal wave moves in an anticlockwise direction around the North Sea, and being derived from the Atlantic Ocean, is gradually absorbed as it travels round the sea. This is largely due to the shallow nature of the North Sea. This means that the force of friction reduces the amount of tidal energy, with the result that the range of the tide diminishes towards the continental coast. This has the result of moving the amphidromic points eastwards, towards the area of reduced range.

The northern one is not precisely located, but it lies somewhere near the coast of southern Norway, and may, in fact, be degenerate, being a small distance inland. However, it does mean that the tidal range on the

south coast of Norway is very small. The second amphidromic point in
the centre is also moved eastwards. It lies a short distance off the coast
of central Denmark, where the tidal range is also small, being less than
4 ft. The southern amphidromic point, on the other hand, is not moved

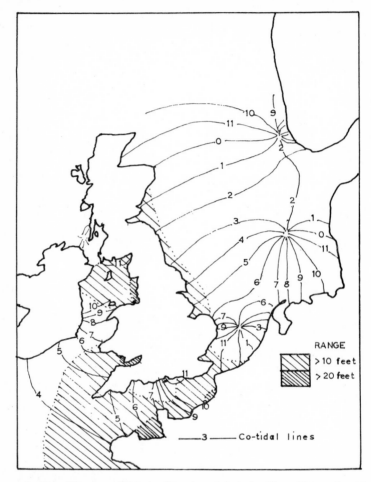

Fig. 5–8. The tides around Britain. (Based on Admiralty Chart No. 5058, with the
permission of H.M. Stationery Office and the Hydrographer of the Navy.)

east to any appreciable extent, partly owing to the closer proximity to
the source of energy, but mainly as a result of the influx of water
through the Straits of Dover. The amount of water coming through the
Straits is, however, only felt in the Flemish Bight, although it does
swing round the co-tidal lines to a certain extent. The tidal range along
the east coast of England increases away from the amphidromic points

and towards the heads of gulfs; it is, therefore, highest in the neighbourhood of the Wash, where the spring range exceeds 20 ft.

5. *TIDAL CURRENTS AND THEIR CHANNELS*

Some observations concerning tidal currents have already been made, such as the anticlockwise movement of the flood currents, which occur at the time of high water in an amphidromic system, but they are worthy of further consideration. It has already been shown that the tractive forces produce a rotatory tidal force, when the declination of the Moon is not zero. This varies in direction with position on the Earth and with the declination of the Moon. The semi-diurnal tractive forces rotate in a clockwise direction in the Northern Hemisphere, and the reverse in the Southern, but the diurnal forces change sign at 45°N and S and at the Equator. They also change sign as the Moon's declination changes from north to south. However, in the Atlantic, where semi-diurnal tides predominate, the movement is mainly in a clockwise direction.

The effect of the Earth's rotation also produces a rotatory current. In the Northern Hemisphere the deflection is to the right; this means that an east-west current, which is flowing east at the flood or high water, will be deflected to the right or south, and will flow in this direction when the easterly flow ceases at the turn of the tide. At low water the current will be flowing west and this will induce a northerly flow three hours later. This results in a clockwise rotation. The subsidiary currents will probably not be so strong as the main current; the line joining an hourly plot of the directions and strength of flow would be nearly elliptical in form, the major axis of the ellipse running east–west.

Rotatory tidal streams will also be set up where the tidal wave is moving up a channel with gently shelving sides. It might be argued that the tidal wave would advance more rapidly in the centre of the channel, but as this would set up transverse gradients, there would be compensating transverse currents. In fact, the wave moves up the channel at a speed appropriate to the mean depth, and variations of level across the channel are prevented by the generation of transverse streams, which give rise to rotatory currents.

Another way in which rotatory currents may be generated is when a progressive wave is travelling along a gently sloping coast. If the high-water current is flowing to the east, it will be at its maximum at high water, and there will be no compensating current at this period. Three hours later, however, the main current will be zero, but the water level on the coast will be falling most rapidly and an offshore current will be running. This will be to the south on the north coast of an east–west channel, and to the north on the southern shore. At hour 6 it will be low water and the level will be flat, so no transverse currents will be running, but the main stream will be flowing west at its maximum velocity. Three hours later the tide will be rising again at its maximum rate; this will also be the time when the main current is reversing and is, therefore, zero. The subsidiary transverse current will be flowing towards the shore to build up the level; this will be to the north on the north coast and to the south on the south coast. The combination of these movements gives a clockwise rotation on the northern shore of the channel and an anti-clockwise one on the southern shore.

It is likely that several of these influences will be operating simultaneously, which will result in a complex pattern of tidal streams. Hydraulic tidal streams may operate in straits linking areas in which the tidal levels are different at either end. These streams can reach great velocities at times. For example, the Seymour Narrows, between Vancouver Island and the mainland, at its northern end has currents approaching 10 knots at some stages of the tide, when there is a 13 ft. difference in level at either end of the strait, due to the fact that it is low water at one end when it is nearly high water at the other end.

In general, waves of tidal length are very long compared to the depth of water, and it may be expected that tidal streams will not diminish in velocity with depth. Such observations that have been made, which are mostly in fairly shallow water, support this contention. In any case it is only in shallow water that the streams are appreciable. In a depth of 50 fathoms, where the surface speed was 1 knot, the maximum velocity of about 1·2 knots was observed 3 fathoms below the surface; there was a very slow decrease towards the bottom below this depth, but even only about 6 fathoms above the bottom the speed was about 0·7 knots.

That tidal currents are effective on the bottom of fairly shallow seas is evident from the characteristic ebb and flood channels which develop in suitable conditions. These channels form where there is plenty of loose sand on the sea floor, which can be shaped by the tidal flow. They also require a more or less rectilinear pattern of tidal currents; that is, currents which flow in two opposite directions, with only very weak transverse streams. A good example of a completely rectilinear system of tidal currents is found off Skegness in Lincolnshire; there the currents flow either due north or south, the flood current flowing in the latter direction. It has been found that where the tidal currents are rectilinear in pattern the flood currents will tend to use one channel, while the ebb currents use a neighbouring, parallel, one. This system of interdigitating channels is often separated by elongated or curved banks of sand, which are deposited in the areas of quieter water between the major current channels.

This type of system, which was first discussed by Van Veen in the southern North Sea, has now been recognized wherever suitable conditions of sediment supply and tidal currents exist. Such channels are often associated with offshore sand banks, such as the Goodwin Sand off Kent, and the sand banks in the Wash. In the Goodwins area there are two main flood channels, which are oriented in a northerly direction, while between them there are southerly directed ebb channels. The interaction of these different channels accounts for the elliptical shape of the bank, and for the channel between it and the Brake Bank, which is situated nearer the Kent coast. They are shown in fig. 5–9. The major axis of the ellipse formed by the banks is aligned parallel to the direction of the tidal streams, in a north-north-east to south-south-west direction (Cloet, 1954a).

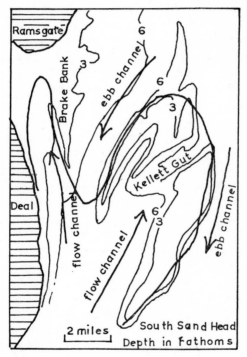

FIG. 5–9. The ebb and flood channels of the Goodwin Sands region off the south-east coast of England. (After Cloet.)

The flood channel usually deepens seawards and becomes shallower, towards a sill at its head, while an ebb channel may prolong a river channel and become shallower as it is traced offshore. The ebb stream may still be running out of the river when offshore the tide has already turned; the flood tide therefore, tends to avoid the ebb channel and initiates one parallel to it. There is a fairly wide variation in the pattern

of the ebb and flood channels, which is sometimes related to the configuration of the coast or estuary in which they occur (Robinson, 1960a).

The tidal currents, and the channels that they create, are of considerable importance from many points of view; they clearly influence
navigation in shallow water and the estuaries where they occur, and they
often play a part in coastal development from the physiographical point
of view, particularly because the currents rarely flow equally in both
directions. Nearly always either the flood or the ebb is the stronger, with
the result that there is a current residual and a net movement in one
direction. This will influence the general direction of movement of bed
material in the area. In order to evaluate the direction and amount of the
flow, a vector diagram of the tidal streams may be constructed. This is
done by plotting the hourly values of the tidal streams as a continuous
figure, each in proportion to its strength in the correct direction. The
net or residual movement can then be found by joining the initial and
final points; its length to scale gives the net velocity, while its direction
is readily apparent. As stronger currents can move more material, the
currents may be plotted as a power of their velocity, in order to arrive
at their net sediment-transporting capacity.

Observation of the character of the bottom in an area over which
tidal currents are flowing also gives evidence of the net direction in
which they are moving material. Sand waves have been found on the
bottom, which have been formed by tidal currents, because they are
orientated perpendicular to the main direction of tidal flow, where this
is rectilinear (Cloet, 1954b). These waves are asymmetrical in profile,
and it is assumed that sand is moved towards the steeper side of the
waves. From an examination of the wave profiles it is, therefore, possible
to infer the direction of tidal transport of material on the sea floor
(Stride, 1959a). The sand waves vary from about $1\frac{1}{2}$ to 7 ft. in height
and 100 to 450 ft. in length. From a study of the sand waves in the
southern North Sea, Stride has suggested that there is a flow of sediment
northwards along the coast of Holland and along the coasts of Lincolnshire and south Yorkshire, while there is a southerly movement north
of Flamborough Head. The direction of movement off East Anglia is
more variable. These movements take place some distance offshore and
are the result of the residual tidal flow.

Sand waves have also been found in water 540 ft. deep on the edge of
the continental shelf, off south-west England, where their height varied
between 25 and 40 ft. and their length had a mean value of 2,800 ft. Their
form suggests a slow westerly movement, under the action of tidal
currents, at the edge of the shelf. This indicates that tidal currents are
strong enough to move sand in this considerable depth of water.

Another type of bottom configuration associated with tidal streams is the linear pattern found by Stride off the coast of south-west England (Stride 1959b). There are linear patches of different types of material elongated parallel to the strongest tidal streams, which are rectilinear in this area. These long patches consist of sand overlying gravel, and are formed where the tidal streams exceed 2 knots in velocity. They are probably due to transverse instability of flow over a rough bed.

At one time many coastal phenomena were explained in terms of tidal currents, but subsequently it was generally accepted that waves play a much greater part in the development of shore forms. While this is probably true of processes in operation on the shore itself, it appears that in the movement of material a short distance offshore the tidal currents are of great importance. They can redistribute bottom material in water of much greater depth than is affected by wave action. This is particularly true of the coasts of relatively enclosed areas like Britain, where the waves tend to be short and the tides high, and their currents strong. On the more open coasts of much of the world the tidal range and currents are smaller and waves are often longer, and can, therefore, be more effective at greater depths. Tidal currents, by changing the bottom relief, can influence wave refraction, and thus affect the action of the waves on the shore indirectly.

6. *TIDES IN RIVERS—TIDAL BORES*

Although many rivers are tidal in their lower reaches, few develop well-marked bores. Even rivers which have bores can lose them, if the bed of the river is disturbed by dredging or other means. There must, therefore, be some critical factor on which the generation of a bore depends. It has already been shown how a wave progressing into shallowing water will tend to develop a steeper front slope, which leads to a more rapid tidal rise than fall. This same process is carried farther when a tidal bore is generated; the rise of water is in the form of a more or less vertical wall of water, advancing up the river.

The best-developed bore in the world is probably that of the Chang Tang Kiang in China. At Haining the depth of the river before the arrival of the bore is only 5 ft., but the bore itself is nearly 11 ft. high at spring tide, moving up the river as a wall of water, at a speed of more than 16 knots. It has been estimated that $1\frac{3}{4}$ million tons of water moves past in 1 min. It is interesting to note that the evidence suggests that at one time this bore did not exist. On the other hand, the Seine in France had a very well-developed bore, called the Mascaret, which used to extend up the river to Rouen, but since dredging and other improvements in the river were started in 1780 the bore has nearly disappeared, and now only affects the lowest part of the river at the highest spring tides. Other rivers having bores include the Hoogly, the Petitcodiac in Canada, and the Severn and Trent in England, although the bore on the latter has been almost eliminated by river improvements.

Clearly a delicate balance between certain forces is necessary to initiate and maintain a bore, as they are relatively rare. They also only affect one tributary in many cases. The Trent, for example, develops a bore, locally called the Eagre, while there is no similar feature in the other rivers flowing into the Humber. It is clear that a bore cannot be accounted for solely by the development of a more and more steeply sloping front to the flood profile of the wave, otherwise bores would not be the local phenomena that they are. From an investigation into the nature of the Trent bore, made by Champion and Corkan, it appeared that the slope of the river bed is a very important factor in the generation of a tidal bore.

In order to understand the generation of a bore it is necessary to consider the movement of water in a sloping channel. It can be shown that if the velocity of the current, moving up the river, is less than the rate of movement of the wave up the channel, the depth of water will increase down the channel. If the velocity of the current is greater than the critical value, which is the velocity of the wave, $\sqrt{gd}$, then the depth will increase upstream, causing an upstream upwards slope of the water surface. The mechanism of the bore can be considered by examining the effect of the bed slope in relation to the velocity of the current.

Where the velocity is very low the surface will be flat and the bed slope will not influence it. If the current is not zero it can be shown that the gradient of the surface relative to the channel slope is given by the formula $\dfrac{i}{1-u^2/gd}$ where i is the gradient of the channel, u is the velocity of the stream and d is depth. Again, the relationship between the velocity of the stream and that of the rate of propagation of the free wave is critical. When the velocity of the stream approaches that of the wave form, the surface slope may become very great; as this value depends on the depth, it is local in its effect. For example, in the Trent the tide rises up a steep slope, the depth is reduced rapidly and the point where $u^2 = gd$ may be reached. This means that over a very short distance there is a large change of surface elevation; this would tend to produce a steep front, which might appear as a wall of water. Where u^2 was less than gd the surface slope would be downwards upstream; this would occur in the deeper water as it does in normal tidal motion as the tide rises.

A steep slope in the river bed is important to the generation of a bore in two ways; firstly, it accentuates the gradient of the water surface, and secondly, it accelerates the attainment of the point where $u^2 = gd$, where the surface slope must change sign. A bore is also more likely to occur at high spring tide, as both the depth and currents are greater at this state of the tide. A narrowing of the channel will tend to produce similar results. Where the critical velocity is reached other factors come in, and the formulae do not hold accurately. Instability is set up and this results in the development of waves, which so often follow the bore as it moves upstream; they are called whelps on the Trent.

Once formed the bore will move upstream, travelling rather as a free wave. The rate at which the bore is propagated upstream depends on its height and the mean depth. This may be modified by the speed of the current flowing downstream in the river, above the bore. The bore travels faster than the progressive wave ($\sqrt{gd}$) at a speed given by

$$c = \left(1 + \frac{1}{2}\frac{B}{d}\right)\sqrt{gd} - U,$$ where c is the speed of the bore, B is its height,

d is the mean depth, U is the river current. The Trent bore moves upstream at about 15 miles/hour or 22 ft./sec. Using the formula B is 6 ft., as the depths before and after the passage of the bore are 6 and 12 ft. respectively, d is therefore 9 ft. This gives $c = 1 + \frac{1}{2}(6/9)\sqrt{288}$ ft./sec. = 23 ft./sec. This agrees very closely with the observed value. The value of u, the speed of the current, is 6 ft./sec. The river improvement works, which normally aim to increase the depth of the river, are therefore detrimental to the formation of bores, because they prevent the critical velocity being reached. Bores are usually associated with spring tides, as at these periods the water is especially shallow at low water, when the flood tide is advancing up the river, and deep as it passes, giving a higher value of B, the height of the bore.

The Trent bore illustrates the close relationship between the gradient of the river bed and the generation of the bore. The lower part of the Trent, when the bore was studied by Champion and Corkan, could be divided into three reaches, shown in fig. 5–10. The lowest part between the Trent Outfall into the Humber and Burton Stather had a very steep slope; the second part, between the latter place and Walkerith, the river slopes less steeply; thirdly upstream of Walkerith the gradient again decreases. It appears that the critical relationship is set up in the second section, where the bore is most marked, and where its rate of movement and size increases to its maximum at Walkerith. From here it travels upstream for some considerable distance, sometimes as much as 20 miles.

The bore is, however, very variable and more recent observations made at various times up to 1952 (Barnes, 1952) show that it has changed its character since the river works were undertaken and appears to have slowed down as it has diminished in height. Its average upstream speed was found to be about 10 miles/hour, although at its maximum it reached nearly 12 miles/hour, or more on some occasions. The conclu-

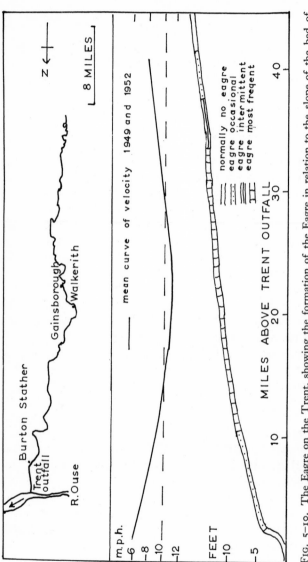

Fig. 5-10. The Eagre on the Trent, showing the formation of the Eagre in relation to the slope of the bed of the river, and the mean speed of its progress up the river. (Modified from Barnes.)

sion may be reached that bores are very individual features, liable to variation in speed and character, or even disappearing, with only minor changes in the nature and gradient of the river bed up which they move.

7. *ABNORMAL TIDES—METEOROLOGICAL SURGES*

Tide tables predict the height of the tide on the basis of the known movements of the heavenly bodies, from the analysis of observed tidal curves. Normally the tides follow closely the expected pattern, but occasionally there are local phenomena which modify the predicted tide. The most common cause of tidal anomalies is the weather. The North Sea is particularly liable to the development of surges due to unusual weather conditions, owing to its shape, but they also affect the English Channel to a certain extent. They tend, however, to be more disastrous in their effects on the North Sea coasts, as the abnormal tidal level is liable to flood low-lying ground, as in Lincolnshire, Essex, and Holland.

Although the surge has no direct connexion with the tide-producing forces, it behaves in some respects in a similar way to the tide, particularly in its progress as a wave in an anticlockwise direction round the North Sea. Surges are not infrequent in the North Sea, eight having occurred during the present century, following a very severe one in 1897. It has been suggested (Farquharson, 1954) that the frequency of storm surges has increased from 1820 to the present, which he suggests may be due to the present rise of sea-level, amounting to about 0·75 ft. in 120 years. There was also a surge in 1894 which reached a height of $9\frac{1}{2}$ ft. above the predicted level at Southend in Essex. This height, however, occurred nearly 6 hours after high water, at which time the surge was only 4 ft. high. It seems very fortunate that the maxima of the highest surges do not seem to coincide with the time of high water. For example, surges over 10 ft. in height have occurred at Southend and Sheerness in 1905, 1921, and 1943, but they all reached their peak between 4 and 6 hours before high water, being only 1, 2 and $2\frac{1}{2}$ ft. high respectively at high water.

It is not known whether there is some physical reason why the maxima of large surges rarely seem to occur at the time of high water of the normal tide, but it is a fortunate fact that they rarely do. For this reason the smaller surges may be more dangerous, as these sometimes almost coincide with high water. At Sheerness in 1897 a 7 ft. surge arrived $1\frac{1}{2}$ hours before high water and in 1928 a $5\frac{1}{2}$ ft. surge reached Sheerness only 1 hour before high water, while a 6 ft. surge in 1936 hit Southend only $\frac{1}{2}$ hour before high water.

The greatest and most damaging of the recent surges was that of 1953, which caused so much damage and loss of life on the east coast of England and in Holland. This surge was exceptional in that the water-level was 6 ft. above the predicted level for 15 hours in some places. At Southend its maximum height was 9 ft., $2\frac{1}{2}$ hours before high water, while it was still $5\frac{1}{2}$ ft. at the time of predicted high water. Other places also recorded abnormal heights; it was 5 ft. high in the Tyne, $7\frac{1}{2}$ ft. at Immingham, $9\frac{3}{4}$ ft. at King's Lynn, where it arrived $3\frac{1}{2}$ to 4 hours after high water. The record levels of this surge would have been exceeded by 5 ft. had the maximum of the surge arrived at the time of predicted high-water level. In Holland levels up to nearly 11 ft. above predicted were recorded, with very disastrous consequences in such a low-lying country.

The meteorological situation is clearly of fundamental importance in the generation of surges. It is, therefore, necessary to describe the type of weather situation which gives rise to a surge. North Sea surges form when a very deep and intense depression to the north of Scotland passes east and south-east into and across the North Sea, often passing on to the land about the position of south Denmark. The wind direction in front of such a depression is from the south-west, but as the front, associated with a vigorous depression of this type, moves across, there is a sudden veer of the wind from south-west to north-west or north. When the pressure gradient is steep these winds will be very strong, as was the case in January–February 1953.

The centre of this depression, as it passed into the North Sea was 966 mb. At the same time a strong north–south ridge of high pressure, with 1,033 mb. pressure at its centre, built up behind the depression. This produced very strong northerly winds, blowing over an exceptionally long fetch, as the isobars ran north–south as far north as Spitzbergen. The winds themselves did a lot of damage in north Scotland, where they reached velocities of about 100 miles/hour on the ground, while the geostrophic wind speed was 175 miles/hour. It is the sudden change of wind direction which is important in forming the surge and the exceptionally strong winds behind the depression are also important, as these drive a considerable amount of water into the North Sea. On such occasions the Straits of Dover at the southern end act to a certain extent as a safety valve, allowing some of the excess water to escape from the North Sea.

The pressure acts as an inverted barometer; high pressure will lower sea-level, while a low pressure will raise it by 1 ft. for a pressure fall of 34 mb. The total amount of water blown into the North Sea by the extremely powerful winds has been calculated by Rossiter (1954), which is another factor helping to raise the water-level. The influence of the changing pressure on the generation of a surge is related to the speed of movement of pressure change. When the disturbance moves with a critical velocity it will generate a greater surge than if the speed is above or below this. It can be shown that this critical velocity is the speed of travel of a free wave in the depth of water available; when the speed of movement of the pressure change moves at the same speed as a free wave a state of resonance will be set up, as in so many other tidal phenomena, and a large surge will be generated. In this way it is clear that slow changes of barometric pressure will not generate surges, as movement is too slow; thus surges are associated with fast-moving storm conditions, in which the strong pressure gradient induces high winds; these high winds also account for the other methods whereby the level of the sea is increased under suitable conditions. In the North Sea the surges seem to be generated off the east coast of Scotland, and once initiated they travel at a rate appropriate to the depth of water as a free wave. They progress in an anticlockwise direction around the sea, increasing in amplitude as far as the Flemish Bight and thereafter decreasing as they move northwards up the coast of Holland and Denmark, and at times they may be traced as far as the Baltic.

Surges can be of two types in the North Sea; those that are generated outside the sea, and which move as a free wave anticlockwise round the sea, which are called external surges, and secondly, those which originate inside the sea itself and are, therefore, called internal surges. A surge of the type which occurred in early 1953 is of complex origin, being influenced by at least three factors: the actual value of the low pressure, the external surge caused by the movement of the low-pressure centre to the north of Scotland and the internal surge, developed as it passed across the North Sea, and finally the effect of the wind in blowing extra water into the North Sea from the ocean to the north.

The level of the whole North Sea was increased by a considerable amount as a result of the operation of the last factor. Rossiter has calculated that about 15×10^{12} cu. ft. of water entered the North Sea between Scotland and Norway between 2100 hrs. on 31 January and noon on 1 February 1953. This caused as increase in the level of the whole North Sea of over 2 ft. during most of this period. The level increased rapidly during the latter part of 31 January and maintained its high level till well into 1 February. The reason for this influx was the action of the gale-force northerly winds, which transported a great deal of water into the North Sea. Owing to the rotation of the Earth, the transport of water in the open sea would be at about 45° to the wind direction, but where the influence of the coasts becomes marked this angle becomes smaller, about 20°; the result of this was that most of the water entering the North Sea did so on its western side, as the deflection is to the right in the Northern Hemisphere, that is along the coast of Scotland. Some of this surplus water was able to escape from the North Sea through the Straits of Dover. The rotation of the Earth again affected the water escaping southwards through the Straits of Dover, resulting in higher sea-levels on the coast of England, to the right of the flow, than on the coast of France. The surge recorded at Dover, in the Straits, was over 6 ft., but by the time it reached Newhaven it was reduced to 4 ft., and across the Channel at Dieppe it was only a little over 3 ft. It is worth noting that the rise in level at Newhaven took place in spite of a very strong offshore wind, which would normally be associated with a fall in level, while the wind was onshore in Dieppe.

It has been estimated that a total of $1\cdot7 \times 10^{11}$ cu. ft. of water escaped southwards through the Straits of Dover; this is, therefore, only about one-hundredth of the extra water entering the North Sea from the north. It was sufficient, nevertheless, to allow a fall of level of $0\cdot9$ ft. approximately in the southern North Sea between Orford Ness in East Anglia and Brouwershaven in Holland. This had a beneficial effect on the water-levels in the southern part of the North Sea, in the area where the external surge might be expected to be at its greatest amplitude.

By deducting the normal, predicted tidal curve from the recorded tide curve it is possible to obtain the curve of the surge at the places where the tide-gauge data were available. From these data, which are shown in fig. 5–11, it is possible to trace the passage of the surge down the coast of Britain and northwards along the continental coast, while its height can also be obtained by this means. The crest of the surge was at Aberdeen at 1500 hrs. on 31 January, by 1800 hrs. the water-level was 4 ft. higher than predicted in the latitude of Northumberland, while by 2100 hrs the surge had reached Yorkshire. By 0001 hrs on 1 February the surge peak had passed between the Humber and the Thames and was approaching the coast of south Holland. Heights above predicted high-water levels were $7\cdot8$ ft. in south Lincolnshire and 9–10 ft. in the Scheldt Estuary. The surge passed north along the coast of Holland and Denmark between 0400 hrs. at Ijmuiden in Holland and 1000 hrs. at Esbjerg on the west coast of Denmark, reaching south Norway at 2200 hrs. on 1 February.

The normal tide and the surge did not travel at exactly the same rate south along the British coast, but in many areas the time of high water of the surge was within 2 hours of the predicted time of high water of the tide, although the actual time of high water was affected by the height of the surge. The surge occurred at a time when the predicted high-tide levels were high owing to spring tides, but had the surge occurred a fortnight later, when one of the highest tides of the year were forecast, the effect would have been much more serious, in many areas raising the water-level a further 2 ft.

However, even as conditions were, record heights were recorded in many areas; the Thames Estuary was severely affected. At Harwich, for example, the predicted high-water level was 5·5 ft., while the height of the water at the time of predicted high tide was 12·2 ft., and the water rose subsequently to 13·1 ft. The consequences in the low-lying areas in the vicinity were very serious, and flooding and damage were extensive. The coast of Holland was even more severely hit, partly because sea-level was also raised by the influence of the winds, which were blowing directly onshore, rather than obliquely offshore as was the situation in England. At the Hook of Holland the surge height at the predicted time of high water was 10 ft.

In considering the effects of such a surge on the coastline, particularly where it is vulnerable to erosion, the storm waves which accompanied

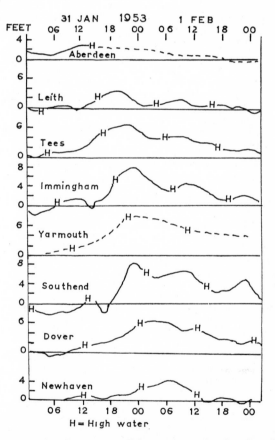

Fig. 5–11. The surge of 31 January to 1 February 1953, showing the residual values observed after deduction from the predicted tide curves. (After Robinson.)

it must be taken into account. It is these waves, which on this occasion may well have been about 20 ft. from trough to crest, which do much damage. They are rendered much more effective than their size would suggest by the fact that they are working much higher up the beach, owing to the exceptional water-level. In many areas, therefore, the damage to sea defences was initiated by overtopping; this weakened the rear and caused their eventual collapse under the onslaught of the extremely high and destructive waves.

REFERENCES

Allison, N. W., An investigation into the causes of the annual variation of mean sea level in the North Sea. *M.N.R.Astron. Soc. Geophys.* **5**, 146–57, 1947.

Barber, N. F., The behaviour of waves on tidal streams. *Proc. Roy. Soc. A* **198**, 81–93, 1949.

Cartwright, D. E., Submarine sand waves and tidal lee-waves. *Proc. Roy. Soc. A* **253**, 218–41, 1959.

Barnes, F. A., The Trent Eagre. *Survey*, Univ. of Nottm. **3**, 1–16, 1952.

Champion, H., and Corkan, R., The bore on the Trent. *Proc. Roy. Soc. A* **154**, 158, 1936.

Chitale, S. V., Bores in tidal rivers with special reference to the Hoogly. *Irrigation and Power* **11**, 110–20, 1954.

Cloet, R. L., Hydrographic analysis of the Goodwin Sands and the Brake Bank. *Geog. Journ.* **120**, 203–15, 1954a.

Cloet, R. L., Sand waves in the southern North Sea and in the Persian Gulf. *Journ. Inst. Navig.* **7**, 272–9, 1954b.

Corkan, R. H., The levels in the North Sea associated with the storm disturbance of 8 January 1949. *Phil. Trans. Roy. Soc. A*, **242**, 483–525, 1950.

Dalton, F. K., Fundy's prodigious tides and Petitcodiac's tidal bore. *Journ. Roy. Astron. Soc. Canada* **45**, 225–31, 1951.

Doodson, A. T., and Warburg, H. D., *Admiralty Manual of tides.* H.M.S.O., 1941.

Doodson, A. T., Rossiter, J. R., and Corkan, R. H., Tidal charts based on coastal data: Irish Sea. *Proc. Roy. Soc. Edinburgh* **64**, 90–101, 1954.

Emery, K. O., *The sea off southern California.* Wiley, 1960.

Fairburn, L. A., The semi-diurnal tides along the Equator in the Indian Ocean. *Phil. Trans. Roy. Soc. A* **247**, 191–212, 1954.

Farquharson, W. J., Storm surges on the east coast of England. *Proc. Conf. on the North Sea Floods* of 31 Jan.–1 Feb. 1953, Inst. Civ. Eng., 14, 1954.

Green, F. H. W., Tidal phenomena with special reference to Southampton and Poole. *Dock and Harb. Auth.* **32**, 143–8, 1951.

Lafond, E. S., Sand movement near the beach in relation to tides and waves. *Scripps Inst. Ocean.* **107**, 1950.

MacMillan, D. H., Tidal features of Southampton Water. *Dock. and Harb. Auth.* **29**, 259–64, 1949.

Marmer, H. A., Tidal investigations on the west coast of South America. *Geog. Rev.* **33**, 299–303, 1943.

Munk, W., and Revelle, R., Sea level and the rotation of the Earth. *Am. Journ. Sci.* **250**, 829–33, 1952.

Proudman, J., The tides of the Atlantic Ocean. *M.N.R.Astron. Soc.* **104**, 244–56, 1944.

Robinson, A. H. W., Ebb-flood channel systems in sandy bays and estuaries. *Geog.* **45**, 183–99, 1960.

Robinson, A. H. W., The hydrography of Start Bay and its relationship to beach changes at Hallsands. *Geog. Journ.* **127**, 63–77, 1961.

Rossiter, J. R., The North Sea storm surge of 31 Jan. and 1 Feb. 1953. *Phil. Trans. Roy. Soc. A.* **246**, 371–99, 1954.

Rossiter, J. R., Methods of forecasting storm surges on the east and south coasts of Great Britain. *Quart. Journ. Roy. Met. Soc.* **85**, 262–77, 1959.

Russell, R. C. H., and Macmillan, D. H., *Waves and Tides.* Hutchinson, 1952.

Sterneck, R. V., Die Gezeiten der Ozeane. *Sitz. Ber. Akad. Wiss. Wien.* **129**, 131–50, 1920; **130**, 363–71, 1921.

Stride, A. H., A pattern of sediment transport for sea floors around south Britain. *Dock. and Harb. Auth.* 467 **40**, 145–7, 1959a.

Stride, A. H., A linear pattern on the sea floor and its interpretation. *Journ. Mar. Biol. Ass. U.K.* **38**, 313–18, 1959b.

Chapter 6

WAVES

INTRODUCTION

PERHAPS the most obvious movement of the water of the oceans is the disturbance of the surface caused by the generation of wind waves. With these may be included the rare, but frequently destructive, seismic waves of tsunami, which, though inconspicuous in the open ocean, may become very large near the coast. It is the wind, however, which is responsible for the formation of the oscillatory waves, which move over the surface of the water and which play such an important part in the modification of the coastline. Looking at the sea in a storm, its surface appears to be in a state of chaotic confusion, and it is difficult to appreciate that amongst the disorder it is possible, to a certain extent at least, to sort out the different wave trains present.

Although they rarely exist alone in nature, it is worth considering the characteristics of ideal, wind-generated oscillatory waves in the ocean. These can be divided broadly into two groups: those that are in deep water and those in shallow water. The definition of deep water is that the depth must be greater than the length of the wave; in deep water it moves independently of the bottom, but in water shallower than this its form and movement are affected by the bottom.

1. *IDEAL WAVES IN DEEP WATER*

Waves in deep water can be defined by their length and height, and particularly important from the point of view of their effect on the beach at least, is the relationship between these two dimensions, which gives the steepness of the wave. The wave length is defined as the distance between two successive crests, measured perpendicular to the wave crest. Closely associated with the wave length are the period and velocity of the wave form. The period is the length of time it takes the wave form to move through one wave length, and the velocity is the speed of advance of the wave form. The three factors are related by $L=C\,T$, where L is the length, C the velocity and T the period. The wave velocity depends only on the wave length, the two factors increasing together; the relationship can be expressed by $C=\sqrt{\dfrac{gL}{2\pi}}$, or in the form

L (feet)$=5\cdot12$ T^2 (seconds). This is useful, because it is easier to measure the period in deep water than the length.

The full formula, from which the one given above is derived, is worth mentioning, as it shows the significant difference between the movement, on the one hand, of wind waves, and on the other of much longer waves, including tide waves and seismic waves. This formula is $C=\sqrt{\frac{gL}{2\pi}\ tanh\ \frac{2\pi d}{L}}$, where g is the force of gravity and d is the depth of water. In deep water d/L is large and $tanh\ \frac{2\pi d}{L}$ is almost unity, which gives the first formula. If d/L is $0\cdot5$, that is the depth is half the wave length, then $tanh\ \frac{2\pi d}{L}$ is $0\cdot9963$, so that for most purposes a wave may be considered to be in deep water when the depth exceeds half the wave length. When, however, the ratio d/L is small, less than $0\cdot05$, $tanh\ \frac{2\pi d}{L}$ approaches the value of $\frac{2\pi d}{L}$. The formula then simplifies to give $C=\sqrt{gd}$; this is the formula already used so frequently in discussing tidal phenomena, when the velocity of the wave depends only on the depth and the length is great compared with the depth. These formulae apply strictly only to waves of low amplitude, but can be used also for low waves of finite height without much error.

The wave height is not fixed in relation to the length, but depends for its value on the wind generating it; theoretically a wave cannot have a height greater than $1/7$ of its length, or it becomes unstable and breaks. This value is very rare in the ocean, and most natural waves are much less steep, the ratio H/L often being below $0\cdot02$. Various conceptions of the ideal surface form of waves have been suggested. The formulae already given were developed by Airy in 1842 and Stokes in 1847, the latter extending the theory to waves of finite height. They suggested that the waves were sinusoidal in form, except when they are of finite height, when their form is more nearly trochoidal; the nature of the motion is irrotational.

One important point concerning their theory of wave character is that the particles, moving in the wave, do not come back to exactly the same place as each wave passes, but progress slightly in the direction of wave movement. This implies that there is a slow transference of water in the direction of wave movement, which is called mass transport. From this point of view their theory differs from that of Gerstner and Rankine, which suggests that the wave form is exactly trochoidal and the orbits exactly circular. As mass transport has been shown to exist it seems that the theory of Stokes, which has been proved convergent by Levi-Civita in 1925 and applied to water of finite depth by Struik in 1926, is the more realistic.

O.–O

The mass transport of water by wind waves is closely related to the nature of the actual movement of water within the wave form. Clearly the water particles cannot move with the velocity of the wave form, which for a 10-sec. wave would be 51·2 ft./sec.; they do, however, describe almost circular orbits, progressing slightly each orbit, in an open circle. The particles move up as the wave crest approaches, forward on the crest, then down as the trough approaches and back under the trough, this completing one orbit each period. The size of the orbit clearly depends on the height of the wave, while the speed of movement also depends on the wave period, as the orbit must be completed each period.

Beneath the water surface there is a rapid reduction in the size of the orbit; this is in geometrical progression for a depth increase in arithmetical progression. Thus for every 1/9 of the wave length downwards the orbit is halved, with the result that at a depth equal to the wave length the orbit is only 1/535 of its surface size, and at a depth of 1·5L it is reduced to 1/12,400 of the surface size. This shows that the waves only affect a very shallow surface layer, compared with the whole depth of the ocean.

The volume of mass transport also depends on the height and length of the waves according to the formula $H^2\sqrt{\dfrac{g\pi}{32L}}$, as the square of the wave height enters the formula, but only the square-root of the length; the amount of mass transport falls off rapidly with decrease of wave height, being nil for waves of no finite height. The surface velocity of mass transport is proportional to the square of the steepness of the wave and is given by $\dfrac{\pi H^2}{L^2}\,C$. This property of waves is of considerable importance to an understanding of their effect on bottom material in shallow water.

The height and length of the wave also determine its energy, which is equally divided in two forms. The kinetic energy results from the movement of the water particles and the potential energy is due to the elevation of the wave crest above the still-water level. Again the amount of energy depends on the square of the wave height, as given by the formula $E=\dfrac{wLH^2}{8}$, where w is the weight of 1 cu. ft., of sea water; this can be expressed also in the form $E=0·64\,w\,H^2T^2$ or $E=41\,H^2T^2$. E is given in ft.lb./foot of wave crest/wave length; H is in feet. T in seconds. Thus the energy also depends mainly on the wave height.

The formulae given above apply strictly only to waves of low amplitude, and must be modified by the addition of another term for waves of finite height, although this has little effect except under extreme conditions. The full formula is $E = \dfrac{w\,L\,H^2}{8}\left(1\text{-}4\cdot 93\,\dfrac{H^2}{L^2}\right)$. In an isolated train of waves, moving through calm water, the kinetic energy remains stationary, while the potential energy moves at the wave velocity. The total energy of the wave train, therefore, moves at half the speed of the wave form; waves appear to die out in front of the train and form in the rear, each individual wave seeming to travel through the wave train.

The ideal waves have long continuous crests, running perpendicular to their direction of movement, but this is not often the case in nature, as there is rarely only one wave train present. It is the interference of wave trains moving in different directions, and of different lengths, which result in the formation of short-crested waves. Even waves moving in the same direction may not have the same length; this gives rise to the usual variability of wave height in the open sea, and of breakers on the coast.

2. WAVES IN SHALLOW WATER

(a) Modification of ideal waves in shallow water

As a wave begins to feel the bottom nearly all its characteristics become modified. The most consistent character, which does not alter as the water becomes shallower, is the wave period. The wave velocity and length are shortened as the water depth decreases. Between the ratios of d/L of $0\cdot 5$ and $0\cdot 05$ the whole formula relating wave velocity to the length and water depth must be applied; this shows that the velocity is reduced as the depth decreases. Curves can be constructed to relate the wave length or velocity for any period to the appropriate depth. This relationship was used during the war of 1939–1945 to obtain an idea of the gradient of enemy-held beaches from air photographs. On these the length of the waves in deep water could be measured and from this the period could be obtained. Then by measuring the decreasing wave length as the waves approached the shore, the depth could be read off from the graph and a profile constructed (Williams, 1947). It is the reduction of wave length which accounts for the important process of wave refraction, by which the wave fronts tend to turn to lie parallel to the bottom contours. The other changes undergone by wave characteristics in shallow water must, however, first be mentioned.

The wave height does not vary so systematically as the length; there is a tendency for the wave height to decrease slightly as the wave first enters water shallower than half the wave length, until the ratio is about $d/L = 0\cdot 06$ when the value is about $0\cdot 9$ the deep water height, thereafter there is a rapid increase in wave height until the wave breaks. This increase is relatively great for waves which were initially flat; a very flat wave may double its deep water height before it breaks, while a steep wave may increase relatively little. Owing to the decrease in wave length and increase in height in very shallow water, the wave steepness will increase very rapidly near the break-point. However, this increase is rarely sufficient to cause the wave to reach the limit of stability, when H/L equals $1/7$.

As the steepness increases the wave form changes, the crest becomes sharply defined and narrower, while the trough becomes wide and flat. This change is particularly noticeable in a long, low swell, which may be inconspicuous in deeper water, but appears to be rejuvenated as it enters shallow water and frequently is the most conspicuous wave train to break on the beach.

As the wave form changes so do the orbits of the water particles. Instead of following open circular paths, they follow open ellipses, the long axis being parallel to the bed. The velocity is also no longer uniform, there being an acceleration under the short, sharp crest, while the seaward flow under the trough takes place more slowly, but for a longer time. This asymmetry becomes more marked near the break-point, and on the bottom the ellipse becomes flattened into a to and fro movement; a short, rapid acceleration takes place under the wave crest with a longer, slower seaward flow under the trough.

(b) Mass transport in shallow water

The pattern of mass transport also changes as the waves enter shallow water. This can be defined as the net movement of water particles which results from the difference between the landward and seaward components of movement. It can be well demonstrated in a model wave tank, in which the waves may be seen in section, by allowing a small piece of dye to fall through the water, leaving behind a thin thread of dye. This is then distorted by the mass transport as shown in fig. 6–1. This experiment shows, that under some waves at least, there is a movement of water towards the land on the surface, a net seaward movement takes place through most of the water column, until near the bottom there is again a net forward thrust immediately above the bottom. Although if the bottom is rippled, the turbulence resulting from this breaks up the thread of dye and the forward thrust is not apparent. This result has been studied experimentally by Russell and Osorio (1957), confirming the theoretical work of Longuet-Higgins (1953) on the mass transport of water in waves in shallow water. This forward bottom movement is found to take place both on a horizontal bed and on a gently sloping one. The velocity of the forward thrust on the bottom was found to increase as the water became shallower for any one wave length.

Russell has suggested that there is a variation in the pattern of the mass transport in waves of different steepness, which would help to explain the very important differences in the action of steep and flat waves respectively, on a mobile beach. In this connexion it is worth noting that in deep water, far from land, there is nothing to hinder the continuous landward progress of mass transport, but near the shore the forward movement of water, as the depth decreases, would increasingly tend to pile up water on the shore and thus to raise the water-level. This tendency must be counteracted by a seaward return drift; hence the seaward flow in the central part of the depth profile is accounted for.

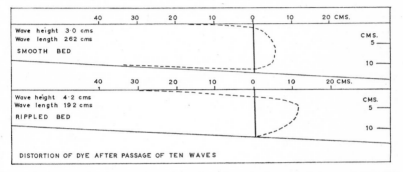

Fig. 6–1. Water movement in a model tank to show the forward thrust on the bottom and surface, with seaward flow in the centre.

Considering first a flat wave in shallow water, it is suggested by Russell that the forward movement of mass transport takes place uniformly throughout the depth of water. Superimposed on this is the return drift, which is largest at the surface and steadily decreases to zero on the bottom; the net result of superimposing these two movements on each other gives a slow seaward movement throughout the bulk of the water, but a narrow layer near the bottom has a strong forward thrust towards the land. As nearly all the sediment in flat waves is moving near the bottom, this is influenced by the landward movement, creating a constructive effect. Thus the well-known constructive effect of flat waves can be at least partially explained, although it must be remembered that this analysis applies only to the movement seaward of the break-point of the waves. Experiments on the transport of sand landward of the break-point have, however, shown that flat waves continue to move sand towards the land throughout, as far as the water-line (King, 1959).

The drift under steep waves may be contrasted with that under flat waves. Russell suggests that under steep waves the landward component of mass transport is greatest at the surface and falls to zero at the bottom, while the return drift is at a maximum in a seaward direction at the surface and also falls to zero at the bottom. When these two curves are combined the resulting net movement is landwards in the upper part of the water, but in the lower part it is seawards, falling to zero at the bottom. Under these conditions the water flow is likely to be turbulent, and material raised from the bottom will drift seawards. Such steep waves are usually under active generation by local onshore winds. These winds will exaggerate this effect by blowing the surface water landwards, and thereby intensifying the compensating seaward drift on the bottom. This can be shown experimentally to take place both inside and outside the break-point. That a similar effect can extend to fairly deep water was shown by observations off the Northumberland coast with a current-meter; where the surface drift was at the rate of 1·4 miles/day to the south by west, at a depth of 22 fathoms, the drift was 2·8 miles/day to the east by north, under the action of an onshore, easterly wind. Thus the destructive effects of steep waves can be greatly enhanced by the action of strong onshore winds.

Again Russell's ideas apply only seaward of the break-point, but other experiments carried out inside the break-point also demonstrated the destructive effect of steep waves in moving sand seawards inside the break-point. The net direction of drift in shallow water is clearly of great importance in analysing the behaviour of waves, when they finally come to expend their energy in the movement of beach material. Thus from the point of view of the coastal geomorphologist, waves in shallow water are of fundamental importance to an understanding of the character and development of coastal land forms. By this analysis it is possible to go one stage further in explaining the well-known destructive effect of storm waves in eroding beaches, with the exception of storm shingle ridges, and of the constructive effect of flat, calm-weather waves in building up the beaches; the former are steep waves, often accompanied by strong onshore winds, while the latter are the long, low swells, owing their reduction in height to their long journey from their place of origin to the beach on which they finally break.

(c) Wave refraction

Before the waves finally come to the break-point, however, they may undergo very considerable change in their direction of movement. The fundamental cause of wave refraction has already been mentioned; it is due to the reduction of wave length with depth. The parts of the wave front that are in deeper water will advance faster than those in shallow water, with the result that the wave crests will become more and more nearly parallel with the bottom contours. The main significance of this bending of the wave crests is to be found in the redistribution of wave energy to which it gives rise. In deep water, where the wave crests are assumed to straight and parallel, the energy is evenly distributed along the wave front. If this is divided into equal parts, the energy in all of them is the same. If the points are continued as lines, everywhere perpendicular to the wave crest, towards the shore, it will be found that as the wave crests bend, so the spacing between these lines no longer remains constant. The lines, which are called orthogonals, as they are at right-angles to the crests, will tend to converge in some areas and diverge in others.

It can be assumed as a first approximation that the energy between the lines, which was equal in deep water, will remain so as they are traced into shallow water. Where the orthogonals converge there will be a concentration of wave energy, and the wave heights will be greater and where they diverge the reverse will apply and the waves will be lower. In this way it is possible to explain the concentration of wave energy on headlands and its dissipation in bays, on the assumption that the bottom contours are parallel to the coastline. The wave crests are bent in such a way that the orthogonals converge on the headlands and diverge into the bays. The waves are, therefore, higher and steeper, and more destructive on the headlands than they are in the bays. This and other types of wave refraction are shown diagrammatically in fig. 6–2.

Even if the coastline is straight, the bottom contours may not be, then zones of convergence and divergence of energy may bear no apparent relationship to the shore; over a submarine valley at right-angles to the coast there will be a zone of divergence and abnormally low waves, while over a submarine ridge the orthogonals will tend to converge, giving waves higher than usual. Where waves are approaching the coast obliquely in deep water, they will tend to turn to reach the coast more nearly parallel, as shown in fig. 6–2. This effect will clearly be more marked in the longer waves, which feel the bottom first, while the shorter waves will not be seriously affected and may finally break on the coast at a considerable angle. Thus long waves will not be associated with long-shore drift to the same extent as short waves, because this depends to a considerable degree on the angle which the waves make with the shore, as they break in shallow water. Longshore drift may also be more effective where the water offshore is deep, because this will also reduce the refraction of the waves.

Where the submarine relief is complex, wave refraction will be similarly complex, and in some situations orthogonals may cross. Such a situation may occur when waves are refracted round both sides of a shoal or island offshore, to meet on the far side from both directions. Such patterns of refraction may account for the formation of features such as tombolos, which tie islands to the mainland.

Wave refraction may also account for the orientation of wave-built structures. Sand berms and sand barriers, which are built up by the long, constructive swells, are particularly affected by the refraction of the waves, because these waves are very long and, as a result, are much refracted before they reach the shore. The smooth curves of such beaches, for example those discussed by Davies (1959) in Tasmania and

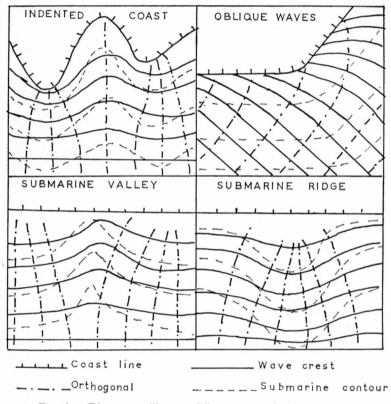

FIG. 6–2. Diagrams to illustrate different wave-refraction patterns.

south Australia, appear to fit the pattern of the refracted wave crests. It is the beaches which respond to the refraction of the waves rather than the reverse, not as is sometimes suggested that the plan of the shore determines the refraction. The submarine relief is probably the most important factor, in conjunction with the direction and length of the dominant constructive waves, in determining the plan of the coast under such conditions, as it is these factors which determine the wave-refraction pattern. Thus beaches of this type will not be orientated to face the direction from which the waves approach in deep water, but their refracted direction, which may well be at a very considerable angle to the former direction, where the dominant swells are long.

Because wave refraction can have such a marked effect on the wave height, it is very useful to be able to determine the amount of refraction waves of any given period, and direction of approach, will undergo by the time they reach the shore. There are methods whereby the wave-refraction pattern can be drawn graphically, if the submarine relief is known. Wave-refraction diagrams are of two types: one shows the pattern of refraction for a considerable stretch of coast for one wave length and direction of approach in deep water. The other shows the effect of refraction at one place for waves coming from different directions of different lengths. When forecasting waves in shallow water it is very necessary to take the wave refraction into account.

(d) Longshore currents and offshore rip currents

One very important aspect of waves in shallow water is the generation of longshore and offshore wave currents; these influence very considerably the movement of material alongshore, which is one of the fundamental causes of coast erosion and accretion. One of the causes of such currents is wave refraction. It has been shown that zones of high waves are likely to alternate with zones of low waves, particularly where the offshore relief is rather complex and the coastline indented and the waves are long. There is greater mass transport where the waves are higher and this should raise the sea level slightly at these points, compared with the zones of low waves. This will create a slope of the water surface from the zones of high waves to those of low waves, which will induce longshore currents in these directions.

These currents have, in fact, been observed by Shepard and Inman (1950). Their observations were made off southern California, where the offshore relief is complicated by submarine canyons which come right up to the beach. From theoretical reasoning it may be supposed that there would be currents from the headlands to the bays, as wave concentration is greatest on the headlands. This will help to account for the erosion of the headlands, because the currents will help to prevent the accumulation of beach material there, and will drift what is available into the bays, where it builds bay-head beaches. It might also be argued that when the waves are long, and therefore much refracted, the zones of divergence and convergence, and hence the currents flowing alongshore, will be better developed. This was, in fact, found to be true from the observations off southern California, although not all the currents were due to refraction.

The deep ocean current flowed offshore, but this had little effect in the shallowest water; there were also currents due to the landward movement of water by mass transport, and to the oblique approach of waves; the wind also exerted an effect, and finally there were the currents due directly to wave refraction. The wind effect was eliminated from the Californian observations as far as possible by observing on calm days. Some of the longshore currents were closely associated with the seaward transport of water, which at times becomes concentrated to form rip currents. These are supplied by longshore feeders when they are strongly developed. The analysis of the observations off California showed that the currents directly due to refraction, flowing away from the zones of convergence of orthogonals, were best developed when long waves were approaching the shore.

The conclusions reached from this study indicated that the direction of the currents along the shore was dependent mainly on the wave period, height and deep-water direction of approach. The last factor had least affect when the waves were longest, as these were the most modified by refraction; under these conditions strong zones of convergence and divergence set up strong longshore currents, which in places exceeded 1 knot in speed. These currents may flow against the direction of wave approach. At the points where longshore currents meet, which may be near points of divergence of orthogonals, they often turn seawards as rip currents. When shorter waves approach the shore they are less refracted and the direction of approach plays an important part in determining the direction of longshore currents, which often follow the direction from which the waves come; the rip currents then tend to be more numerous, but much smaller. When the angle of approach of short waves is fairly large, the longshore currents will be almost continuous in one direction, with speeds exceeding 1 knot. Under calm conditions, as obtained when the observations were made, it was found that by far the greater number of observations showed the same movement on the surface and at depth.

Rip currents are much more conspicuous on shores on which the very long swells, generated by strong winds far away, are common. They are very localized and may change position with changing wave conditions. They form where the return drift is concentrated into a fast-flowing seaward current, which is often increased by strong longshore feeder currents (see fig. 6–3). The higher the waves the stronger will be the rip currents, because this increases the landward mass transport. They may be identified on the beach because they reduce the breaker height, where they pass through the surf zone; they do not, however, extend very far seaward of the breaker zone, beyond which they dissipate rapidly. They may be dangerous to bathers, who may be carried offshore in their strong flow; however, it is usually possible to swim in again alongside the rip current, where the breakers are higher and the mass transport on the surface is landwards. Rip currents are variable in velocity, being faster after a series of high waves, when the water-level on the shore has been raised temporarily; they flow more strongly seawards when the high waves are followed for a short time by lower ones. Observations by McKenzie (1958) in New South Wales have shown that

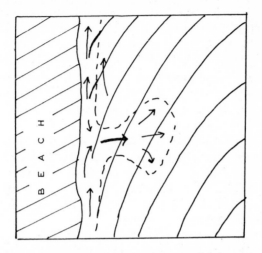

FIG. 6–3. Diagram to show the character of a rip current.

rip currents on the sandy beaches are stronger, but much less numerous, during periods when the waves are exceptionally large; these large rips were fed by strong feeder currents, up to $\frac{1}{2}$ mile long and 8 ft. deep; such strong currents are responsible for cutting channels across the beach. He also confirmed that smaller waves tended to produce smaller but more numerous rips.

(e) **Breaking waves**

The waves expend most of their great energy in breaking. The point at which waves break is determined to a considerable extent by their height; as a general rule it is true that a wave will break in water which is about 4/3 its own height at the break-point. Thus a 3 ft. high wave at its break-point will break in water which is 4 ft. deep. The deep water height of low waves, however, may be almost doubled before they break, so that they break in water twice as deep as their deep-water height.

The cause of the breaking of waves is not primarily the result of friction between the wave and the floor over which it is passing, although it may lose some energy in this way if the slope is very gentle, but it will not break as a result of this friction. The change in the orbital velocity and size of the orbit explains the process of breaking more easily. As a wave approaches shallower water its orbit enlarges to the elliptical form, but the time it has to accomplish its orbit remains the same, as the period of the wave is not affected by the shallowing water. At the same time the velocity of the wave form is decreasing, and there comes a time when the velocity of the water particles in their orbit approaches that of the wave form; when the orbital velocity exceeds the wave form velocity, the water will overtake the wave form and the wave will break. This accounts for the possibility of surf riding on a wave which is just about to break, for only on the crest of a wave in this state does the water itself move at the same speed as the wave form. Another factor which leads to the breaking of a wave is the fact that as the orbit increases in size the amount of water in the wave form is decreased by the reduction in length, with the result that there is not enough water to complete the orbit; the front of the wave becomes hollow and the crest, being unsupported, crashes down into the trough, as the wave breaks.

Breakers can be of two types, which depend on the nature of the wave and the character of the bottom. The plunging breakers are those in which the crest collapses into the trough, enclosing a pocket of air and completely destroying the wave form in the process of breaking. The other type is known as spilling breakers, in these the wave crest advances as a line of foaming water, which is moving forward at the speed of the wave form. On a flat beach there may be several surf waves, as these are called, advancing at the correct speed for the depth in the surf zone; it is this type of wave which is used for surf riding, as the breaker does not lose its identity, but gradually gets lower and lower until it becomes a thin layer of swash on the beach.

The plunging breakers are best developed on a steep beach from waves which were originally fairly flat, while the spilling breakers form on a gently sloping, usually sandy beach, when the waves in deep water were fairly steep. There is, however, a gradual transition between these two main types, which vary with the factors on which their character depends. Nearly all the energy of a wave is lost as it breaks, but what is left moves the remaining water up the beach as swash, and this returns down the beach, under the action of gravity, as the backwash.

(f) The reflection and diffraction of waves

Not all waves break; whether a wave breaks or not will depend on the nature of the coast against which it finally arrives. If a wave approaches a vertical cliff or sea-wall, whose foot is in deep water, it will not break and its energy will not be absorbed. As with tidal waves under somewhat similar circumstances, the wave will be reflected from the vertical barrier. Under ideal conditions this will lead to very little loss of energy, and an equal wave will travel in the opposite direction, supposing the primary wave reaches the barrier parallel to it. This reflection will set up a standing oscillation, similar to that already described for tidal movement. This is sometimes called a deep water clapotis, but it will not be developed in this form if the incident wave arrives against the barrier at an angle. The reflected wave will then make an equal and opposite angle with the barrier. The two waves will interfere with each other in such a way that their crests and troughs sometimes coincide and sometimes cancel each other. The result is a diagonal pattern of high crests alternating with low troughs.

The phenomenon of diffraction is also worth mention, as it accounts for the presence of waves in areas which might be expected to be sheltered from them. This is particularly important with regard to wave action in harbours. If waves are travelling towards a break-water, with their crests parallel to it, as shown in fig. 6–4, those in deep water beyond the end of the break-water will continue to move forward in the same way, but as they pass the break-water they will spread out and become lower in height in its shelter. In plan they will form the arc of a circle, centred

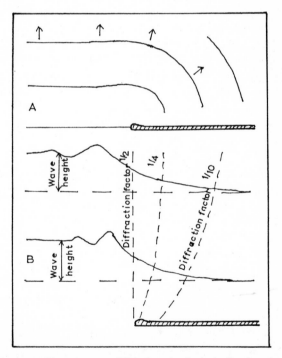

Fig. 6–4. Diagram to illustrate wave diffraction. A, above, is the plan view of the wave crests, and B, below, shows the wave height and diffraction factor for $\frac{1}{2}$, $\frac{1}{4}$ and 1/10 of the open sea wave height. (After Russell and Macmillan.)

on the end of the break-water. As these circular fronts must derive their energy from the wave crests advancing in deep water, these must lose height along a line at right-angles to the break-water towards the direction of wave movement. In fact, the waves along this line are halved in height, with an increasing reduction of height along the curved arcs as energy is transmitted along the wave crest, as shown in the figure.

In this way it is possible to explain why areas in the geometrical shadow of an obstacle, such as a break-water, have a certain amount of wave action. Although the theory of diffraction, as applied to light waves, is not strictly applicable to sea waves, experiments have shown that results worked out from it are not far wrong, usually giving slightly higher waves than those actually recorded.

(g) The effect of waves on structures

Waves can at times do considerable damage to break-waters and sea-walls, as well as to natural cliffs of solid rock. It is worth considering the conditions under which such damage is likely to take place. It has already been shown that if the water is sufficiently deep in front of a sea-wall or break-water, the whole of the wave energy will be reflected and the only force exerted on the structure will be the hydrostatic head of the rise and fall of the water-level. Even if the water is not deep enough to allow a complete reflection, if it is so deep that the wave does not break against the structure, most of the energy will be reflected. This will form a shallow water clapotis, in which it is possible to see the retreating wave moving through the advancing one. This can often be seen when the waves are advancing against a sea-wall at high tide. Again this type of reflection will not cause any damaging pressures on the sea-wall.

Damage is much more likely to be done if the wave breaks against the structure; in this situation the particle velocity within the wave form is equal to that of the wave form and water moving in this way may exert considerable pressure on the sea-wall. It has been observed that the speed of the water at the crest of the wave may, in fact, be equal to twice the wave velocity at times.

The most intense shock pressures will, however, be set up if, when the wave breaks against the sea-wall, it encloses a pocket of air in doing so. This air pocket becomes intensely compressed, and it throws up the enclosing water with great violence, which may set up extreme shock pressure. Such pressures are difficult to measure, as they take place over a very short period of time. The pressure due to breaking waves may be short-lived, as experiments at Dieppe demonstrated; their high pressures were recorded for periods varying from $1/20$ to $1/200$ sec.; for example, one wave produced a shock pressure of 12,700 lb./sq.ft., but the total time the pressure exceeded 6,000 lb./sq. ft. was only 1/100 sec.

Experimental work by Bagnold has also shown that shock pressures are very short-lived. He found that, even in the most uniform waves that could be generated in a model wave tank, the shock pressures varied greatly, and only occurred when a pocket of air was enclosed. They were very much greater when the pocket of air was very thin. The total amount of pressure each wave produced was fairly uniform, but its distribution varied. Thus extreme pressures only lasted a brief time, while less severe ones lasted longer. The observation that the thinnest pocket of air produces the highest pressures suggests that the air pocket acts as a cushion, separating a vertical wave front from a vertical wall against which it is brought instantaneously to rest and its momentum lost. It is such shock pressures which are most liable to do serious damage on the coast, although their rarity and brief action in time is balanced by the more frequent and longer-lived, but less intense, forces exerted in other ways.

(h) Solitary waves

When the depth of water is so small that the velocity of the wave no longer depends on it, d/L being less than 0·05, the waves move independently of each other, as their velocity now depends only on the depth, according to $C=\sqrt{gd}$; such waves are called solitary waves. Each one consists of a crest, which is separated from its neighbours by flat water in which the water particles are at rest; those under the crest move in the direction of wave propagation. In order to maintain a uniform water-level a slow seaward flow is probably superimposed on the landward movement. The movement of particles in such a wave is up and forwards as the crest approaches, while as it passes they slow down and move downwards, although the superimposed seaward movement would convert this latter part of the orbit into a seaward flow.

This type of wave is of interest, as it is possible to calculate theoretical velocities for the flow on the bed for different wave heights. Experimental work, which was designed to measure these velocities, has shown that the results agreed more closely with the results worked out theoretically, using the solitary wave theory, than those worked out from the Airy-Stokes wave theory for low progressive waves. It seems likely that solitary waves of this type may exist in very shallow water in nature; perhaps they occur where waves re-form after breaking on a submarine bar.

3. *WAVE SPECTRA AND WAVE GENERATION*—'*SEA*'

The waves in the open ocean and on the coast are much more complex than the ideal waves which have been considered already. It is the great complexity of waves in the open ocean, particularly in the generating area, where they are known as 'sea', that has led to the development of the method of analysis which splits up the complex wave profile into its constituent parts, to form the wave spectrum. This is somewhat similar to the method of harmonic analysis, which is used in tidal work, and provides data giving the relative frequency of the different period bands present in the wave pattern at any time.

A wave analyser has been developed at the National Institute of Oceanography (Tucker, 1956). This instrument makes it possible to analyse the wave trace, which shows the actual variations in the water-level, into its constituent periods, as shown in fig. 6–5. The resulting wave spectrum shows that the energy of the wave is usually concentrated around a fairly narrow frequency band. The frequency is the inverse value of the period of $1/T$. From a study of the energy distribution in the complete wave pattern, it is possible to arrive at a value for the significant wave height, which is usually taken to be the mean height of the highest $1/3$ of the waves, and the significant period, which is the period of these waves. The significant height can also be expressed in terms of the mean height of all waves, H_{mean}; its value is $1 \cdot 6$ times the mean height, while the maximum height is about $2 \cdot 4$ times the mean height. Directional wave spectra have also been developed (Darbyshire, 1961)

Various analyses show that the wave spectrum usually covers a wide range of wave periods; thus Neumann (1953), who has used the wave-spectrum technique to relate waves to the winds that form them, has shown a typical spectrum in which the frequency varies from less than 0·06 to over 2. The periods covered by this frequency range are from 20 sec. to 5 sec., which is a very great range. Within the range, however, there is a marked peak, which Neumann suggests becomes more marked as the wind force rises and the energy of the waves increases. Thus in a sea generated by a 20-knot wind he shows a low peak with a frequency of 0·124 or a period of 8·1 sec. When the wind force is as great as 40 knots the maximum energy is concentrated strongly around the frequency of 0·06 or 16 sec. period; it is in this band, therefore, that the highest waves would be expected to occur.

More recently Darbyshire (1959b) has analysed observations made in the North Atlantic by a weather ship. He uses the spectrum technique to relate the various dimensions of the waves, as actually observed and analysed, to the winds generating them. Provided the fetch is large, he has found that the wave spectrum has only one form, even though the generating wind force varies. The spectrum which he gives is generally of the same form as that suggested by Neumann; there is a sharp peak in which the wave energy is concentrated and the waves highest. This frequency he calls f_0 and from this value the energy falls off more

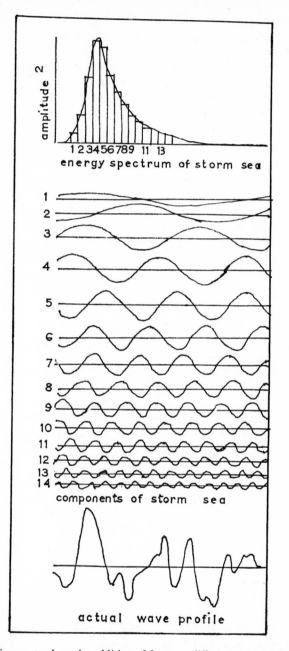

FIG. 6–5. Diagram to show the addition of fourteen different components of a wave spectrum to form the actual wave profile. The proportion of energy in the different parts of the spectrum is indicated in the upper part of the diagram. (After Deacon.)

O.–P

rapidly to the high period or low frequency side and less rapidly towards the lower periods.

A useful result of his analysis is the relationship which has emerged between the different variables, on which the wave size depends, and the relationship between the form of the spectrum and the significant wave dimensions. The significant period he shows to be related to the period which has the most energy in the spectrum by $T_f = 1\cdot14\ T_1/_3$, thus the period with the highest energy is only slightly larger than the significant period, while the wave height, which is dependent on the wave energy in the spectrum, can be related to the square of the wind speed, assuming a large fetch.

This shows that although it is convenient to express the wave dimensions in terms of their significant height and period, these values are by no means the only elements present in any wave pattern. They merely represent the narrow band in which the wave energy tends to be concentrated; waves of very different periods are also present, but they normally only contain a small amount of energy and, therefore, the wave heights associated with them are low. This demonstrates the great complexity of the wave pattern in the sea and the great difficulty there is in explaining the generation and subsequent growth of waves. Several theories have been put forward to account for the initial generation of waves and a variety of techniques have been developed to forecast or hindcast wave dimensions from meteorological data.

Wave generation. Many of the theories put forward to explain the method by which energy is transferred from the air to the water have been shown to be incorrect in some respect, but a recent theory by Phillips (1957) appears to be rather more successful, although there are still difficulties in establishing a complete explanation.

One of the early theories was put forward by Jeffreys in 1925; he suggested that the air flow was laminar over the windward slope of the wave and turbulent on the lee slope, which is partially sheltered by the wave crest, giving lower velocities there. An important factor in his theory was the sheltering co-efficient, which is related to the proportion of the windward slope of the wave offering resistance to the wind. The value he deduced for this co-efficient seems to have been too great, and his theory cannot account for the original generation of waves from a flat surface, although it does seem to apply better in the early stages of wave generation than when they become large.

The work of Sverdrup and Munk showed that the tangential stress of the wind on the water was an important aspect of wave generation; this varies with the square of the wind velocity, above a certain threshold. When the water particles move in the same direction as the wind they acquire energy from the wind, but energy is lost when the particles move in the opposite direction. Because of mass transport there is a net gain of energy. The wave velocity is much greater than the water particles' velocity, which could allow the wave form to move faster than the generating wind velocity. When the wave velocity exceeds the wind velocity generating them energy is transferred in two ways; the waves gain energy by wind stress when the particles of water are moving in the same direction as the wind, but they lose it by pressure of the wave form on the wind. In the earlier stages the increase of energy builds up the height of the wave more than the length, but when the wave form is moving faster than the wind, most of the energy goes towards increasing the length and with it the wave velocity.

The more recent theories of wave generation by Eckart (1953) and Phillips (1957) consider that the flow of the air is fully turbulent and that the normal pressure, due to gusts of wind, is distributed at random. It appears that the pattern used by Eckart was not sufficiently random, and Phillips's results appear to be more accurate. He assumes that a gusty wind starts to blow on a surface previously at rest. This causes pressure fluctuations on the surface, which are both normal (perpendicular to the surface) and tangential. Eddies are caused by the wind and these tend to develop slowly and to move at a speed related to the wind velocity. These local pressure centres are carried in the air stream and, when their rate of movement is similar to that of a developing disturbance on the water surface, a state of resonance will be set up. This initial disturbance may develop into a growing wave, because if it is moving at a speed similar to the wind-pressure pocket, they move together and the wave can grow. This, however, assumes that the pressure pattern is not changing and is, therefore, an oversimplification.

When the wave dimensions increase other factors come in and the waves grow in a different way. According to this analysis there does not seem to be a minimum wind velocity necessary to develop waves; even the lowest winds which cause some disturbance on the surface may form waves, although these may not grow. The smallest wind velocity which is likely to generate resonance waves is about 23 cm./sec.

It is suggested that with light winds the wave spectrum is narrower, the waves appearing more uniform, than with strong winds, when a wider wave period band is present. It has been shown by Phillips that the wave height grows, after the initial stages, at a rate which is uniform with time, at least until the wave height exceeds a certain point. His theoretical results agree fairly closely with some observations over a fairly restricted range of wind duration.

Despite these advances Francis (1959) has stated that the structure of the larger waves is so complex that all the theories break down before the largest waves are reached, and it is these which have most significance from many points of view, such as the behaviour of ships at sea and the attack of waves on coastal defences. It is, therefore, necessary to develop empirical relationships between the main factors on which wave growth and wave characteristics depend.

The most important of these factors is the wind strength, but other factors must not be ignored. The duration of time during which the wind is blowing is very important, because, however strongly a wind is blowing, if it only blows for a short time large waves cannot be generated. The other factor of significance is the fetch, which may be defined as the stretch of open water over which the generating wind is blowing. In an enclosed sea this will be limited by the nearest shore in the direction from which the wind is blowing, while in the open ocean it will depend on the meteorological situation, on which the distance over which winds of constant direction are blowing depends.

The effect of fetch can readily be seen where the wind is blowing offshore; near the shore the waves are very small, but they gradually increase away from the coast as the fetch lengthens. There are, in fact, two distinct zones; in the one near the shore the waves are increasing in size away from the coast, because the fetch is increasing in this direction, but each wave maintains its size, which is limited by the fetch. In the second zone, farther offshore, the fetch does not impose a limit to wave size beyond a certain point which varies with the strength of the wind. The waves in this zone will all be of equal size at any one time, but will continue to grow until they reach the maximum size for that wind speed and duration, assuming that the wind continues blowing in the same direction.

Different authorities differ greatly in their interpretation of the fetch required to develop waves of maximum size. Darbyshire, for example, considers that a fetch of about 100 miles is sufficient to develop waves to their maximum size, even when the winds are strong. Neumann, Pierson, and James hold different views; they consider that the fetch necessary to produce the maximum-sized waves depends on the strength of the wind, which itself largely determines the wave size. They suggest that much longer fetches are necessary than those given by Darbyshire (1957a), thus a 34-knot wind would require 400 nautical miles fetch to produce the maximum waves possible, while a 50-knot wind needs 1,420 nautical miles and 69 hours duration. This latter situation is likely to be very rare; thus it is difficult to test the upper part of their curve. The data of Bretschneider also indicate that waves require a very long fetch to reach their maximum size, when the winds are very strong, as shown in fig. 6–6.

The depth of water over which the wind is blowing will also exert some influence on the growth of waves, and Darbyshire has found that

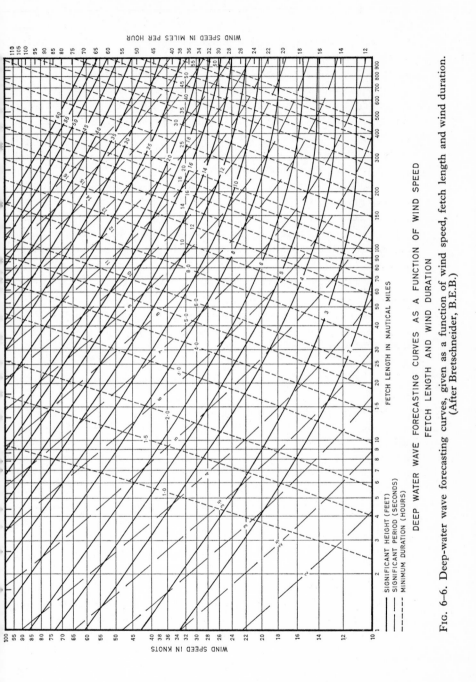

FIG. 6–6. Deep-water wave forecasting curves, given as a function of wind speed, fetch length and wind duration. (After Bretschneider, B.E.B.)

the formulae applicable to shallow water differ from those fitting the deep-water data. Further complications are introduced by the instability of the air immediately in contact with the sea, or the air-sea temperature difference. One observation showed that when there was a decrease of 11 °C of the air temperature relative to the sea temperature, the wave height was doubled for the same wind speed. It has been stated that a 25 per cent increase of wave height results from a $5\frac{1}{2}$°C temperature difference between air and water. Other observations in the Irish Sea have suggested that the effect of instability is marked only when the waves are not fully developed (Darbyshire, M., 1958), and the whole problem is still under discussion.

All these variables make it very difficult to assess the waves generated by any given storm, particularly as there were probably some waves present before the disturbance developed. Clearly the most favourable regions for the generation of really large waves will be those parts of the ocean where the winds blow strongly and constantly in direction over wide stretches of open sea. These conditions are most nearly fulfilled in the westerly wind belt of the southern ocean. Winds in the stormy latitudes of the North Atlantic are much more variable in position and direction, not allowing such regular wave trains to be formed. It is the very long waves, with their great energy, which can be traced farthest from their source across the ocean.

4. *WAVE ATTENUATION—'SWELL'*

When a wave moves out of the generating area into calmer waters it becomes modified, and is known as 'swell'. However, where the original winds were very strong the waves, because of their great energy, travel for very long distances before losing their identity. As soon as swell travels out into calmer water the shorter waves tend to die out because they lose their small amount of energy fairly quickly; this has the result of making the swell appear more uniform and longer crested than the sea from which it originated. A spectrum of swell waves is usually deficient in the short wave lengths, although local winds may super-impose a series of small waves on the swell; this renders it difficult to see in the open ocean, particularly if it is low. From many observations of swell on the coasts of the continents in the Southern Hemisphere, it seems that a common figure for the length of the swell generated in the southern ocean is about 1,000 ft. long, having a period of 14 sec.

When swell moves out from the generating area there are different views as to the modifications that it undergoes; some authorities suggest that the swell lengthens as it moves away from the generating area, but most workers agree that there is no marked change in the wave length of the individual wave trains as they move out from the generating area. It is generally agreed that the waves move as individual trains, each travelling with a velocity appropriate to the wave length; they therefore become spread out, with the longest waves outstripping the shorter, to arrive first at some distant shore.

As the waves move out they become longer crested and more uniform and sinusoidal in form, with smooth rounded crests. Their height is reduced as they move away from the generating area, a process which is accelerated if they encounter a headwind. The reduction in wave height is due to three possible causes: firstly, dispersion; secondly loss of energy due to air resistance and turbulence, and thirdly, divergence.

Darbyshire (1957b) has studied the attenuation of waves in the north Atlantic Ocean over distances of 400 to 1,600 miles from the storm area, from records of waves taken instrumentally on the Weather Ship *Weather Explorer*. The analysis of the records showed that the reduction of wave height was independent of wave period, and could be expressed simply in the form $H_T/H°_T=(300/R)^{\frac{1}{4}}$, where H_T is a function of the wave height at the recording point, being the square root of the sum of the squares of the peaks for each 1-sec. interval on the wave spectrum; $H°_T$ is in the same form, but refers to the wave height at the edge of the generating area. This was arrived at by the use of the formulae for wave generation and may, therefore, not be quite accurate; R is the distance from the recording point to the centre of the storm. Despite the uncertainty of the wave height on the edge of the generating area the results are very consistent. They seemed to be independent of the speed of the following wind in the decay area. The formula shows that wave height is reduced fairly rapidly with distance from the storm, being halved in about 1,000 miles, but decreasing much more slowly thereafter, as shown on the fig. 6–7.

The causes of this reduction were analysed. The first, dispersion, resulted from the spreading out of the wave trains as each moved out from the generating area with its own appropriate velocity. The longest waves reach farthest ahead, thus spreading out the zone over which the energy was distributed and leading to a reduction in wave height. Within any one period band, such as was used for this analysis, this effect would not be marked and could not account for the observed reduction, although it is probably this factor which accounts for the apparent increase in wave length which some authorities associate with swell waves. The second factor is the loss of energy, but too little is known as yet concerning the method of transfer of energy from water to air, and vice versa, for a reliable estimate of this factor to be made.

The third factor can, however, account in considerable measure for the observed result. Divergence is the spreading out of a wave front laterally as it moves out from the storm area; this must clearly result in a loss of energy per unit length of crest and, therefore, of wave height. Darbyshire considers that this factor is important in effecting the reduction of wave height in the decay area. He has used the formula given successfully in comparing predicted and observed swell heights. In fact, the attentuation of waves seems to be better understood than their growth, as forecasts of swell are usually more reliable than those of seas in the generating area.

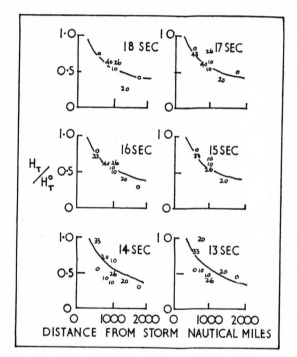

FIG. 6–7. Reduction of wave height in relation to distance from a storm centre and strength of following winds. (After Darbyshire.)

One of the early analyses of swell waves, published by Barber and Ursell (1948), used a record of swell waves measured by a wave gauge at Pendeen in Cornwall. This record was analysed to give the wave spectrum, from which the progress of swell of a particular frequency band could be traced on successive records. They based their analysis on the assumption that wave trains travel across the ocean at speeds equal to half the wave velocity. By projecting the waves backwards in time and distance from their point of arrival, the position and time from which they set out could be found. Where these propagation lines meet is the most likely centre of the storm, whose distance away can then be read off from the scale and the time determined. An example of the wave spectra and propagation diagram is shown in figs. 6–8a, b, c. Meteorological charts can then be studied and the storm from which the swell travelled can be identified from these data.

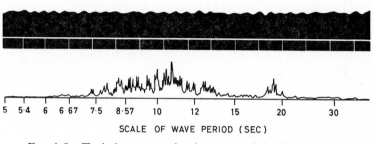

FIG. 6–8a. Typical wave record and spectrum. (After Darbyshire.)

The swell, in the example analysed, first reached the coast of Cornwall at 1900 hrs. on 30 June 1945, when it had a period of 18 sec. Later observations showed a steady decrease in period, as the shorter waves arrived, but the height increased. The origin of these swell waves was traced back to an intense tropical hurricane, which reached its maximum intensity on 26–27 June, when it was situated off the coast of North America between Cape Hatteras and Nantucket, Mass. This was about 2,700 to 3,000 miles away from Cornwall. Other swells recorded on this coast have been traced back to storms in the Southern Hemisphere near the Cape of Good Hope. It is interesting to note that the value of the wave period showed fluctuations, that have been explained as the result of interference due to tidal currents, as their periodicity agreed with that of the changes in the tidal streams.

That swell waves can travel even longer distances than these without losing their identity has been shown by the examination of wave records in California. Wiegel and Kimberley (1950) have concluded that swell reaching California, during the summer months, must have originated in the Southern Hemisphere in the south Pacific Ocean between 40° and 65°S and 120 to 160°W. This is about 7,000 miles from California. The swell, generated in the winter in the stormy latitudes of the southern ocean, arrived with periods between 12 and 18 sec., sometimes reaching values as high as 22 sec. Its usual height was about 2 to 6 ft., but at times it reached a maximum of 10 to 12 ft., suggesting that the original waves

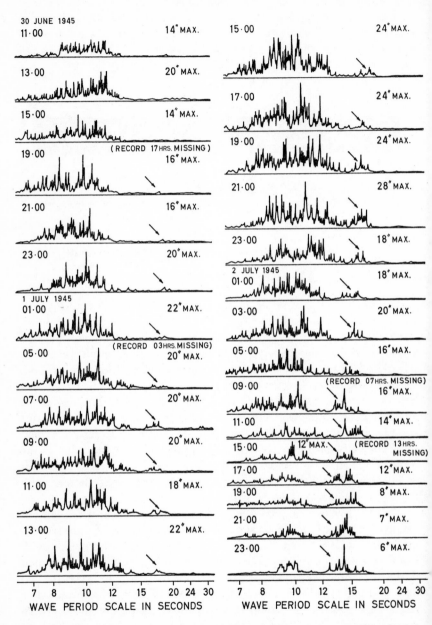

FIG. 6–8b. Wave spectra at Pendeen, Cornwall, 30 June to 2 July 1954. (After Barber and Ursell.)

must have been very large indeed, and could only have been generated in the region of strong and persistent westerly winds.

When considering the arrival of waves at any point, therefore, it is necessary to take full account of the swell waves, whose point of origin may be thousands of miles away across the ocean. It is this fact which in large measure differentiates the wave records of areas in enclosed seas

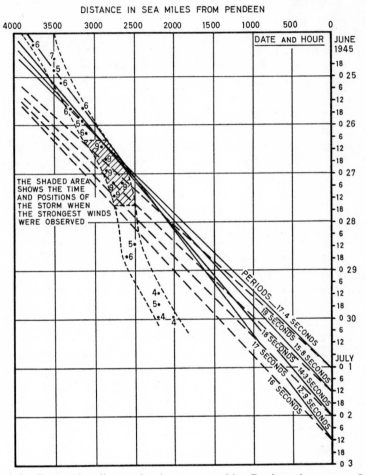

FIG. 6–8c. Propagation diagram for the waves reaching Pendeeen between 24 June and 2 July 1945. (After Barber and Ursell.)

and those to which the long swells have access on the shores of the open ocean. It is also the long swell waves which are most modified by refraction as they enter shallow water, because, being very long, they feel the bottom long before the shorter waves, generated locally by less strong winds.

5. WAVE OBSERVATIONS

Until recently the methods used to forecast waves depended on visual observation. Now, however, methods have been developed which enable waves to be instrumentally measured both in deep water and in shallow water. The forecasting techniques, which aim to relate wind speed, fetch and other variables to the wave dimensions, can be based on surer foundations.

The measurement of waves in shallow water can be done in various ways, the most useful of which is probably the pressure-wave gauge. This instrument, which measures the variations of pressure due to the variations in depth over the gauge as the waves pass over, may be situated in any desired depth of water. It gives a continuous trace of the wave height, in a form which is suitable for analysis to provide a wave spectrum.

The problem of measuring waves in deep water is much more difficult, but a satisfactory ship-borne wave recorder has been developed at the National Institute of Oceanography (Tucker, 1956). This apparatus, which can be fitted into the hull of a ship, is designed to measure the height of the water surface above the point in the hull where it is fitted, and to relate this height to a reference level below the ship; the addition of the two values gives the wave height. The first amount can be found by the change in pressure due to the increase of water depth, but the second is not so easily measured. It is derived from a measure of the acceleration of the vertical component of wave velocity by integrating it twice. The result shows the fluctuations of the surface, which can be analysed in a similar way to give the wave spectrum. The instrument is fitted at a level 10 ft. below the water-line, which cuts out waves of periods shorter than 4 sec. The records have an accuracy of $\pm$ 10 per cent. Another useful instrument, designed by Barber (1954), measures the direction from which waves approach in shallow water. This is clearly of value, because the direction of approach is very important in considering the total volume of transport of beach material alongshore.

Since instrumental values for the waves have become available it is much easier to obtain a reasonably accurate picture of the actual pattern of wave height and period in different areas, as it is all too easy to exaggerate visual impressions of wave heights, particularly in a storm at sea. The highest wave which had been recorded by 1959 was 60 ft. high; it was recorded on 26 November 1956 at a position 61°N, 15°20'W.

Darbyshire (1959b) has analysed the relative frequency of wave height and period in the Atlantic and in the Irish Sea, as well as at various coastal stations; this gives useful information concerning the dimensions of waves likely to be experienced in different situations. The waves which were used for the analysis in the Atlantic were in the generating area. The height of the crest above the mean water-level was found for each period band of 1 sec. and related to the force of the wind. For Force 4 winds in the Atlantic the most common period was 6 sec., and the height above the mean water-level averaged about 1 ft.; for Force 6 the values were 7 sec. and 2½ ft., and for Force 8 they were 11 sec. and nearly 10 ft., while for Force 9 the figures were only a little greater.

Only fairly recently has information become available of instrumental wave measurements in an enclosed sea off Britain. Wave records taken by the lightship in Morecambe Bay at a position 53°55′N, 3°29′W, have given interesting information concerning wave generation in coastal waters with large tides. The maximum waves recorded in the Irish Sea were 28 ft. high with a period of 7 sec. on 1 November 1957, but waves of this height are very rare. Taking observations for the whole year, even 10-ft. waves only occur about 2 per cent of the time, while waves occurring about 20 per cent of the time are only 1 ft. high. The higher waves are all concentrated in the winter half of the year (Darbyshire, M., 1958). By far the most common significant period was about 5 sec., occurring about 30 per cent of the time; this was exceeded mainly in December and January, when it only reached about 7 sec. There was a close correlation between wind direction and wave height, the higher waves being generated by the winds blowing over the largest fetch. One of the interesting results of this investigation is that for a given wind speed the waves were much shorter, and they required a shorter fetch to reach their maximum size than in the open ocean.

These results may be compared with those given for observations in the open Atlantic and on the coast of Cornwall. These observations show that in the open ocean the wave heights are very much greater than those recorded on the coast of Cornwall. In February 1953 the average height in the ocean was over 23 ft., while for the coastal observations in the same month of 1946 the mean height was just over 11 ft. The difference was rather greater in winter, but was nevertheless noticeable throughout the year. There is also an interesting difference between the significant periods in the two areas. The average periods of the waves was much longer at the coastal station than it was in the open ocean, although again the observations were made in different years. Periods over 15 sec. were much more common on the coast, where they may occur for as much as 45 per cent of the time in some months, while they never exceeded 5 per cent of the time in mid-ocean, even in winter.

To account for the lower waves recorded near the coast, it is suggested that wave generation is not so efficient in shallow water. The longer periods recorded at the coastal station may be the result of the attenuation of some of the shorter, higher waves, generated in the open ocean, before they reach the coast, where the long-period swells, therefore, predominate. The wave sizes seem to follow a fairly similar pattern in different areas, with the highest waves being extremely rare, while a particular height is dominant in each region. Thus for the Atlantic weather-ship data this height was about 10 ft. for all the observations, although waves of 50 ft. were sometimes recorded. At Perranporth, on the other hand, although waves over 30 ft. occasionally occurred, the most common height was about 4 ft. A somewhat similar value held for observations at Casablanca in North Africa.

6. *WAVE FORECASTING*

It would be very valuable for many purposes to be able to forecast accurately the wave dimensions from meteorological data. To do this accurately requires detailed knowledge both of the theory of wave generation and a detailed picture of the weather situation over the ocean, neither of which is available. The methods which have been developed, therefore, are mainly empirical in character, and seek to relate observed wave dimensions to the winds generating them. The results are often expressed in the form of curves, from which the desired wave dimensions can be read off from observed data of wind strength, duration and fetch. Some of these curves are based on visual wave observations and cannot hope to be more accurate than the information on which they are based. Others, for example those of Darbyshire, are based on instrumentally observed wave data. There are three main variations of these forecasting data, devised respectively by Sverdrup and Munk, and modified by Bretschneider, called SMB for short; Pierson, Neumann, and James, PNJ for short, devised a different version, while the third was put forward by Darbyshire (D). It is not easy to be sure which gives the most reliable results, and these can differ very significantly, as the following examples will show.

Taking a fetch of 50 nautical miles and a wind speed of 30 knots, the significant height according to SMB would be 11·1 ft., PNJ give 6·6 ft., and D 8·3 ft.; for a 40-knot wind the figures are respectively 20 ft., 23 ft. and 14 ft. The SMB method does not make use of the spectrum technique, which is used by the other two methods. The figures given above are for a very short fetch; when the fetch is longer the results are rather different, because Darbyshire considers that wave height is independent of fetch when this exceeds about 100 nautical miles, while the other methods allow the waves to continue to grow as the fetch increases. For higher values of the fetch, therefore, the wave heights given by Darbyshire are considerably lower than those given by SMB and the PNJ values are very high indeed.

Darbyshire has given data which suggest that the PNJ formula for wave height results, at times, in a 100 per cent overestimate, when compared with observed significant wave heights, while his own values were much nearer the observed ones. The fetch in the particular instance cited was 1,000 miles. With a fetch of only about 150 miles the PNJ results seemed too small. In many examples the results given by the SMB method are even greater than those which PNJ suggest. One difficulty in comparing the different curves is that Darbyshire uses, in the earlier formulae at least, the gradient wind, while the other methods use the surface wind, measured at a height of 33 ft.

Charnock (1958) has suggested that it would be better to use the friction velocity, but this is not so readily obtained. Because of the difficulty of application of the gradient wind. Darbyshire (1959b), in his latest analysis of the relationship between wave height and wind speed, has used the wind as measured at the weather ship, from which the wave observations were made. Assuming that the relationship between the gradient wind and the surface wind is $3/2$, his results are very similar to the earlier ones, being given by $H = 0 \cdot 0038 \ U^2$ (earlier) and $H = 0 \cdot 0036 \ U^2$ (later), where H is the square root of the sum of the squares of all the peaks in the spectrum in feet and U is the gradient wind in knots. The newer relationship between the wind at the surface, W, in knots and the significant wave height is $H_{1/3} = 0 \cdot 0133 \ W^2$. According to his analysis, therefore, the wave height varies as the square of the wind speed. The wave period containing the peak of the wave-spectrum energy, T, was related to the square root of the surface wind speed by $T_f = 1 \cdot 94 \ W^{\frac{1}{2}}$; this value held until the wind force was very strong, when the result became more accurate if the formula was given as $T_f = 1 \cdot 94 \ W^{\frac{1}{2}} + 2 \cdot 5 + 10^{-7} \ W^4$. These formulae assumed that the waves are fully developed; that is, no limits are imposed by the fetch or wind duration.

The newest data concerning the SMB technique provide curves which enable a variety of different situations to be analysed. Not only are the deep-water conditions allowed for, but the different conditions which apply to wave generation in shallow water are taken into account. One graph, from which the deep-water wave characteristics of significant height and period can be obtained, is plotted with the wind speed on one axis and the fetch length on the other, as shown in fig. 6–6, and the minimum duration necessary to obtain full-size waves is also given. The curves for the wave height show that this increases steadily as the fetch increases. For example, taking a 30-knot wind, in a fetch of 100 miles, a wave just over 10 ft. high would be expected, but when the fetch is increased to 1,000 miles the wave height should be over 20 ft., and should require 55 hours duration, instead of only 9 hours in the smaller fetch.

Curves are also given which allow the decay of waves to be estimated; here again there is a difference between the methods, in that the significant periods are held to increase with decay distance in the SMB graphs. Complications arise owing to the fact that the storm generating the waves is itself moving, and this movement becomes very important in the instance of a hurricane, which is treated in the recent revision of the SMB technique by Bretschneider (1959).

The PNJ method (1955), by providing a series of additional sets of curves, also allows for the angular spreading of the waves as they move away from the generating area, the fetch over which the storm waves are blowing, the situation in which the storm is moving about the same speed as the waves generated by it, and finally, the result of the rapid cessation of the storm winds. The technique of wave forecasting will not be perfected until there are many more precise data on which the results can be based, and until it is possible to assess accurately the very complex part played by the weather situation, wind force, direction and duration being particularly important. Other factors which must be considered are the stability, or air-sea temperature differences, the effects of shallow water, tidal currents and wave refraction, all of which affect the wave dimensions. Until this can be done it seems reasonable to assume that each technique will work best in the area for which it was devised, assuming that the same methods are used to obtain the wave height. None of the methods are absolutely reliable, although impressive accuracy is sometimes achieved.

7. LONG WAVES AND SEISMIC WAVES (TSUNAMI)

(a) Long waves or surf beat

There are a number of waves in the ocean whose lengths are considerably longer than the normal, wind-generated waves, whose periods do not normally exceed about 24 sec. A type of long wave, sometimes called surf beat, was recorded by Munk (1949), and discussed by Tucker (1950). These waves had a period of about 2 min. and a height of about 1/11 of the normal waves; they sometimes give trouble in harbours and have been recorded from places as far apart as Tema in Ghana and Perranporth in Cornwall. At Ghana the waves of this type had periods between 1 and 10 min., with periods of 2–4 min. being most common. Their height was about 1/20 that of the normal waves, reaching a maximum of about 5 in. The similar type of waves which were recorded at Perranporth had heights about 1/12 of the normal waves, and their period was also 1 to 5 min. Here the long waves had a height of 5 in., when the ordinary waves were 6 ft. high.

It has been suggested that groups of extra high waves, which are likely to appear from time to time in a complex wave spectrum, cause these long waves. The mass transport increases rapidly with the wave height and near the break-point; this results in an abnormally great volume of water moving towards the shore as the groups of larger waves break; this is compensated by a return flow, which sets up the long waves. The increasing mass transport in the breaker zone sets up a shoreward wave, which is reflected from the shore; in this way it initiates the long wave or surf beat.

(b) Microseisms

Another type of wave associated with ocean storms is worthy of brief mention, on account of its importance in forecasting the approach of damaging storm waves or swell (Iyer, 1959; Darbyshire, 1960). It has been found, by careful comparison of wave records and records of very small seismic disturbances, that these microseisms are related to storm waves. The period of the microseism is half that of the storm wave, and both have a spectrum of waves. The interesting point about the microseisms is that they frequently arrive some time before the waves reach the coast. If it were possible to relate the direction from which the microseisms travel to the direction in which the storm waves are travelling, they would provide a very valuable warning system, especially in those areas where weather observations out to sea are scanty.

The main cause of the microseisms seems to be the interference between two wave trains of equal period, but different amplitude, travelling in opposite directions. This situation will arise in a small depression, in which there is a sharp veer of the wind as the disturbance passes any point; this will generate waves moving in opposite directions. In some instances the interference between waves of the same period could be achieved by reflection from a steep coast. When waves of equal period but different height meet head-on, Longuet-Higgins has shown that they will exert an effect on the bottom even in deep water, and in this way microseisms can be set up. These will travel much more rapidly in the Earth's crust than the waves on the ocean surface. The problem of finding the point of origin of, and the direction of approach of, the microseism is complicated by the fact that they, like ordinary waves, suffer from refraction, and from the fact that a number of different periods of seismic waves are involved. The results of this work, however, would be of considerable value if it allowed accurate forecasts of the arrival of damaging storm waves to be made.

(c) Seismic waves (tsunami)

Another type of long-wave activity is the direct result of seismic activity, rather than the cause of it. These are the very long waves

O.–Q

generated by a submarine earthquake, which are often called by the Japanese name of 'tsunami', and were at one time referred to by the misleading term 'tidal wave', which is misleading in view of the fact that they are in no way connected with tidal phenomena. It is reasonable to suppose that any sudden movement in the crust of the Earth, which sets up waves travelling through the crust of the Earth, will also affect the water of the oceans. The Pacific is particularly liable to tsunami, partly on account of the crustal instability of the land around its edge, but such waves also occur in the Atlantic. The damage done by the seismically generated waves, due to the Lisbon earthquake of 1755, made this only too apparent. This earthquake also affected Loch Lomond to the extent of producing an oscillation of $2\frac{1}{2}$ ft. amplitude and 10 min. period.

The waves produced by earthquakes are rightly called long waves, as their length may well be about 100 miles, although their height in the open ocean may be only 1 to 2 ft. Because the waves are so long, their velocity depends only on the depth of water, even in the deep ocean, as their length is great compared with the depth of water. If the mean depth of the oceans is taken as 2,500 fathoms, the speed of the tsunami would be 472 miles/hour. They are normally so long and low that they are not felt by ships in the open sea, but as they approach close to the shore their height is increased and they may break on the shore with devastating effect as waves 20 to 30 ft. high.

The earthquake of 1 April 1946 in the Aleutian Islands generated seismic waves which moved out across the ocean to reach Hawaii after 5 hours. They arrived in increasing size, the third wave being the highest, as shown in fig. 6–9. The time interval between the first two was 12 min. Waves from this same earthquake reached as far as the Antarctic, where a hut was washed away (Shepard, 1959). Still more extensive and widespread damage was done by the tsunami resulting from the earthquake in southern Chile on 22 May 1960. This exceptionally severe shock produced waves which reached and caused damage in New Guinea on the other side of the Pacific.

The velocity with which these waves travelled across the ocean varied between 419 miles/hour and 466 miles/hour to Wake Island, which they reached about 19 hours after the shock (Robinson, 1961). As the water depth decreases close to the shore, the speed of the wave slows down and its height increases. An 11-ft. wave was recorded on the Californian coast, while a 30-ft. wave caused much damage in Hokkaido and Honshu in Japan. Lyttleton Harbour, New Zealand, and even Sydney in Australia were affected by this tsunami. The period between the arrival of the wave crests varied between 10 and 25 min. The effects of the tsunami were much more disastrous in Japan than they were at

Hawaii, which is very much nearer the source of the disturbance. Partly because of the relatively minor effect the tsunami had in Hawaii, it was not thought likely that it would reach Japan with much energy left; this assumption was, however, very far from justified, as the damage in Japan demonstrated. It also indicates that there is still a lot to be learnt

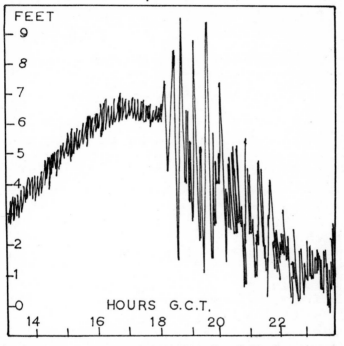

FEET

HOURS G.C.T.

FIG. 6–9. Tide-gauge record for San Luis Obispo Bay, California, to show the effect of the earthquake waves generated by the earthquake of 1 April 1946 in the Aleutian Islands. (After Deacon [Lang].)

about the way tsunamis travel across the ocean, but more particularly about the way in which they are influenced by the shallow water around the coast in relation to their direction of approach. Thus a tsunami may give waves only 5 ft. high only a few hundred miles from the point of origin, but 30 ft. high waves at places as much as 10,000 miles away. It is clear, however, that long waves of this type can travel immense distances without loss of energy.

REFERENCES

Barber, N. F., Finding the direction of travel of sea waves. *Nature* **174**, 1048–50, 1954.

Barber, N. F., and Ursell, F., The generation and propagation of ocean waves and swell. I. Wave periods and velocities. *Phil. Trans. Roy. Soc. A* **240**, 527–60, 1948.

Bretschneider, C. L., Revisions in wave forecasting, deep and shallow water. Chapter 3. *Coastal Engin. Conf.*, 30–67, 1959.

Charnock, H., A note on empirical wind-wave formulae. *Quart. Journ. Roy. Met. Soc.* **84**, 443–7, 1958.

Darbyshire, J., A note on the comparison of proposed wave spectrum formulae. *Deutsch. Hydrog. Zeitsch.* **10**, 184–90, 1957a.

Darbyshire, J., Attenuation of swell in the north Atlantic Ocean. *Quart. Journ. Roy. Met. Soc.* **83**, 351–9, 1957b.

Darbyshire, J., The spectra of coastal waves. *Deutsch. Hydrog. Zeitsch.* **12**, 153–67, 1959a.

Darbyshire, J., A further investigation of wind-generated waves. *Deutsch. Hydrog. Zeitsch.* **12**, 1–13, 1959b.

Darbyshire, J., Microseisms and storms. *Adv. Sci.* **17**, 149–57, 1960.

Darbyshire, J., Prediction of wave characteristics over the North Atlantic. *Journ. Inst. Navig.* **14**, 339–47, 1961.

Darbyshire, M., Waves in the Irish Sea. *Dock. and Harb. Auth.* **39**, 245–8, 1958.

Davies, J. L., Wave refraction and the evolution of shoreline curves. *Geog. Stud.* **5**, 1–14, 1959.

Eckart, C., The generation of wind waves over a water surface. *Journ. Appl. Physics.* **24**, 1485–94, 1953.

Francis, J. R. D., Wind action on a water surface. *Proc. Inst. Civ. Eng.* **12**, 197–216, 1959.

Iyer, H. M., Recent work on microseisms in the United Kingdom. *Indian Journ. Met. Geophys.*, 255–64, 1959.

King, C. A. M., *Beaches and coasts.* Arnold, London, 1959.

Longuet-Higgins, M. S., Mass transport in water waves. *Phil. Trans. Roy. Soc. A* **245**, 535–81, 1953.

McKenzie, P., Rip current systems. *Journ. Geol.* **66**, 103–113, 1958.

Munk, W. H., Surf beats. *Trans. Am. Geophys. Un.* **30**, 849–54, 1949.

Neumann, G., An ocean wave spectra and a new method of forecasting wind-generated sea. B.E.B. *Tech. Memo,* 43, 1953.

Phillips, O. M., On the generation of waves by turbulent wind. *Journ. Fluid Mechs.* **2**, 417–45, 1957.

Pierson, W. J., Neumann, G., and James, R. W., Practical methods for observing and forecasting ocean waves by means of wave spectra and statistics. *Hydrog. Off. Pub.* **603**, H.O., U.S. Navy, 1955.

Robinson, A. H. W., The Pacific tsunami of May 22nd, 1960. *Geog.* **46**, 18–24, 1961.

Russell, R. C. H., and Macmillan, D. H., *Waves and tides.* Hutchinson, 1952.

Russell, R. C. H., and Osorio, J. D. C., An experimental investigation of drift profiles in a closed channel. *Proc. 6th Conf. Coastal Eng.*, Miami, 1957, 171–93, 1958.

Shepard, F. P., *The Earth beneath the sea.* Baltimore, 1959.

Shepard, F. P., and Inman, D. L., Nearshore circulation related to bottom topography and wave refraction. *Trans. Am. Geophys. Un.* **31**, 196–212, 1950.

Tucker, M. J., Surf beats: sea waves of 1 to 5 minute period. *Proc. Roy. Soc. A,* **202**, 565–73, 1950.

Tucker, M. J., A ship-borne wave recorder. *Trans. Inst. Nav. Arch. Lond.* **98**, 236–50, 1956.

Wiegel, R. L., and Kimberley, H. L., Southern swell observed at Oceanside, California. *Trans. Am. Geophys. Un.* **31**, 717–22, 1950.

Williams, W. W., The determination of the gradient of enemy-held beaches. *Geog. Journ.* **109**, 76–93, 1947.

CHAPTER 7

SEDIMENT IN THE OCEAN

INTRODUCTION

THE oceans form a vast receptacle into which much of the waste products of subaerial erosion eventually find their way, via the rivers, glaciers and wind. A great number of the remains of oceanic organisms also accumulate in them, as well as material brought into the water more directly from the interior of the Earth via the volcanoes which stud much of the ocean floor, particularly in the Pacific Ocean. The sediments also include a minute amount of extra-terrestrial material in the form of meteoric dust.

The classification and character of these materials can give much valuable information concerning the nature of the ocean and the processes at work within it, as well as having at times a more direct bearing on such important topics as the modification of the world climate and all that depends on it. In fact, in the depths of the oceans have been found some of the most valuable data concerning climatic changes during the glacial period.

1. *CLASSIFICATION OF OCEANIC SEDIMENT*

The deposits in the oceans can be subdivided broadly into two main categories, the shallow-water sediments and the deep-water ones, although recent work on the character of the deeper sediments suggests that terrigenous sediments may find their way into the deep oceans at positions very far from land. The classification is not so much based on the position in which the sediments are found as on their origin and character.

Thus the major divisions are made between terrigenous material derived from the land, organic material, which may have been brought to the seas in solution from the land, part of it being converted into the skeletons of minute oceanic organisms, which accumulate when they die as sediment on the ocean floor, and the volcanic ash deposits. By far the greater area is covered by deep-sea, pelagic sediments, which are easier to classify than the much more variable sediments of the coastal zones. They may be broadly subdivided into inorganic and organic deposits as follows:

I. Inorganic deposits. These contain less than 30 per cent organic material, and are known as red clay.

II. Organic deposits. The common term for the material which contains more than 30 per cent organic matter is 'ooze'. These deposits are subdivided according to their major chemical basis, and secondly by the organisms which predominate in them.

IIa. Calcareous oozes. These contain more than 30 per cent calcium carbonate in the form of minute skeletons of different planktonic animals and plants; there are three main types.

i. Globigerina ooze is formed of the tests of pelagic foraminifera.

ii. Pteropod ooze contains shells of pelagic molluscs.

iii. Coccolith ooze contains many coccoliths, which are the protective structure of minute Coccolithophoridae.

IIb. Siliceous oozes. These contain a large amount of silica, derived from the siliceous skeletons of small planktonic creatures, plant and animal; they are divided into two types on this basis.

i. Diatom ooze, which contains remains of planktonic plants in the form of frustules.

ii. Radiolaria ooze, which contains the skeletons of these planktonic animals.

The inorganic deposits, which are the bulk of the shallow-water sediments, can best be classified according to their size and sedimentary character, in such divisions as sand, silty sand, silty mud, and clayey mud. Revelle has suggested that the terrigenous deposits of the shallower water should be classified by size as follows:

Sand—more than 80 per cent coarser than 62 microns diameter;
   very coarse sand 2,000–1,000 microns;
   coarse sand 1,000–500 microns;
   medium sand 500–250 microns;
   fine sand 250–125 microns;
   very fine sand 125–62 microns.
Silty sand—between 50 and 80 per cent coarser than 62 microns.
Sandy silt—more than 50 per cent coarser than 5 microns and
   more than 20 per cent coarser than 62 microns.
Silty mud—more than 50 per cent coarser than 5 microns and
   less than 20 per cent coarser than 62 microns.
Clayey mud—less than 50 per cent coarser than 5 microns.

Silt ranges between 62 and 4 microns (1,000 microns is 1 mm.), while clay particles have diameters less than 4 microns, coarse clay lies in the range from 4 to just below 2 microns, and medium clay 2 microns to just under 1 micron, while the finest clays go down to 0·12 microns. In order to avoid mineralological implications clay grade sediments are sometimes called 'lutites'.

At the other end of the scale the very coarse deposits may be defined as boulders above 256 mm., cobbles from 64 to 256 mm., pebbles from 4 to 64 mm. and granules from 2 to 4 mm. This is according to the Wentworth system of classification of size of particle. From the point of view of deposition in the sea, the settling velocity is important; the following figures refer to distilled water at 20°C.

Fine sand		1,040 m./day.
Very fine sand		301 m./day.
Silt	31·2 microns	75·2 m./day.
,,	15·6 microns	18·8 m./day.
,,	7·8 microns	4·7 m./day.
,,	3·9 microns	1·2 m./day.
Clay	1·95 microns	0·3 m./day.
,,	0·98 microns	0·074 m./day.
,,	0·49 microns	0·018 m./day.
,,	0·25 microns	0·004 m./day.
,,	0·12 microns	0·001 m./day.

The figures suggest that the finest particles can be carried very far from land, before they eventually come to rest on the sea floor, although even the coarser deposits may be carried into the abyssal plains by turbidity currents. The discovery of the extent to which such processes operate, even in the deep ocean, has made it more difficult to define the limits of terrigenous deposits. Other methods of distinguishing the shallower sediments is by their source, such as deltaic, estuarine, glacial, coral, volcanic or other processes, including both organic and inorganic processes.

2. THE CHARACTER OF THE OCEAN SEDIMENTS

The character, source of material and rate of deposition of the different deposits in their wide variety of environments will be mentioned next.

(a) Pelagic sediments

THE ORGANIC OOZES. *Calcareous ooze.* Globigerina ooze is one of the most common deep sea deposits and is formed by the accumulation of the calcareous skeletons of foraminifera, mainly the planktonic form, Globigerina, which consists of rounded calcareous tests. The average calcium carbonate content of five samples of this ooze from the Pacific was 82 per cent, varying from 75 to 89 per cent. Compared with many other deep-sea deposits this ooze is badly sorted, its sorting co-efficient being 6·4, while the median diameter of the samples was 6·4 microns, with quite a large proportion of the material in the sand size grade, over 100 microns, although this sample may not have been typical.

The lower limit for the definition of Globigerina ooze is 30 per cent foraminiferal tests, or according to some authorities 30 per cent lime, of which more than half must be foraminifera. Some of the calcium carbonate in the deposit may be due to chemical precipitation. In some areas the calcium carbonate may be as low as 30 per cent, in others over 90 per cent, with the mean about 65 per cent. The greater concentration of calcium carbonate in the deposit tends to occur in the shallower water, as a greater proportion of the calcium carbonate is dissolved in the water as the small tests sink to the deeper levels; this type of ooze is rarely found in the deepest water below 5,000 m. Often the deposit is nearly white in colour. The number of species of which the sediment is formed decreases from the tropics to the higher latitudes, while in the Atlantic the amount of lime in the deposit also decreases in the same direction, having a maximum in the tropics (Sverdrup, Johnson, and Fleming, 1946).

The other calcareous oozes contain remains of pteropods and other organisms. In the pteropod ooze the actual percentate of pteropods seldom exceeds 30 per cent, but they are much more conspicuous because of their greater size. Nevertheless the lime content of the ooze remains high, varying between 50 and 90 per cent, the average being 80 per cent. The depth at which this ooze is found is limited to between 1,500 and 3,000 m., with the lime content highest around 2,000 m. The coccolith ooze is too rare to require further mention; although coccoliths occur in most calcareous oozes, they rarely form the bulk of the deposit.

The source and variability of the percentage of calcium carbonate is an important aspect of this group of deposits. It is found that the percentage of lime in the bottom deposits reflects that in the surface water, according to Trask, who established this correlation. The amount of solid lime in the surface waters increases with salinity and temperature, which helps to account for the higher organic lime content in the tropical regions. Lime is built into the organisms in the zones where upwelling waters bring nutrients to the surface, where photosynthesis allows the organisms to convert the lime into parts of their skeletons. An extra thickness of bottom accumulation may occur in those areas where warm and cold currents meet, and cause the destruction of many individual creatures, whose remains sink down to the bottom. The calcium-carbonate content also depends on the dilution with terrigenous matter, which tends to increase towards the coast, while volcanic matter will have a similar effect.

Another very important aspect of the lime content is solution; this takes place as the tests sink to the bottom, and when they reach it, the latter being more important according to Kuenen (1950). It is probable that solution is more effective at depth, because of the lower temperature and salinity and possibly also the greater pressure. Solution cannot take place in stagnant conditions, as there is no means whereby the saturated lower layer can be moved, to allow more solution to take place. On the other hand, solution is likely to take place effectively in those areas where the water has come from high latitudes, and in which the carbon-dioxide content is higher.

The north-moving bottom water of the south Atlantic Ocean gradually loses its effectiveness to dissolve calcium carbonate, because its degree of saturation increases as it moves north; it is low in the southern part of the ocean. Most of the calcium carbonate in the sea comes from the dissolving of limestone on the Earth, which was itself originally deposited in the sea, although its original source must have been the igneous rocks, some of which contain a proportion of lime. There is, therefore, a cycle of calcium-carbonate formation, deposition and solution, which goes on in the ocean and also involves the ancient marine sediments, now in the form of limestone and chalk, which outcrop on the land surface and are also subject to solution, thus returning the calcium carbonate to the sea from whence it came.

Siliceous oozes. The siliceous oozes become more important in areas where the organic production of calcium carbonate falls off, and where solution of this material exceeds its production. One of the factors which favours the increase in number of diatoms, which form the basis of diatom ooze, is a reduction in salinity, for example off large rivers, where the salinity is lower.

Diatoms are siliceous algae which are planktonic in character, belonging to the phytoplankton. They make up a relatively large proportion of the total deposit in areas at higher latitudes, and in positions where the sinking currents can dissolve the calcium carbonate, and thus reduce the proportion of this mineral. These tiny plants grow near the surface, where the nutrients are concentrated, particularly in the higher latitudes. The area where the Antarctic Circumpolar Water rises to the surface to the south of the Antarctic convergence is a zone where much nutrient material is carried up from the depths to be converted into diatoms by photosynthesis, in the upper layers of the sea, through sunlight. The tiny organisms then sink to the depths to accumulate as diatom ooze.

This deposit differs from the calcareous ooze in being very much better sorted, its sorting co-efficient being 1·85 instead of 6·4; thus the greater bulk of the material falls into the silt grade in the size classification. There may still be quite a high calcium-carbonate content in the deposit at times, which varies between 2 and 40 per cent, while it may contain from 3 to 25 per cent mineral grains, which may have been transported by floating ice in the higher latitudes. The line separating the diatom and Globigerina ooze follows closely the zone of the Antarctic convergence, where the Antarctic Intermediate Water sinks down and flows to the north; the diatoms thrive to the south of this line and the foraminifera to the north in the Southern Hemisphere. Some of the smaller and thinner frustules in the diatom ooze appear to dissolve before they reach the bottom, as only the larger ones are conspicuous in the deposit.

The other type of siliceous deposits is found in low latitudes; again it is formed where the solution of lime on the bottom is particularly active. Silica is secreted by a group of protozoa called 'Radiolarians'· These are planktonic animals which have highly complex and ornate skeletons, and although they are greatly outnumbered by the foraminifera in the surface fauna, special conditions of sedimentation allow them to become predominant in the deep-sea deposit over fairly restricted areas. The term 'Radiolarian ooze' is used when the tests make up more than 20 per cent of the deposit, while they may exceptionally make up a maxim amount of 60 to 70 per cent. This type of ooze is the least limy, containing less than 20 per cent of calcium carbonate, the average amount being 4 per cent and sometimes only amounts to a trace. On the other hand, the inorganic material is often fairly conspicuous in this type of ooze; at a maximum the finer mineral particles, less than 50 microns, make up 67 per cent, while the average amount is nearly 40 per cent. In colour, therefore, this deposit often resembles the inorganic red clay.

Radiolarians have been found in large numbers in some fossil sediments, now outcropping on the land, for example the Devonian and Carboniferous rocks of Australia, where the deposits are up to 3,000 m. thick. It seems, however, that these deposits were shallow-water sediments, forming in a geosynclinal environment, close to the shore, and it is unlikely that they are true pelagic deposits, although it is not known clearly how they originated. Another form in which silica may be deposited in the sea is in the shallow water sponges, which grow on the bottom.

Siliceous oozes are more common in the Pacific Ocean, partly because the amount of calcium carbonate declines more rapidly with depth in the Pacific. The deep and bottom water of this ocean contains four times as much silicate as the Atlantic and more phosphate and nitrate (Revelle *et al.*, 1955).

There is clearly a complex relationship between the organic processes, whereby lime or silica is secreted to form the organic portion of the deep-sea deposits, and those that undo this work by dissolving the plant and animal remains as they sink to the floor and accumulate to form the oozes. The relative proportion of the deposit which is made of this organic calcium carbonate or silica also depends on how much it is diluted by inorganic mineral remains, while chemical precipitation of calcium carbonate adds a further factor.

The conditions may be summarized as follows: sediments rich in organic matter will tend to occur where (1) there is an abundant supply of organic matter, (2) a fairly rapid rate of accumulation of inorganic matter, particularly if it is fine grained, (3) little oxygen in contact with the sediment. This last factor reaches its most extreme form in seas or basins in which the water is stagnant in the lower levels, as in the Black Sea. On the other hand, deposits will be low in organic content if (1) there is a small supply of organic material, (2) if there is a relatively low rate of accumulation of non-decomposable material, (3) if there is an abundant supply of oxygen. The reason for (2) may at first sight seem a little misleading, as it might be supposed that if the deposition of inorganic material were relatively fast, it would dilute the organic portion of the sediment, but what, in fact, it does is to protect this from solution, specially when it is fine grained, so that water cannot readily penetrate through it. It also prevents the destruction of the organic matter by benthic (bottom-living) animals. Concerning the relationship of oxygen supply to organic content, it has been shown by Richards and Redfield (1954) that there is a clear-cut inverse relationship between the organic content of the sediments and the oxygen content in the overlying waters in the north-west of the Gulf of Mexico.

It is clear that lime is the most important single element of the organic deposits of the deep-sea environment. The average lime content of all the pelagic sediments has been calculated to be about 37 per cent, while it forms only 25 per cent of all terrigenous deposits. This lime is unevenly deposited in the major oceans; there is an average of 41 per cent lime content in the Atlantic sediments, while those of the Pacific have only 19 per cent. According to Revelle *et al.* (1955), present pelagic sediments are high in calcium carbonate.

INORGANIC DEPOSITS. *Red clay.* Large areas of the oceans, amounting to about half in the Pacific, are covered by the most important inorganic deposit of the deep-sea basins, which is called 'red clay'. This is deposited in areas where the organic remains are dissolved into solution before they reach the bottom. Red clay may be of extremely fine grade, 83 per cent being in the clay grade and only 17 per cent in the silt grade, while one sample had a median diameter of only 1·1 microns, and the upper quartile was as low as 3·5 microns; this sample was fairly well sorted, having a sorting co-efficient of 2·86. These values, however, refer to an extreme example of the deposit rather than to the average. Some red clays contain no calcium carbonate, others have up to 29 per cent, but the average is about 7 to 10 per cent; siliceous remains are also few, amounting to a maximum of 5 per cent, with a minimum of zero and an average of o·7 to 2·4 per cent. The average of 126 samples showed that the maximum proportion of particles under 50 microns was 100 per cent and the minimum 31 per cent, with an average of 86·5 per cent.

The red clay, which is brownish red or chocolate brown, is therefore, a very fine-grain deposit; its colour is due to the presence of ferric hydroxide or oxide, with a little manganese oxide. It has been found that the clay contains many clay minerals, as well as decomposed volcanic dust, which at one time was thought to constitute the greater part of the deposit. The extremely finely divided clay minerals resemble those found on land, and have probably reached their present position from the land as relics of subaerial weathering; their fine grade allows them to drift for long distances across the oceans. They may have been carried by the ocean currents for great distances, owing to their very low settling velocity.

Manganese nodules and other deposits are often associated with red clay, and it seems likely that nickel and cobalt are being concentrated in the deep-sea floor of the Pacific. These nodules are not entirely restricted to areas of red-clay deposits, being also found amongst some organic deposits, but they are most often found in red clay. Recent work with underwater cameras (Shipek, 1960) has revealed these nodules, forming on a deposit of red clay at a depth below 4,500 m. (14,750 ft.) in the eastern Pacific. Another interesting point that these photographs revealed was the presence of ripples at depths of 1,647 and 1,320 m. (5,400 and 4,330 ft.) in calcareous oozes, which suggests that bottom movement is not entirely negligible, even at these depths. It may well be caused by the action of long waves or tsunami waves, or ocean currents.

Red clay accumulates very slowly, so that it takes a long time for objects dropped on the sea bed to be buried; thus sometimes amongst the red clay are found remains of creatures, such as sharks' teeth, ear bones of whales, or even inorganic matter, such as pebbles dropped from floating ice-bergs, lumps of pumice and other debris. Some of these objects can be dated; for example, the sharks' teeth were Tertiary in date, which shows that red clay accumulates very slowly.

Because red clay forms the bulk of the sediment where the organic material has been dissolved, it is found often in the deeper parts of the oceans where the calcareous oozes do not penetrate. The mean depth for 126 samples of red clay was found to be 5,407 m., while the minimum depth was 4,060 m. and the maximum depth was 8,282 m.; these depths may be compared with the mean depth at which the other main deposits are found which are as follows: Globigerina 3,612 m., Pteropod, 2,072 m., Diatom 3,900 m. and Radiolarian 5,292 m. The siliceous oozes occur deeper than the calcareous ones, because silica is much less soluble than calcium carbonate, while red clay is hardly soluble at all.

RATE OF DEPOSITION. One very important point concerning the deep-sea deposits is their rate of deposition, which plays an important part in the analysis of cores, and is also of interest from the point of view of the age and structure of the oceans. It has been mentioned in chapter 2 that the total thickness of sediments on the sea floor, as revealed by seismic observations, is on the whole very small, often amounting to less than 1,000 m. About 200 m. is an average thickness in the red-clay-covered areas of the Pacific and 400 m. in the equatorial calcareous belt. It is interesting to relate this to what is known about the rate of deposition, to give some ideas of the date at which sedimentation first started. There are several difficulties in such an analysis; the earlier sediments may have been buried beneath later lava flows, changes in the environment at the surface or the circulation at depth may give rise to variation in plant and animal organisms, and to such factors as the degree of saturation with calcium carbonate and other variables, which help to make any estimate less reliable. Nevertheless it is worth considering some of the data available.

The possibility of dating some layers of the cores by radio-carbon methods gives rather more reliability to the estimates of the more recent sedimentation; for these reasonably accurate dates can be given. Some of the more recent results give very variable values for the rate of accumulation, which depends much on the type of environment in which the sediment was accumulated.

A large number of different methods have been adopted to arrive at some value for the sedimentation rate, such as the amount of matter in suspension in sea water. Other methods employ the layers of glacial strata which have been laid down in some areas, while the counting of foraminifera has been used to give the rate of production, related to a study of the deposition in the same area; this may give fairly accurate results. Probably the most valuable basis for the estimation of sedimentation rates is the use of radioactive methods, which have been applied by Piggot and Urry (1942) and subsequently by many other workers in different areas. Some assumption as to the uniform rate of deposition of ionium and radium during the period represented by the core must be made. From the depth of core available this method goes back to a date 70,000 years ago; cold-loving foraminifera in the deposit suggest glacial interstadials, during the last major ice advance.

The sedimentation rates estimated for different environments varied greatly, as was to be expected; 24 cm./1,000 years was recorded in a sample taken at the lower edge of the continental slope, near the end of the Labrador Current. On the edge of the Mid-Atlantic Ridge the rate was found to be 11 cm./1,000 years, while in the western basin in the Atlantic, in impure Globigerina ooze, the rate was 4 cm./1,000 years. The same ooze in the Caribbean Sea gave a rate of 0·6 cm./1,000 years, and an even slower rate was found in red clay 500 km. off the coast of California, which formed at the rate of 0·5 cm./1,000 years. Kuenen (1950) has gathered together some of the data on the rate of sedimentation, and points out that one of the causes of inaccuracy is the shortening of the core in the sampler, which implies that the rate of sedimentation is reduced unless allowance is made for this by increasing the results by 40 per cent. The values he gives for red clay, adjusted in this way, vary between 0·4 and 1·3 cm./1,000 years, and for Globigerina ooze 0·8 to 4 cm./1,000 years, while diatom ooze has only one sample at 0·7 cm./ 1,000 years. Terrigenous deposits are so variable that figures do not help much. It is interesting to compare these rates with those for sedimentation in geosynclines and basins; the maximum rate, for example, in the North Sea during the Triassic and Jurassic is worked out as 3·4 cm. /1,000 years.

Recent work undertaken in the Atlantic by Ericson *et al.* (1961) shows that during the last 11,000 years, or post-glacial time, 108 cores had a range of sedimentation rate from 5 cm. to 700 cm. in thickness during this period; this range of rates is from 0·5 cm. to 63·6 cm./1,000 years. It seems from their results that the average rate of sedimentation in glacial times was 1½ times as great as the post-glacial rate in the forty-six cores which penetrated sufficiently far. These forty-six cores showed a post-glacial rate of accumulation of 3·5 cm./1,000 years, while the glacial rate was 5·1 cm./1,000 years. The maximum rate of sedimentation found for the post-glacial period was 63·6 cm./1,000 years, located on the continental rise south-east of Cape Hatteras; an even higher rate of 274·4 cm./1,000 years was recorded in the bottom of a canyon north-west of Cape Verde, French West Africa. These very high rates of accumulation can probably be accounted for by the special circumstances in which they were found. They are not likely to be due entirely to pelagic deposition, which suggests that terrigenous deposits can find their way into the pelagic environment. That this is true was clearly shown by the observations of Ericson *et al.*

In connexion with the rate of deposition it is worth noting that seismic refraction methods have shown that the Pacific sediments reach a thickness between 170 m. and 1,000 m., with the average a little less than 500 m. Taking an average rate of deposition of 0·5 cm./1,000 years, 500 m. would accumulate in 100 million years. This goes back into the Cretaceous period. It is interesting to note that no sediments older than this have been found in the Pacific (Revelle *et al.*, 1955). The figures for the Atlantic suggest a sediment layer of between 500 and 1,000 m., but it seems likely that the average rate of deposition is faster in the Atlantic than it is in the Pacific. It is suggested that 1,000 m. could accumulate in the Atlantic during the time it would take 200 to 400 m. to accumulate in the Pacific.

There are various possible interpretations of the relatively thin layer of sediment, which at the present rate of accumulation would not go far back towards the beginning of geological time. The rate of sedimentation in the past may have been slower than now; this could possibly be explained by the more vigorous oceanic circulation, to which the cold sources of deep water in high latitudes now give rise, but which may well have been absent when there was no ice. Another possibility is that the oceans only developed in their present form during the Cretaceous, which would agree with some of the findings relating to the problem of continental drift, or alternatively, the earlier sediments may have become consolidated or covered by volcanic lava, with the result that they do not react as unconsolidated sediment when seismic waves are interpreted. It is quite possible that all these explanations apply to some part of the ocean, but that none is applicable over the whole area.

In considering the rate of sedimentation and the type of sediment deposited, a number of environmental factors must be taken into account. The most important of these are (1) the general relief pattern of the area under consideration, (2) the relation of the area to the sources of inorganic and terrestrial material, (3) the physical and chemical conditions, both at the bottom and in the water above the area. There are also many minor variables which may cause local differences.

It should also be pointed out that deposits in some situations are liable to subsequent movement or erosion. Ripple marks have been observed to a depth of 12,000 ft.; these and scour marks are found on the top of most sea mounts which have been photographed and in other exposed situations (Heezen, 1959).

ATLANTIC SEDIMENTARY TYPES. These factors may be considered in relation to the Atlantic, in which there are two distinct types; one is truly pelagic in character, but the other carries the terrigenous environment far into the deep ocean, and therefore, provides a link between the two major environments. Ericson *et al.* comment on these two types; the first, the true pelagic type, is called sediment of continuous accumulation, and consists of Globigerina ooze, more or less mixed with inorganic matter of very fine grade, which in places becomes true red clay. These deposits were built up by the continuous addition, particle by particle, of matter. The other type is deposited by turbidity currents, thus growing rapidly for a short time and then remaining nearly static till the arrival of the next turbidity current. This process is more effective in the Atlantic, due to the larger number of rivers, in relation to its area, draining into it, and the smaller area, 20 per cent as opposed to 30 per cent in the Pacific, more than 1,000 km. from land. Also the pattern of deep-sea trenches prevents this process being active in much of the Pacific apart from the area off north-west America (Revelle *et al.*, 1955).

The sediment deposited by turbidity currents differs markedly from that of the other type. It is very much coarser than normal deep-water sediment, and it includes well-sorted layers of silt, sand, or even gravel at times. An example is the core taken 170 km. south-east of the edge of the continental shelf in the floor of the Hudson Canyon at 38°23′N, 70°57′W, at a depth of 3,470 m. Above the gravel is a layer of lutite with foraminifera, while the gravel layer is nearly 300 cm. thick. This type of deposit often includes material which has obviously been derived from shallow water, such as mollusc shells of shallow-water species. Another characteristic of intermittent deposition is the interbedding of terrigenous material and true pelagic deposits; the latter accumulate between the turbidity currents, while the former can at times be recognized by its bedding, which may be graded.

This characteristic graded bedding is the result of the settling out of mixed material; as the turbidity current slows down the coarsest particles settle first, then the finer and finer layers are laid down, giving a gradual decrease in particle diameter upwards through the sediment. Experimental work by Kuenen (1953) has shown that artificial turbidity currents frequently settle in this way, and it has provided a clue to the correct interpretation of many of the deep-water sands, which show this feature. Similar structures may be seen in rocks, now exposed on land, which helps to define the conditions under which they were originally deposited, as well as providing good evidence of the way up the rock originally lay, which may well be valuable in areas affected by strong earth movements.

In sediments which show typical graded bedding the deposits may range from well-sorted sand below to pure fine-grained lutite above. In order to get the complete sequence very quiet conditions must prevail in the final stages, as the lutite settles out very slowly. The lower side of a graded bed shows an abrupt change in character, which suggests that the deposition started abruptly, cutting across an old surface of deposition. At times the sandy layers near the bottom show signs of small-scale current bedding, which suggests that deposition took place in fairly fast-moving water, in which case the sands at the bottom may not be well sorted. At times, as Kuenen (1953) points out, slump structures may be found in graded bedding; such features suggest that deposition took place on fairly steep slopes, on which the sediment was not stable, leading to subsequent movement. Proximity to the source of sediment may result in poor bedding and these two characteristics often go together. Where the deposits came to rest in deep basins or on gentle slopes the following characteristics are commonly found: (1) great regularity of bedding, (2) absence of true slump structures, (3) deep-water pelagic sediments occur between the graded beds, (4) the upper part of the graded bed consists of very fine sediment, (5) absence of current ripple marks (6) various directions of supply are sometimes indicated.

Ericson *et al.* (1961) have described the different deep-water environments in which pelagic and terrigenous deposits may be expected, respectively. The most likely areas in which the first type of sediment will be found are the nearly level tops of isolated rises, these situations are least likely to be disturbed by turbidity current activity. The sediments which are typical of turbidity currents are found in a number of different environments; graded layers have been found in submarine canyons, which supports the theory that these currents play a part in the formation of the canyons; they also occur on the gently sloping plains, which often form the deep-water deltaic-like sedimentary area at the mouth of the canyons. Another environment in which they have been found is in deep trenches; the steep sides of these do not allow a great thickness of sediment to accumulate without instability causing slumping, resulting in the stirring of the sediment, and subsequent settling in a graded state.

As a result of the localized deposition of terrigenous matter in this way, there is a great variety in the depth at which it is found and the rate at which it accumulates; several metres may be deposited during one period of deposition of short duration. The action of turbidity currents in levelling off the floors of the deep basins by spreading a uniform sheet of material over their floor is clearly important in accounting for this particular deep-water relief feature. In some basins, such as the Sigsbee Deep in the Gulf of Mexico, it can be shown that low-velocity turbidity flow, on a broad front, has spread a recognizable layer of graded bedding over an area of about 3,000 sq. miles. These are relatively fine sediments which agrees with a low velocity of flow in the turbid water; thin silts grade up into a thick layer of lutite.

These deposits may be contrasted with those laid down at the mouth of the Hudson Canyon, at a depth of 15,000 ft. (3,200 m.). The samples, described by Ericson *et al.* (1951) were taken from the submarine delta which has formed at the mouth of the Hudson Canyon. Sand was a common constituent of these cores, varying from thin films to layers up to 6 m. (19·6 ft.) thick; on the average 30 per cent of the cores were sand. This was well graded and bedded and was intercalated with normal deep-sea sediment, and its obvious source was on the continental shelf, while turbidity currents must have carried it to its present position.

In this way, therefore, deposits from shallow water near the land can be carried out to the deep-ocean basins, and great care must be taken when ocean-sediment cores are used for estimating the rate of deposition and the changes of climate, that none of this extraneous matter is included, or if it is present that it is allowed for, which can be done on account of the characteristic type of bedding and other features. The distribution of the cores showing sand and silt in the central Atlantic is shown in fig. 7–1.

(b) Nearshore sedimentation

Sedimentation in the nearshore environment is very complex, there are many variables involved and the relief is normally complex in this zone. Deposition in the immediate neighbourhood of the coast has been complicated by the fact that sea-level was about 300 ft. lower during the glacial period, with the result that much of the material deposited around the coast may originally have been left there by subaerial agencies. An example of this type is the Dogger Bank in the North Sea, which Stride (1959) has shown to be largely morainic in origin, from a study of seismic refraction and cores.

A large proportion of the sand in the North Sea and parts of the Irish Sea probably originated as glacial and fluvio-glacial deposits, which have been reworked by the tidal currents into the familiar sand banks of these areas. Shepard (1948) has drawn attention to the deposits characteristic of the continental shelves off glaciated regions, where coarse sediment may be found out to the edge of the shelf. Thus many areas in higher latitudes show the influence of glacial deposition in the character of the nearshore terrigenous sediments. In few areas does the material grade in size outwards from the shore towards the edge of the shelf; very often the finer material accumulates in hollows on the shelf, while at the edge the material may be coarser or rock may outcrop. However, off large rivers the sediment is usually finer and mud may be a common constituent of the sediment. Under suitable conditions deltaic sediments may be deposited to very great thicknesses, as the accumulation of sediment is accompanied by a sinking of the foundation to allow room for further sediment.

According to Kuenen, the shallow water or Neritic sediment environment covers only about 10 per cent of the water-covered area; these sediments are, however, very important stratigraphically, as most of the rocks now exposed on the Earth's surface were once shallow-water marine sediments. Most of the terrigenous material is deposited in this zone, where its final resting-place is determined by the action of marine

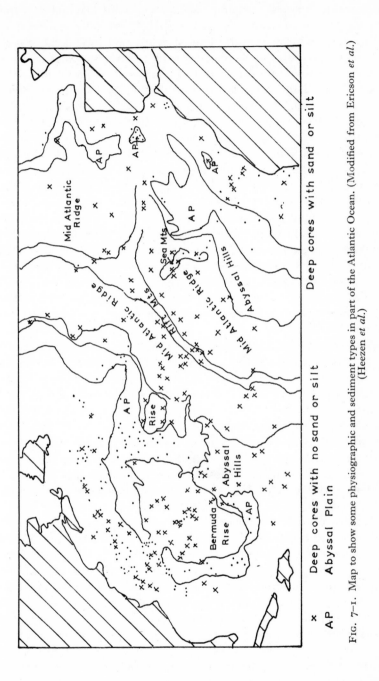

x   Deep cores with no sand or silt   Deep cores with sand or silt

AP   Abyssal Plain

FIG. 7–1. Map to show some physiographic and sediment types in part of the Atlantic Ocean. (Modified from Ericson *et al.*) (Heezen *et al.*)

processes, such as wave action in shallow water, tidal and other current activity. Waves themselves cannot, however, effect the movement of sand or gravel below a rather limited depth, probably of the order of 30 to 40 ft., according to observations made in various areas. Large-scale movement below these depths must be achieved by means other than wave action. Tidal currents are probably effective to much greater depths, as the sand waves on the edge of the continental shelf off south west England show; these were found at a depth of 540 ft. There is still too little known of the effect of long waves, seismic waves and internal waves to assess their part in the movement of material in the deeper water, while it has already been suggested that ocean currents are sometimes capable of moving material, such as the Gulf Stream in flowing over the Blake Plateau.

Another important aspect of the neritic zone is the deposition of organic sediment. Much of the limestone in its various forms, which now outcrops on the Earth's surface, was originally formed in fairly shallow water, where terrigenous material was not being deposited at the time. Some of the calcium carbonate which now forms calcareous rocks, such as the chalk, may have been deposited by chemical precipitation. It is interesting to note that although limestone is common in the stratigraphical record, there are very few areas in the modern shallow-water area where it is forming at the present time. One such area is in the Bay of Mont St. Michel, where deposits contained 75 per cent of calcium carbonate in depths of 10 to 30 m. In other areas the beach material consists of remains of foraminifera with a calcium-carbonate content of over 90 per cent, such as some of the beaches of Connemara, West Ireland. Fine calcareous oozes are now found in the shallow waters around some of the West Indian islands, but such environments are of very restricted area. This difference between the present and past distribution of calcareous deposits in shallow water could possibly be explained by the general lowering of sea temperatures at the present time.

It is also possible that the pelagic foraminfera secreting limy skeletons did not exist before the Cretaceous, so that the locking up of large amounts of calcium carbonate as Globigerina ooze on the deep-sea floor has only taken place since the Cretaceous period, which would lower the concentration of calcium carbonate in sea water. It has been calculated that in another 100 to 150 million years the pelagic foraminifera will have used up all the available lime, which will then be locked up on the floors of the deep oceans. This would require a considerable modification of oceanic life. The precipitation of lime at the present time in the shallow water around the Bahamas, in the form of aragonite mud, is taking place because too much carbon dioxide is being assimilated from the water by plant organisms. This leads to oversaturation of lime and the deposition of calcium carbonate. Where the water is saturated with lime, precipitation will be induced either by increase of temperature or decrease of pressure.

The detailed study made recently by Emery (1960) has revealed some of the relationships between marine sediments and their environment in the complex region adjacent to the coast of southern California. This area includes many different environments, most of them falling into the relatively shallow zone. The include: marshes, gravel beaches, sand beaches, mainland shelf, island shelves, bank tops, sills of basins, slopes, submarine canyons, basins and troughs, and the deep-sea floor. The first three types of sediment need not be discussed in detail, as they are marginal to the sea, occurring at such levels that they are exposed above water-level for most of the time. On the mainland shelves the deposits are variable, which can partly be accounted for by the fact that some of the sediment is residual, and therefore, not in sympathy with modern processes of sedimentation in the area. Most of the shelf area is, however, covered by modern sediments, amounting to 95 per cent off Santa Barbara. These deposits are mainly sand and silt,which decrease in grain size offshore; they contain little calcium carbonate, but some clay. The relict sediments were deposited when sea-level was much lower than it is now. Sands are much coarser than the present sediment on the shelf. Organic deposits consist mainly of shell fragments. In this area the shelf sediments form only a thin layer on an eroded shelf surface. There is thus a marked difference between this type of shelf and one of continuous deposition, as off Texas. The island shelves are broadly similar, although local differences are apparent, depending on the character of the island. Fig. 7–2 illustrates the character of the sediment in the different zones.

Many of the bank-top sediments contain a large proportion of calcium carbonate, which is coarser than the detrital sediment in the vicinity. Another common feature of the bank tops is glauconite which is often found in areas where detrital sediment is lacking, as it would be on a bank top. It rarely comprises more than 20 per cent of the deposit, but it is coarse grained. The sills of the basins show a very wide variety of sediment. On the slopes, although sediment has been shown to rest on slopes as steep as 70 deg., the layer of sediment is relatively thin and absent in places. In others, as one nearshore slope showed, a layer of sediment 6 m. thick of median diameter of 22 microns lay on a slope between 9 and 18 deg. steep. These sediments contain much water and can maintain high angles as a result of a certain rigidity, which if disturbed leads to loss of strength and subsequent slumping. There seems to be more rock exposed on the continental slope than on the basin slopes; where sediment was found it could be classified as Globigerina ooze, as it contained more than 30 per cent calcareous foraminifera. The sediments of the basins and troughs were found to be largely detrital and sedimentary calcium carbonate.

There is a general increase in the lime content in the offshore direction, which can be correlated with the grain-size pattern; this decreases

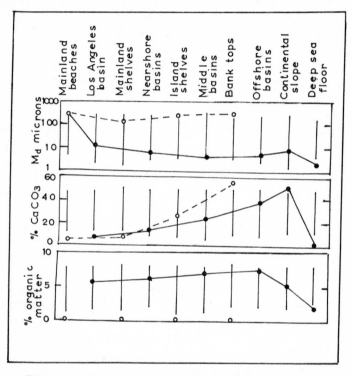

FIG. 7–2. Diagrams to illustrate the organic matter, calcium carbonate and normal detrital matter in different environments on the continental borderland off southern California. (Modified after Emery.)

from the inner to the middle basins, then increases on the continental slope, but decreases again on the deep-sea floor. The lime content, consisting of coarser particles than the detrital material, causes an increase in grain size offshore in the outermost basins and on the continental slope. The deep-sea deposits in the vicinity are red clay.

Various estimates for the rate of sedimentation have been put forward; thus Shepard and Revelle worked out a rate of 13 cm./1,000 years. More recent estimates have used radio-carbon dating, which can give more accurate result. There is a great variability throughout this intricate area, the values varying by a factor of 34; the greatest rate is

123 mg./sq. cm./year in the Santa Monica basin, the smallest 3·6 mg./sq. cm./year on the deep-sea floor. The greatest rate of deposition is found in the nearshore basins, which applies to both detrital and calcium-carbonate deposition, as shown in fig. 7–3. The rate for detrital-sediment accumulation is at a maximum in the basins now on the shore, such as the Los Angeles basin, and is also fast in the near-shore basins, falling

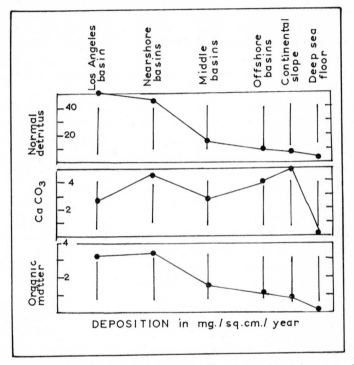

FIG. 7–3. Diagrams to illustrate the volume of sedimentation of organic matter calcium carbonate and normal detrital matter on the continental borderland off southern California. (Modified after Emery.)

off very markedly in the middle and offshore basins to very low values on the continental slope and deep-sea floor.

There is also a wide variation in the rate of deposition of calcium carbonate, which varies by a factor of 45 from 0·2 to 8·9 mg./sq. cm./ year. The deposition is very high in the near-shore basins, but reaches a peak on the continental slope, with higher values in the offshore than the middle basins, and practically none on the deep-sea floor. The relative proportions of the different materials deposited is worked out as follows: detrital 84·2 per cent, calcium carbonate 13·2 per cent, and organic matter (at depth) 2·6 per cent = 100 per cent. These figures show the very important part played by detrital or terrigenous sediments in an area not far from the continental coast, while in the open ocean in this vicinity the proportions are very different.

(c) The formation of petroleum in oceanic sediments

The ocean sediments are worthy of study from another point of view, in that they can give useful information concerning the processes of petroleum formation, a product which is becoming of increasing importance to modern civilization. There is still some doubt as to the origin of petroleum (Emery, 1960), but it is usually thought to be organic in origin. One of the problems of the origin of petroleum is that, once formed, it may migrate away from its source. The problem of the origin of this important substance is really a chemical one, although its environment of formation is relevant to a study of ocean sediments. Nearly all the petroleum is associated with marine fossils, and therefore it probably originates in a marine environment or at least forms from marine deposits. In order to account for the development of petroleum it is necessary to have an environment in which organic matter can be sealed off from oxidization and the action of scavengers, where in time it may be converted into petroleum, possibly by the effects of anaerobic bacteria. It is also necessary to provide a reservoir rock into which it can migrate and from which it can be extracted.

The conditions associated with turbidity currents can provide this environment (Ericson *et al.*, 1961). The turbidity current can sweep up a large amount of finely divided organic matter in its path, which may be deposited in a relatively restricted area and so become concentrated. It is sealed from the activity of mud-boring creatures at the base of the deposit, as these can only penetrate 10–20 cm., while the deposit of one turbidity current may exceed this thickness. The next turbidity current might provide a layer of sand above the deposit in which the organic matter is isolated, and thus form a reservoir for the developing petroleum to pass up into, and from which it can be extracted. The depths at which petroleum forms is greater than that to which corers can as yet extend, so that the process cannot be seen in operation, but the oil deposits of the Los Angeles basin, which were formed in Miocene and Pliocene marine deposits, illustrate the conditions in which oil can form, and which appear to be very similar to those in the basins offshore along the Californian borderland. The sediments, which are nearly 4,000 m. thick, consist of shale interbedded with sand brought by turbidity currents. The shales have 2·6 per cent organic matter and a median diameter of about 14 microns. The organic content was originally higher; it is estimated that it may have been about 6·1 per cent. Oil is often associated with anaerobic conditions found in such stagnant

conditions as exist in the Black Sea, in which black shales are accumulating (Dunham, 1961).

It is interesting to mention the tentative estimates of Emery concerning the total production of organic matter which has any chance of
becoming petroleum. He suggests that of the 100 per cent of organic
matter that is produced by phytoplankton in the Los Angeles basin
only 6·4 per cent reaches the bottom of the sea as sediment; at a depth
of 3 m. this is reduced to 4·2 per cent, while in the shales it is only 2·8
per cent. But the proportion which is likely to be exploited as petroleum
is only 0·005 of the original total of 100 per cent. This can be expressed
in a different way, by stating that one barrel of petroleum requires the
growth of the equivalent of 19,000 barrels of organic matter. If the
hydrocarbons only are considered, and oil consists largely of these, the
preservation is a little more efficient, as 1·3 per cent out of 100 per cent
is recoverable as petroleum. This source of power is a very inefficient
method, therefore, of using the original energy of the Sun; this allowed
the photosynthesis by which the organic matter was originally created,
which has in time been converted into the petroleum.

3. *DISTRIBUTION OF SEDIMENTARY TYPES*

It will be clear that the bulk of the ocean floor is covered by pelagic
sediment, although the distribution of shallow-water sand and silts or
even gravel, by turbidity currents, rather blurs the limits of the deep-
ocean sediments, in the Atlantic at least. Nevertheless it is possible to
delimit the major zones in which each type of deep-sea deposit pre-
dominates and some of these are very restricted in their distribution.
The general pattern of their distribution is shown in fig. 7–4.

Some of the most important facts concerning the distribution of
sediments are the following: (1) The pelagic sediments are found only
in the large ocean basins. (2) The most common types of sediments are
the red clay and Globigerina ooze; it is estimated that the former covers
38 per cent of the total area, while the calcareous oozes cover together
47·7 per cent, of which only a very small area is not Globigerina ooze.
(3) The diatom ooze is restricted to a narrow, almost continuous band
around Antarctica, and to a belt across the north Pacific. (4) The radiolarian ooze is found only in the Pacific, where it forms a wide band in the
equatorial regions. (5) Pteropod ooze is only found in the Atlantic Ocean,
in a north–south belt on the mid-Atlantic ridge around latitude 20°S.
(6) The terrigenous belt is very variable in width, although there is a
tendency for a greater width in higher latitudes, while in lower latitudes
calcareous deposits of benthic creatures are more important. In the
North Polar basin and around the coasts of the north Pacific and

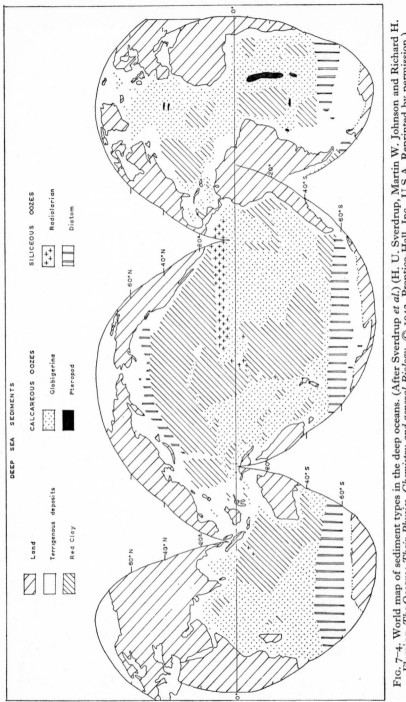

Fig. 7-4. World map of sediment types in the deep oceans. (After Sverdrup *et al.*) (H. U. Sverdrup, Martin W. Johnson and Richard H. Fleming, *The Oceans: Their Physics, Chemistry and general Biology.* © 1942. Prentice-Hall, Inc., U.S.A. Reprinted by permission.)

DEEP SEA SEDIMENTS

Land

CALCAREOUS OOZES

Globigerina

Pteropod

Terrigenous deposits

Red Clay

SILICEOUS OOZES

Radiolarian

Diatom

Atlantic terrigenous sediments dominate. (7) The distribution is determined to some extent by depth, with the deepest parts covered by red clay, and the moderate and deep areas by this material and Globigerina ooze. (8) Although there is some merging of sediment types in the marginal areas, on the whole the types are very distinct over wide areas, which facilitates and enhances the value of a study of the types and their distribution.

The distribution of the different types of deposits in the oceans can be summarized as follows, according to Sverdrup *et al.*:

Sediment	Indian Ocean	Atlantic	Pacific
		percentage	
Calcareous oozes	54·3	67·5	36·2
Siliceous oozes	20·4	6·7	14·7
Red clay	25·3	25·8	49·1
	100·0	100·0	100·0

This table and the facts about the distribution given above bring out several interesting points concerning the distribution of the different sediments. The calcareous deposits are most important in the Indian and Atlantic Oceans, which may be partly accounted for by the greater depth of the Pacific, where red clay is the most extensive deposit. On the other hand, it seems likely that the more vigorous oceanic circulation of the Atlantic Ocean, in which the only deep water is formed and in which the oxygen content is higher, is also important. This indicates more vigorous renewal of surface water by upwelling and hence a more rapid replenishment of nutrient supply on which the foraminifera depend. The importance of nutrient supply is seen by the pattern of distribution of some of the more restricted oozes. The diatom ooze, which is found only in areas where active upwelling takes place, illustrates this point clearly. It is found in the zone where the Antarctic Circumpolar Water is formed from upwelling water masses, as already mentioned. This explains why this ooze is found in a belt all round the Antarctic, except where terrigenous material dominates to the south-east of South America.

Another reason why the Pacific may be poorer in calcium carbonate than the Atlantic is the correlation which Trask has found between low salinity and low carbonate values. Observations have shown that the north Pacific, north of 10°N, is very deficient in calcium carbonate, considerably more so than the south Pacific, although the Atlantic contains much more than either as shown in fig. 7–5. One possible reason for the greater amount of calcium carbonate in the Atlantic might be that the rivers supply more of this material to the Atlantic than the Pacific. A further possible reason could be a net transport of calcium carbonate from the Pacific to the Atlantic, which is consistent with the higher calcium content in the subsurface waters of the Pacific.

The reason for the lower calcium-carbonate content of the north Pacific sediments is more difficult to explain. It must mean that there is a net transport of calcium carbonate south across the Equator, as most of the rivers enter the north Pacific. A possible factor is the greater solubility of calcium carbonate in the north Pacific, on account of the low oxygen content and, therefore, greater amount of carbon dioxide; thus calcium carbonate in the water and on the bottom may be more readily soluble. This problem is still far from being finally solved.

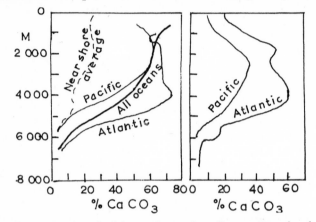

Fig. 7–5. The proportion of calcium carbonate in sediments at varying depths. The left-hand diagram shows the average calcium-carbonate content of the pelagic sediments, while the right-hand diagram shows the same for all types of sediment. (After Sverdrup *et al.*) (H. U. Sverdrup, Martin W. Johnson and Richard H. Fleming, *The Oceans: Their Physics, Chemistry and general Biology.* © 1942. Prentice-Hall, Inc. U.S.A. Reprinted by permission.)

The distribution of the most restricted oozes, the calcareous Pteropod and the siliceous Radiolarian, is mainly determined by the fact that these are warmth-loving species and only flourish in restricted areas. These two oozes cover respectively only 1 per cent and 2 per cent of the ocean floor. The present distribution of the oozes has not remained the same permanently, as changing conditions have modified the pattern somewhat. These changes in the pattern of distribution, and also in the species of organisms represented, and the rate of sedimentation have been used to elucidate the changing climatic conditions, and to provide a time scale for these, which has been made more accurate since radioactive techniques have been used.

4. *THE ANALYSIS OF DEEP SEA SEDIMENT CORES*

Although there are many complications in the analysis of deep-sea cores, they have provided very valuable evidence on the changing temperatures of the oceans, which can be correlated with the evidence available from other sources to give a more complete picture of the sequence of climatic change during the Pleistocene period. In favourable deep-sea locations positions can be found where there is an uninterrupted sequence of deposits; this is rarely possible on land, where deposition at one stage is liable to subsequent erosion.

The necessary preliminary to the development of this type of analysis was to obtain undisturbed a long core of sediment, preferably from an area of slow deposition, which means that the lowest layer of sediment will then be of considerable age. In fact, some of the cores obtained from the Pacific penetrate right through the Pleistocene sediments into the Tertiary ones beneath. It is necessary to avoid, where possible, the extensive areas where the strata have been disturbed by submarine slumping and turbidity currents. The original coring tubes, which were used to obtain long cores, were designed by Kullenberg (1947); the corer used a piston, which helps to enable long, undistorted cores, up to 20 m. long, to be recovered. Some of the problems of interpretation may be mentioned, before the results of such observations are considered.

A series of results obtained from the equatorial Atlantic were consistently interpreted as showing increasing deposition and quantity of calcium carbonate during periods of higher surface temperature, which were correlated with the inter-glacial periods. On the other hand, another series of observations, from the equatorial Pacific, gave equally consistent results, but they were the exact reverse. There the rate of calcium-carbonate deposition appears to increase during the colder periods, which was interpreted as due to the increased deep-water circulation during such periods, with the resultant more vigorous circulation in the equatorial zone and better supply of nutrients. These fed a more numerous foraminiferal population and so led to more rapid deposition of calcium carbonate, and in places even the alternation of red clay with Globigerina ooze. These two reverse results may both be correct, and give warning of the danger of making generalizations without taking all the relevant factors into account. The changing productivity of the oceans is only one of the means by which the changing climate can be assessed, but it is useful if it can be correlated with differing rate of sedimentation or different type of sediment, such as red clay alternating with calcareous ooze.

Another method of using the deep-sea cores to determine change of climate is to study the changing species of foraminifera, which can usually be related to the temperature at which they flourish best. The actual dating of the different layers of sediment provides the best means of relating the changing conditions of sedimentation to specific climatic variations, which on land give rise to glacial and inter-glacial periods.

Several techniques have been used to accomplish this; the ionium method was used by Urry, while Emiliani (1955) has used the relationship between o^{18} and o^{16}, related to the isotopic composition of the oxygen in the water. This method provides a means by which the temperature of the water may be determined, but it cannot provide any dating of the material.

The work of Hough (1953) on cores taken in the south Pacific has given a long record of Pleistocene climatic change. According to the ionium dates of Urry, his core, which was 194 cm. long, goes back 990,000 years, although the older part of the curve is extrapolated. The core, from 08°56′S, 92°05′W, consists of alternating red clay and Globigerina ooze; the latter is thought to have formed during the warm periods. The data from this core and another further south suggest that the last glacial period started about 64,000 years ago, which agrees fairly well with other estimates. The core shows six colder sub-stages during the last glaciation. The base of the core was thought to penetrate towards the beginning of the first of the four major glacial epochs, while the last inter-glacial was calculated to lie between 268,000 and 64,000 years ago, and a 70,000-year glacial period preceded it, which would be the Saale of north Europe and the Illinoian of America.

The work of Broecker *et al.* (1958) relates the changing climate to the rate of deep-sea sedimentation. Their work was done with a mid-equatorial Atlantic core, using carbon[14] dating techniques to date the layers and to measure the rate of sedimentation between them. The results showed that there was a major change in the rate of sediment accumulation about 11,000 years ago, the recent rate being considerably less than the earlier rate. The clay-deposition rate fell by a factor of 3·7, while the carbonate factor fell by 2·1; both are related to a change in temperature. There was a uniformly high rate of sedimentation between 25,000 and 11,000 years ago, while an intermediate rate of clay deposition took place before 25,000 years ago. These observations suggest that clay and probably carbonate deposition was highest during the greatest extent of glaciation.

The greater rate of clay deposition under cold conditions could be accounted for by various factors, such as the lowering of sea-level, which would mean that less material would be trapped on the continental shelf, and glacial action caused increased erosion and, therefore, greater availability of debris, specially in the finer grades. The increase in calcium carbonate could be due either to different oceanic circulation or increased supply via the rivers. The organisms are also affected by temperature changes, particularly the coccolithophores, which provide much of the very finely divided calcium carbonate.

The date of 11,000 years ago, at which the deep sea core data suggest a strong change of climate, agrees well with estimates made by other methods. In fact, radio-carbon dates nearly all agree that the mild Allerød period started about 11,000 years ago; this date marks the beginning of the post-glacial climatic improvement, although it was followed by a short deterioration. Working back from these dates and using the rate of sedimentation of 5·25 cm./1,000 years, the whole of the last glacial period runs to 64,400 years ago. If the intermediate rate of deposition is taken, then the result would be 80,700 years ago. A mean value of 70,000 years agrees well with the generally accepted length of the last glacial period. The rates of sedimentation suggested by this study are as follows:

	Post-glacial	*Glacial gm./sq. cm./1,000 years*
Clay	0·22	0·82
Total carbonate	1·34	2·80
Foraminifera	0·40	0·57
Coccolith	0·94	2·23

More recent work by Broecker *et al.* (1960) has shown that a large part of the Atlantic has probably warmed up by 6 to 10°C over a period of less than 2,000 years, with its mid-point within 300 years of 11,000 years ago. Further evidence of the effect of this change is the stagnation of the Cariaco Trench off Venezuela, where the upper 5 to 10 m. of sediments contain hydrogen sulphide, which rests on oxidized clay there is organic material below this anaerobic layer. The cause of the stagnation is the warming of the water; water cold and dense enough to allow it to sink to replace the cold water at the bottom of the trench was no longer available.

The advantage of the method of oxygen isotope analysis of Emiliani (1955) is that it obviates the danger inherent in some of the other methods; for example, the carbonate content of the deposit and the proportion of species of foraminifera are both liable to subsequent modification as a result of bottom solution, which does not affect the isotope method. The cores used came from the Pacific, the Atlantic and the Caribbean Sea, the latter giving the best results, as the cores were longest. The temperature differences suggested by the analyses was about 6°C. The dates of various levels in the cores have been determined by radioactive methods.

The longest core studied showed six complete temperature cycles with the oldest minimum 880 cm. from the top; if the cycles are of approximately the same age length, which may be justified from their similar thickness, then this level of the core represents 260,000 years. These results also suggest that the rate of sedimentation is falling off owing to a reduction in the number of foraminifera. The results from the Pacific agreed with the earlier conclusion of Arrhenius (1952) that high-carbonate phases correlated with low-temperature periods. It is suggested that the Plio-Pleistocene boundary may lie at a depth of 610 cm., which is immediately followed by a phase of high-carbonate activity and preceded by a period of high temperature. There are about fifteen complete carbonate cycles above this level. It is suggested that this represents a total of 600,000 years, which would cover the whole Pleistocene. This does not, however, appear to allow sufficient time for all the developments which must be fitted into this period (Gage, 1961).

The cores taken in the Atlantic, which penetrate into the Tertiary, do not show signs of cyclic temperature changes. A study of the benthic foraminifera suggest that the bottom temperatures in the Pacific were about the same as today in the glacial periods, while those in the eastern equatorial and northern Atlantic were about 2·1 °C cooler. Inter-glacial bottom temperatures were not more than 0·8°C higher than the present in the equatorial Pacific.

The correlation which Emiliani proposes with glacial events on land seems to fit very well as far back as the last major ice advance, which he suggests started about 75,000 years ago, but earlier than this the time scale seems to be very much too short, and the results do not agree with the more recent work of Ericson *et al.* (1961).

Ericson *et al.* use a number of different techniques to get all the available information from a series of cores taken in the Atlantic deep-sea sediments. The variations in foraminiferal species were studied as well as variations in the rate of sedimentation. Micropalaeontology is used to deduce changes in climate, while radio-carbon dates give precision to the results; beyond the time limit of this dating method correlations are made on the basis of a study of the coiling direction of planktonic foraminifera. Some of the cores penetrate below the Pleistocene deposits, and the oldest extends throughout the Tertiary into the Upper Cretaceous, according to the dates indicated by the foraminifera.

The cores used in the analysis cover a very wide area and range of environment; these include the mid-Atlantic ridge, its rift zone, the abyssal plain, submarine canyons as well as various submarine hills and rises and the continental slope. The slow continuous type of deposition is the most useful for this type of analysis. The observations made on the cores penetrating the oldest material have yielded very interesting results. For example, deposits which must have been dropped from floating ice have been found well to the south of the present position of the north Atlantic Drift at 46°55′N, 18°35′W. This indicates wide changes in the past circulation of the north Atlantic. In the older material, which was found in about one in ten cores, no material older than Cretaceous has been found, which also applies to samples taken from the Pacific. In some instances the older sediments are exposed near the surface owing to erosion of the overlying layers; this applies particularly to the steeper parts of the continental slope and other areas of high gradient.

The cores showing continuous pelagic sedimentation were analysed in various ways. These cores contain both oozes and red clay; the latter material accumulates so slowly that a core can cover the whole Pleistocene succession. They are not so useful in other respects, however, as there is no means whereby the changes in climate can be identified. The most useful cores for climatic analysis are those containing foraminifera and these are best preserved in the relatively shallow water, in which solution has not destroyed some of the evidence, as happens in the deeper areas. By correlating a large number of widely separated cores in the Atlantic and Caribbean, it has been possible to establish valid faunal zones, which have been given letters, and which can be related to the average thickness of the sedimentary layers and correlated with the glacial periods, using the appropriate time scale.

The results of the analysis show that the period since 250,000 years ago can be divided into six faunal zones. Radio-carbon dates go back to about 20,000 years ago, beyond which the dates can be extrapolated on the basis of the rate of sedimentation. The periods covered by the zones and the equivalent glacial epochs are shown in fig. 7–6. Zone (u), (w) and (y) are the colder-loving fauna, while zones (v), (x) and (z) are the warmer type of fauna.

In a few cases there is a correlation between the colour of the sediment and the climate, as deduced from the foraminifera faunal type; the warmer zones are brown, while the cooler ones are various shades of

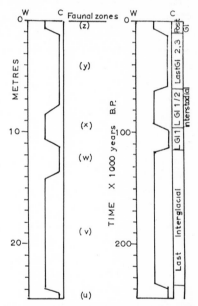

FIG. 7–6. Generalized climatic curve and average thickness of sediments in the deep Atlantic and Caribbean. W refers to warm types and C to cold types. (After Ericson *et al.*)

grey. The uppermost layers show a cyclic variation from dark grey to light grey in four sections, nine cycles being indicated in each; so far no explanation for this pattern has been found. The colour change, however, can be related possibly to the periods of desiccation and pluvial phases in Africa. The brown corresponds to the dry periods, as these sediments are most likely to obtain their terrigenous content from the rivers of northern Africa, owing to the pattern of ocean currents. The grey colour could be due to carbonaceous matter brought down by the rivers in the pluvial periods, which would correspond with the glacial periods farther north. The cores showing these colour variations were found in the eastern Atlantic near the Equator, on the eastern flank of of the mid-Atlantic Ridge; cores in the west Atlantic and Caribbean did not show this feature.

Zone (x) shows an assemblage of foraminifera very similar to the present, which suggests that at this time similar oceanographical conditions obtained. The main zones which were worked out by these methods have already been indicated in fig. 7–6 and their possible glacial correlations can be seen. Zone (x) is thought to have been deposited during an interstadial in the last glaciation, rather than in the last inter-glacial. The temperature fluctuation deduced for the period agrees on the whole with that given by Emiliani (1955), although his earlier dating is not reliable. The cores suggest that at no time during the past 50,000 or 60,000 years has the climate been as warm as it is now. This evidence from the Atlantic can be checked with that obtained by Arrhenius (1952) from the eastern Pacific. He found, partly on the basis of variation in sedimentation rate, that the last cool phase in the Pacific started about 70,000 years ago. This date is a reasonable estimate for the beginning of the last major glacial advance. Piggot and Urry (1942) give 60,000 years ago for this event, obtained by the ionium method from a core taken from the north Atlantic. A similar date is given by Fisk and McFarlan (1955) from a study of the radio-carbon dates of shells and wood in the Mississippi delta region. The river cut a deep trench at about this time, owing to the falling sea-level, resulting from advancing ice. The beginning of this fall is dated at 60,000 years ago, while the maximum fall reached by sea-level occurred at least 30,000 years ago. The deposits dated at this time were found in the trench cut by the river at a level of 80 ft. below sea-level near New Orleans; another wood sample of 28,000 years of age was found at a depth of 273 ft. below present sea-level near Donaldsville, Louisiana.

Thus a study of deep-sea sediments has led to a consistent dating of climatic changes, which can be related with a fair degree of certainty to glacial and inter-glacial episodes on the land, while the continuity of the oceanic records of such temperature changes is often much more complete than that of the terrestrial record, and several lines of investigation give confidence in the results of the analyses.

REFERENCES

Arrhenius, G., Sediment cores from the eastern Pacific. Swedish Deep Sea Exped. 1947–1948, *Report*, 5 fasc. 1, 1952.

Broecker, W. S., Turekian, K. K., and Heezen, B. C., The relation of deep sea sedimentation rates to variations in climate. *Am. Journ. Sci.* **256**, 503–17, 1958.

Broecker, W. S., Ewing, M., and Heezen, B. C., Evidence for an abrupt change in climate close to 11,000 years ago. *Am. Journ. Sci.* **258**, 429–48, 1960.

Byrne, J. V., and Emery, K. O., Sediments of the Gulf of California. *Bull. Geol. Soc. Am.* **71**, 983–1010, 1960.

Emery, K. O., *The sea off southern California*. Wiley, 1960.

Emiliani, C., Pleistocene temperatures. *Journ. Geol.* **63**, 538–78, 1955.

Ericson, D. B., Ewing, M., and Heezen, B. C., Deep sea sands and submarine canyons. *Bull. Geol. Soc. Am.* **62**, 961–6, 1951.

Ericson, D. B., Ewing, M., Heezen, B. C., and Wollin, G., Sediment deposition in the deep Atlantic. *Geol. Soc. Am. Sp. Pap.* **62**, 205–20, 1955.

Ericson, D. B., Ewing, M., Wollin, G., and Heezen, B. C., Atlantic deep-sea sediment cores. *Bull. Geol. Soc. Am.* **72**, 193–286, 1961.

Fisk, H. N., and McFarlan, E., Late Quaternary deltaic deposits of the Mississippi River. *Geol. Soc. Am. Sp. Pap.* **62**, 279–302, 1955.

Gage, M., New Zealand glaciation and the duration of the Pleistocene. *Journ. Glaciol.* **3**, 940–3, 1961.

Heezen, B. C., Dynamic processes of abyssal sedimentation: erosion, transportation and redeposition on the deep-sea floor. *Geophysical Journal* **2**, 142–63, 1959.

Heezen, B. C., Tharp, M., and Ewing, M., The floors of the oceans: I The north Atlantic. *Geol. Soc. Am. Spec. Pap.* **65**, 126 pp., 1959.

Hough, J. L., Pleistocene climatic record in a Pacific Ocean core sample. *Journ. Geol.* **61**, 252–62, 1953.

Kuenen, P. H., *Submarine geology*. Wiley, 1950.

Kuenen, P. H., Turbidity currents, graded and non-graded deposits. *Journ. Sed. Pet.* **22**, 83–96, 1952.

Kuenen, P. H., Significant features of graded bedding. *Bull. Am. Ass. Petrol. Geol.* **37**, 1044–66, 1953.

Kullenberg, B., The piston core sampler. *Svenska Hydrog. Biol. Komm. Skr.* **3**, band 1 46 pp., 1947.

Piggot, C. S., and Urry, W. D., Time relations in ocean sediments. *Bull. Geol. Soc. Am.* **53**, 1187–1210, 1942.

Revelle, R., Bramlette, M., Arrhenius, G., and Goldberg, E. D., Pelagic sediments of the Pacific. *Geol. Soc. Am. Sp. Pap.* **62**, 221–36, 1955.

Richards, F. A., and Redfield, A. C., A correlation between the oxygen content of sea water and the organic content of marine sediments. *Deep-Sea Res.* **1**, 279–81, 1954.

Shepard, F. P., *Submarine geology*, 1948.

Shipek, C. J., Photographic study of some deep sea environments in the east Pacific. *Bull. Geol. Soc. Am.* **71**, 1067–74, 1960.

Stride, A. H., On the origin of the Dogger Bank. *Geol. Mag.* **96**, 33–44, 1959.

Sverdrup, H. U., Johnson, M. W., and Fleming, R. H., *The oceans, their physics, chemistry and general biology*. Prentice-Hall, New York, 1946.

Trask, P. D., editor, Recent Marine sediments. *Am. Soc. Petrol. Geol.*, 736 pp., 1939.

Wiseman, J. D. H., and Ovey, C. D., Recent investigations on the deep-sea floor. *Proc. Geol. Ass.* **61**, 28–84, 1950.

Wiseman, J. D. H., Past temperatures of the upper equatorial Atlantic in A discussion on the floor of the Atlantic Ocean. Part I Sediments. *Proc. Roy. Soc. A.* **222**, 287–407, 1954.

CHAPTER 8

SOME ASPECTS OF LIFE IN THE OCEAN

INTRODUCTION

PLANTS are the essential basis of life both on the Earth and in the oceans. They alone can synthesize living matter from the chemical nutrients in sea water; this is achieved with the aid of light, derived from the Sun, by the process of photosynthesis. Animals can then live on the plants, and can multiply and people the ocean with their infinite variety of forms, each adapted to deal with the special conditions of its environment; whether it be the deepest waters of the ocean basins, or the inter-tidal zone, each environment poses its own problems to its inhabitants.

It is the Sun which provides the energy by which the nutrients are made into living matter, on which all the other marine organisms depend, more or less directly according to their feeding habits. Clearly, therefore, the most important zone from the point of view of marine plants is the layer into which the Sun's rays can penetrate, and this is very shallow in comparison with the total depth of the sea. Water absorbs lights much more rapidly than air, while at least 10 per cent is lost by reflection from the surface. The clearness of the water greatly affects the penetration of light, causing variation in the depth at which plants can grow; in the clearer seas, such as the Caribbean, it may be 110 m., while on continental shelves in temperate seas it may be reduced to 40 m. or less, and near the coast may fall as low as 15 m. or less, depending on the amount of matter in suspension in the water.

The depth to which only 1 per cent of the light penetrates is the lower limit at which planktonic plants can grow in the ocean. The seaweeds, growing on the bottom, can extend a little farther, to depths where the light intensity is less than 0·3 per cent of the surface value. In the clear waters of the Mediterranean this depth may be 160 m. Fish cannot see below 500 m., while it appears quite dark below 1,000 m., although even at this depth and below fish can live. Another essential feature for the production of marine plants is an available supply of nutrient materials in the water; thus light and nutrients are both essential to life.

1. *THE BASIS OF MARINE LIFE*

(a) Phytoplankton

The term 'plankton', which is derived from Greek, can best be translated as 'that which is made to wander or drift', according to Hardy

(1956). This means that the planktonic plants, or phytoplankton and the zooplankton, are carried passively by the currents, while the 'nekton', which means 'swimming' in Greek, are those organisms strong enough to swim where they please, although even the powerfully swimming fish must pass their earliest life phases in the plankton, as they are then in the form of eggs, or larvae too small to move against the currents.

The phytoplankton are the minute plants, drifting at the mercy of the surface currents, on which all the other marine creatures depend for their living, directly or indirectly. Because they have no means of self-propulsion, they must be able to maintain their position in the upper layers of the ocean, where they obtain the life-giving light, by floating. In order to float various methods are adopted; the phytoplankton use the principle that the smaller an object, the larger is its surface area in relation to its volume. The greater surface area will increase the friction against the water and help them to remain afloat. For this reason most of the phytoplankton is extremely small.

Their small size has another important advantage, as well as helping to keep them afloat; they absorb their necessary mineral nourishment through their surface, so that it is clearly an advantage to have this large, relative to their volume. The importance of this small size is made clear when it is recalled that the volume increases by the cube of the linear measurement, while the surface area does so only by the square.

Where conditions are favourable the production of phytoplankton is very great, but each unit is very small. Temperature, salinity and light are all important, but the supply of nutrients is also vital. Temperature affects their rate of growth and reproduction, which in general declines as the temperature falls, while a higher temperature, in reducing the viscosity and density of the water, makes it more difficult for the plankton to keep afloat in the upper layers where sunlight penetrates. Salinity has the inverse effect, a reduction leading to a decrease in the density of the water.

Nutrients are vital to the development of the phytoplankton; their reproduction rate, therefore, depends to a considerable extent on the availability of nutrients. This in its turn depends on a number of different factors. The nutrient elements in sea water are in weak concentration, but nevertheless they must be present to allow plant growth. According to Lee (1958) the main elements are as follows:

Element	*Parts per million by weight*
Phosphorous	0·001–0·10
Nitrogen (dissolved gas not included)	0·01 –0·7
Silicon	0·02 –4·0
Copper	0·001–0·01
Iron	0·002–0·02

In order to be of use to the phytoplankton these nutrients must be in the uppermost layers of water, where there is also light. For this reason the water will be most fertile in those zones where the nutrients are being continuously replenished from the supplies at depth, where they cannot be used directly. Once the surface supply has been used up by the plants, the sea will lose its fertility, unless the nutrients are replaced; in the same way as the soil becomes exhausted on land if fertilizer is not added.

It is possible to speak of marine deserts and areas of great fertility; the former are areas where the nutrients, once used, are not replaced, while the latter are those areas where processes of heating, cooling or wind action allow the renewal of water on the surface from below. The nutrients are replaced at depth by the slow sinking of the bodies of the dead organisms, which are broken down by bacterial action to provide the nutrients, particularly phosphates and nitrates, which are the essential plant foods. Thus any process which can stir up and turn over the water is important, as it can bring up the nutrient-rich water to replace the water at the surface, whose fertility has been exhausted.

Temperature affects the nutrient supply, because warming, in rendering the water less dense, will make the stratification more stable, while cooling, by producing denser water, may allow the surface water to sink and it will then be replaced by water from below. Changes in salinity may work in the same way; more saline water, being denser, will tend to sink, and therefore renew the fertility, while a decrease in salinity will work in the opposite direction.

Perhaps more important in this respect, in some areas at least, is the wind. The wind can stir up the water, by the formation of waves, which will cause nutrients from shallow depths to be brought nearer the surface; its effect by itself does not extend to great depths, but it can be important in very shallow seas, in which there is much material in suspension, so that light penetration is very limited. This applies particularly to seas such as the North Sea. Some of the most fertile areas of the sea are those where the wind blows offshore for most of the year. Such zones have already been mentioned in discussing the surface currents as regions of upwelling. On these coasts water is brought to the surface from moderate depths and is very rich in nutrients, nourishing a vast quantity of plant and other marine life. The process is self-generating, as the large amount of life sinking to greater depth can make more nutrients, which will again be brought to the surface by upwelling. This process goes on most effectively in those areas in mid-latitudes on the west sides of continents, such as California, the coasts of Chile and Peru, south-west and north-west Africa, parts of north-west Australia and the coast of Somaliland and southern Arabia.

Another process whereby water is brought to the surface from below has also been mentioned earlier; this is due to the action of the rotation of the Earth, which causes zones of divergence and convergence—for example, the equatorial divergence, as discussed in chapter 4. These zones of upwelling, where the process is continuous, are permanently fertile and produce a fairly steady crop of phytoplankton, the variations depending largely on variations of temperature, which control the growth rate. Another zone of fertility is associated with the formation of the Antarctic circumpolar water mass, which is formed by upwelling of large quantities of water in the region to the south of the Antarctic Convergence, as already discussed in chapter 3. In other areas, however, the phytoplankton activity shows a strong seasonal rhythm.

The waters of the North Sea and other temperate seas illustrate the pattern. The production of phytoplankton is very low during the winter months from October to February, and the numbers of plants in the water is low. There is, however, normally a very sudden upsurge of activity in March, known as the spring flowering, when the rate of reproduction reaches extremely high figures; but this phase of vigorous activity does not last for long. The rate of increase of the phytoplanktonic organisms is such that in a week they may increase one hundredfold, while in two weeks they may have multiplied ten hundredfold. By April, however, the peak passes and the numbers decline as rapidly as they increased, till in May they are down to the low winter level. There is a second upsurge, called the autumn flowering, which usually takes place during late August and the first part of September, although it does not reach such large proportions as the spring flowering. The cycle and some of the factors on which it depends is shown in fig. 8–1.

This cycle has a very important effect on the large fishing industry in the rich waters of the North Sea. In winter the waters of the shallow North Sea are well stirred up by winds and tidal currents and nutrients are well distributed throughout the water, but the weak light and dirty water prevent much planktonic activity, while the lower temperature also slows down production. In spring, however, the sea warms up slightly and the sun becomes more powerful and starts the process of reproduction as the light intensity increases. This progresses very rapidly in the nutrient-rich waters, until all the upper layer of nutrients have been used up. By this time in early summer the upper layers of water are getting warmer, and the water stratification is becoming stable, so that the deeper nutrients can no longer reach the surface. At the same time the zooplankton is grazing down the standing crop of phytoplankton. Towards the end of the summer the surface waters begin to cool, while the strong winds of the equinoctial period stir up the water and allow the nutrients to reach the surface once more. The lesser light intensity of this part of the year means that reproduction does not reach its high level of the spring. As winter proceeds the light decreases to a limit below which the activity is again reduced to a low level, and the nutrients accumulate, ready for the spring flowering of the following season, when the light intensity again increases.

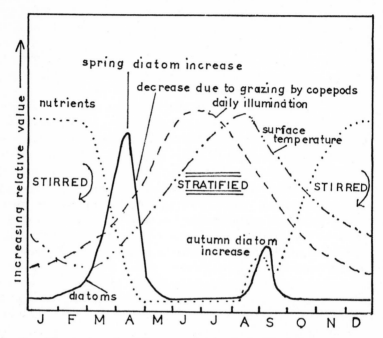

Fig. 8–1. The yearly cycle of diatom production in the North Sea and some of the factors to which it is related. (After Lee in Lake [ed. Steers].)

The effect of the heating of surface waters is even more marked in the tropics, as there it is a permanent state, and this has led to the belief that the tropical waters are relatively poor in phytoplankton, compared with those of higher latitudes, except in the zones of upwelling. However, it has been suggested that the greater depth of light penetration and the higher temperatures of the tropics may render production there almost as efficient as some areas in high latitudes (Graham, 1956).

One of the areas where the nutrients are particularly rich is the southern North Sea off the Thames Estuary, where the sewage of London reaches the sea. These very rich waters provide an extra 2,900 tons of phosphorous a year, which leads to a catch of fish in this region twenty-five times that in the Baltic and double that of the rest of the North Sea, amounting to 100,000 tons annually. This region may be contrasted with the oceanic desert of the Sargasso Sea, where, although there is plenty of light, the water remains stratified throughout the year and nutrients cannot be replaced.

Sometimes the phytoplankton is so dense in the water that it appears slimy, or takes on a colour related to that of the organisms within it. The Red Sea, for instance, gets its name from the colour of the water, when a particular species is exceptionally abundant. Many of these minute plants are diatoms, and these sometimes impart a brown-green colour to the water. Some of the smaller members of the phytoplankton are the coccolithophores, whose protective plates, called coccoliths, form a constituent of some deep-sea oozes. Others are called dinoflagellates, because they have tiny whip-like organs to help them keep afloat. These are even smaller; when magnified 1,500 times, they are still less than $\frac{1}{2}$ inch long. Sometimes the coccolithophores are so numerous that they give a milky appearance to the sea; such 'white water' is said to be an indication of the presence of herrings.

It is extremely difficult to get an accurate idea of the number of phytoplankton in the water, but an estimate by Johnstone, Scott, and Chadwick (1924) suggests that in an average April in the Irish Sea there are about 727,000 per cubic metre; this may be compared with the number of animals in the same volume, which was 4,500. This shows how very much smaller the phytoplankton are than the zooplankton.

The total amount of primary food produced by the phytoplankton might be expected to exceed that produced on land by plants; in fact estimates suggest that the total production of all the sea amounts to about $11 \cdot 5 \times 10^{10}$ tons of carbon annually, which is about the same as the estimate for the land. The larger area and greater depth at sea does not compensate for the more efficient processes on land. The phytoplankton, in using the radient energy of sunlight, does not do so very efficiently; it has been calculated that much less than 1 per cent of the Sun's energy is used for plant production in the sea. The carbon is produced by photosynthesis from the carbon dioxide obtained by solution from the air, from carbon salts in solution and from respiration, although the atmosphere forms the reservoir of carbon dioxide. The amount of production available in the form of edible fish is only a small proportion of the total production, as far as human food is concerned, because so much is lost by each stage in the food chain; the fish amount to only about 1/1000 to 1/10,000 of the food value of the marine plants.

(b) Zooplankton

The zooplankton depends for its livelihood on the phytoplankton, on which it feeds. These little creatures, although they are small and still float passively with the currents, are very varied in character. There are the tiny jellyfish, arrow worms, small crustacea or copepods;

Calanus, which belongs to the latter group, is important, as it forms the main food of the herring. Some members of the plankton are only temporary inhabitants of this environment, being the young and larval stages of various other creatures, which will eventually be able to live a more independent life, in their adult form.

Different planktonic animals can live under different conditions of temperature and salinity; they are, therefore, at times indicative of the water mass in which they can flourish under the most suitable conditions. The water masses of the western approaches to Britain can be differentiated by their planktonic fauna; arms of Atlantic water extend eastwards into the English Channel, and their extent at any time can be determined both by the colour of the water and by the characteristic arrow worm which lives in the planktonic community. The Channel water and that of the North Sea and the more coastal type is characterized by *Sagitta setosa*, this is the green water, while the water to the west and north, in the Atlantic, is deep blue and is the home of *Sagitta elegans*. The boundary between these two water masses is sometimes very sharp.

Other interesting water movements have been associated with planktonic fauna of a special type. Thus Mediterranean water, flowing out at the bottom of the Straits of Gibraltar, turns in part north and gradually approaches the surface, coming to the upper levels along the western continental shelf off west Britain. This water brings with it a planktonic fauna typical of far more southern latitudes. Thus a study of plankton can lead to a knowledge of water movement, which could not otherwise be proved readily. The northward extent of this southern water varies from year to year, but may stretch as far as the Shetland Islands, where it reaches the surface. The distribution of these water types is shown in fig. 8–2.

Some members of the zooplankton have developed a remarkable habit of vertical migration; they sink down to the lower layers during the day and climb to the surface again during the night, sometimes migrating through a depth of more than 100 m. This movement is illustrated in fig. 8–3. At first it was thought that this movement might be related to the different behaviour of various species with regard to the light; some always try to move away from sources of light. Other suggestions were that each species has a particular optimum light intensity, which it follows up and down, during the day and night. This factor does seem, in fact, to play a considerable part in this movement, as experiments have shown. These have indicated that *Calanus*, which is only the size of a grain of rice, can swim upwards at a rate of nearly 50 ft./hour, while larger creatures can achieve rates of 305 ft./hour, or more over shorter periods.

The reason for this vertical migration, in terms of the advantage of the animal, is more difficult to find. It gives an animal, which cannot move about by its own powers to a new environment, the possibility of changing its conditions by moving into different layers of water vertically.

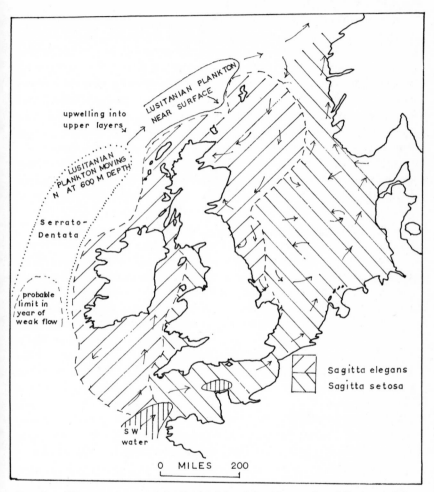

Fig. 8–2. Water types around the British Isles defined by species of *Sagitta* and the northward extension of Lusitanian plankton, to the west of Britain. (Modified from Hardy.)

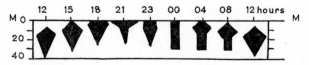

Fig. 8–3. Vertical migration of the planktonic Copepod *Calanus*. (After Russell.)

These animals can only move about a few hundred feet per day; this movement horizontally would not alter their environment, but vertically in this range they could reach a variety of conditions. Other factors probably also affect vertical migration and it is a complex problem, not yet fully understood.

The distribution of both phytoplankton and zooplankton is patchy, and they often seem to be mutually exclusive. This may be due to the grazing of the phytoplankton by the zooplankton, or perhaps some product of the process of plant production leads to antibiotic conditions, which excludes many of the animal species. Some species are, however, positively correlated with dense phytoplankton. It is on the abundance of the plankton that the very varied life of the sea is founded. The movements of some of the important fish, from the point of view of human food, can be related more or less directly to the distribution and type of the plankton. Some fish and other marine creatures feed directly on the plankton, and they are naturally more directly affected by it; the herring and whalebone whales are important examples.

2. THE LIFE ON THE OCEAN FLOOR—BENTHOS

The creatures that live in and on the bottom of the sea are called the Benthos; they are very varied and play an important part in the food chain, both as prey and predators. The character of the bottom, and the depth, play a large part in determining the type of animals found in each habitat. The variety of creatures is greatest on the continental shelves, in the zone where light can reach to the bottom and the benthos can feed on living phytoplankton, as well as zooplankton and other food. They seem to be more plentiful in regions where the plankton production is high; for example, in the Kattegat it has been estimated that in an area of 3,500 sq. miles 230,000 tons of first-class food and 380,000 tons of second-class food for bottom-living fish, such as plaice, is produced. Their importance in the food chain is, therefore, clear; this large amount of benthos has been estimated to produce 13,000 tons of plaice annually.

There are three main methods whereby the benthos feed; some filter the finest food particles from suspension, others live on the detritus which is deposited on the bottom, while yet others are carnivorous and compete with man and other predators for the bottom living fish. The greatest variety of forms are associated with a rocky bottom, but the largest area of the sea floor is covered with sediment, including mud, sand and gravel, each of which has its own typical fauna. Some animals live in, rather than on, the bottom. Most of the animals of the rocky floors live on particles suspended in the water, which they filter out;

these fine particles are mainly planktonic in character. A lot of these creatures, existing on such small food particles, are polyzoa, consisting of many small individuals living together in a colony as one unit, such as the corals or *flustra*.

Some of the bivalve molluscs are also suspension feeders; their gills are enlarged to enable them to sieve large amounts of sea water. The mussels, which live on rocks, and the oysters and scollops, living on gravelly or sandy bottoms, belong to this group. Other molluscs, such as the razor shell, *Ensis*, the cockle, *Cardium*, and clam, *Mya*, bury themselves in the bottom sediment, but feed through a siphon, which projects above the surface. They can then remain safely buried in the sand whilst feeding.

The deposit feeders make use of the detritus and remains which fall to the bottom. The worms are a branch of this type of feeder, some make a U-shaped burrow in the sand and pass the material through their bodies, extracting nourishment from it as it passes through. Some worms bury themselves in the bottom, while exploring the surface for food with their tentacles. Heart-urchins, *Echinocardium*, and brittle stars, *Amphiura filiformis*, bury themselves in the bottom and feel for their food, the former eating sand grains, covered with organic matter, while the latter use their flexible arms in search of food.

One of the common groups of benthic animals are the foraminifera. Unlike the planktonic foraminifera which secrete limy shells, such as *Globigerina*, some of the benthic types make themselves houses. Some of these houses are of great interest; they are built by these tiny animals, without sense organs such as eyes, and which appear to be no more than masses of primitive protoplasm. For example, *Psammosphaera rustica* builds a polyhedral or nearly spherical chamber, using for the construction minute sponge spicules, the longest being only 2 to 3 mm. in length. These are built into a framework, then the spaces are filled with carefully fitted fragments of sponge spicule of just the correct length, the longer 'tent poles' project from the structure and help to prevent it sinking into the ooze on the sea floor. That such primitive animals, without sense organs, can select their building material and fashion it into a structure which has rightly been termed a marvel of constructional skill shows that there are still mysteries to be solved concerning the nature of simple organisms (Hardy, 1956).

The benthos are an important means whereby the finely divided food on the ocean floor is made available for the larger creatures, who are not adapted to filter the finest particles of nourishment for themselves. The benthos also prey on some of the bottom-living fish. There is, therefore, an intimate relationship between the different types of marine creatures. One great advance in the study of benthic fauna and their ecology was the work of Petersen, who developed a grab in which he obtained samples of the sea bed and the creatures living in it. He could divide the bottom into zones according to its characteristic faunal assemblage, the type of bottom and availability of food being important factors. The results also give useful information concerning the availability of food for bottom-living fish.

A survey of the Dogger Bank has shown how patchy is the distribution of different species. For example the bivalve, *Spisula subtruncata*, which is important plaice food, was surveyed in detail. Very young specimens were found in one area, where their density increased to over 8,000/sq. m. in one small patch. The one-year-old specimens were concentrated some distance away, where the maximum density, again in a small patch, exceeded 1,000/sq. m., while at two years old the area was even more restricted. This indicates the large mortality this species suffers; fish were not the only predators, some being eaten by a carnivorous gastropod.

The bottom-living invertebrates also pass through a larval planktonic form, when they drift about with the currents. Some, however, have the ability to postpone their metamorphosis into the adult form, for days or even weeks, till they reach a favourable type of bottom. Some larvae are probably lost when the currents are abnormal and they do not reach a suitable ground before they change form, and some may be carried beyond the continental shelf to water too deep for their survival on the bottom. There are two opposing tendencies at work during the planktonic larval phase: firstly, the need to mature quickly to propagate the species, and secondly, the need to remain afloat long enough to spread the species widely.

The third category of benthic animals is important; these are the carnivorous types, which compete with man and other predators for the demersal or bottom-living fish, and whose importance in this respect has only fairly recently been shown. Some of the bristle worms or *polychaetes* are voracious carnivores. One of these is known as the sea mouse, *Aphrodite*; it burrows into the substratum and feeds on the worms. Some molluscs eat others, which in turn form the food of the plaice. The beautiful sea slugs or *nudibranchs* browse on sea anemonies, hydroids or even seaweed; they are usually coloured in such a way that they blend with their main food. Starfish are one of the most voracious carnivores, eating bivalve molluscs by opening their shells with their own muscular arms. In fact, they are perhaps the most serious rivals of the demersal fish in obtaining food from the bottom.

Recent work by Thorson has shown that plaice take about 3 to 5 per cent of their weight in food each day in the warmer part of the year, but only 1/10 of this during the colder season. Considering many bottom fish, he reached the conclusion that they rarely took more than 5 to 6 per, cent of their body weight in food per day. Most invertebrates, however, take a much higher proportion; for example, a gastropod, *Conus mediterraneus*, took 25 to 50 per cent of its weight of worms, *Nereis*, at one meal, while newly settled starfish ate up to three times their own volume of clams in six days. In youth the invertebrate predators take up to 25 per cent of their own weight of food a day, while active adults take about 15 per cent a day; on the whole they take about four times the food taken by bottom-living fish each day.

An interesting assessment of the use of food suggests that 1,000,000 tons of food is available in the Kattegat, consisting of *lamellibranchs, gastropods, polychaets* and *crustacea;* this must feed 5,000 tons of fish and 75,000 tons of invertebrate predators. If they both consumed food at the same rate, the fish would have 6 to 7 per cent of the supply, but, since the invertebrates eat four times as much as the fish, this percentage falls to only 1 to 2 per cent. Even if the food supply were increased the quicker-developing invertebrates would take advantage of it long before the fish were able to. This shows what a serious menace to the fish stocks these invertebrate predators can be.

Thorson has solved another problem; the predators usually have a longer life than the prey—thus it would seem likely that when the new generation of prey arrives, the longer-lived predators would consume them before they had a chance to grow and reproduce. For example, the newly settled bivalves must escape the searching arms of the brittle stars during the period when they are small enough to be eaten easily by them. This is achieved by the brittle stars entering on a passive period, during which they reproduce but do not feed, for two months. By this time most of the bivalves have grown large enough to escape being eaten when the brittle stars begin to feed again. The same sort of relationship between predator and prey applies to other benthic species and seems to be the method of survival developed by natural selection for the survival of each species.

Another important element of the benthic fauna are the *crustacea,* which include the crabs, shrimps and lobsters. They live mainly on rocky or stony ground, where they can be caught in pots, particularly off the west coast of Britain. Only one of the many types of crab is eaten by man; the others include many interesting species, such as the hermit crab, which lives in empty shells of gastropods. Recent work has shown that benthic animals are not entirely confined to the shallower waters of the continental shelf. Even in the greatest depths at which photographs have been taken, there are signs of benthic creatures (Laughton, 1959a and b).

3. *DEMERSAL FISH*

The fish which live near the bottom of the sea are called demersal fish, and they can be divided into two broad types: there are the round fish, such as cod, haddock and hake, and the flat fish, whose adaptation to life on the bottom is further advanced, these include such fish as plaice, sole and halibut.

The fish which live right on the bottom are well adapted to this environment, having undergone structural modification, by which their bodies are flattened and both eyes have moved over to one side of their head. The plaice, *Pleuronectes platessa*, is a good example of this species, as it has been intensively studied and is also a valuable commercial species, particularly in the North Sea. It has been modified in such a way that it lies on the bottom with its right side uppermost; its colouring has developed so that it blends perfectly with its surroundings, while it has developed a habit of moving its fins in such a way that sand, stirred up as it settles, falls on the edge of its body to break the hard outline.

This bottom-living fish lays floating eggs. A large female plaice may lay up to half a million eggs at each spawning. The main area where the plaice spawn is in the Flemish Bight at the southern end of the North Sea, where the eggs are laid in mid-winter; it is in this zone that a tongue of rather more saline Atlantic water penetrates through into the North Sea from the English Channel. It has been estimated that 60,000,000 plaice come to this area to spawn each winter. Other smaller spawning-grounds are off Flamborough Head, off north-east Scotland, and in the Irish Sea and north-west Heligoland. The eggs, deposited in the Flemish Bight, drift towards the coast of north Holland, a movement which has been confirmed by the study of drift bottles as shown in fig. 8–4. The eggs drift north-east at about $1\frac{1}{2}$ to 3 miles a day, and this brings them, and the young fry as they hatch, as members of the plankton, on which they feed at first, to their nursery-ground.

At first, and until it is a month old, the little fish has the normal shape of any round fish, but between 4 and $6\frac{1}{2}$ weeks old it becomes changed into a tiny flat fish, which is only $\frac{3}{4}$ in. long at this stage. During this critical period the young fish are very dependent on the wind and currents. If the winds should be abnormal, thus preventing the normal north-easterly movement, or perhaps carrying the little fish too far, they will fail to reach their most favourable nursery-grounds. The amount of planktonic food available at this early stage is also an important factor. These factors lead to great variation in the success of different broods and to the stock in different years. Those that spawn earliest may not have so much planktonic food available as those spawned later, when the spring flowering is available for food.

The plaice stay in their nursery-grounds in the coastal waters off Holland and south Denmark for two years. Then as they grow they gradually move northwards into deeper water, increasing in size till at

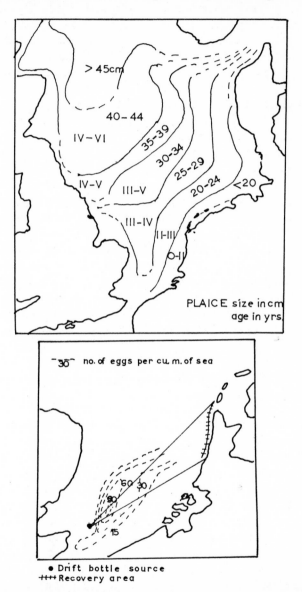

FIG. 8–4. The lower figure shows the area of spawning of plaice in the southern North Sea in relation to the drift of bottles released in the same region and their recovery zone on the Dutch coast. The upper figure shows the northward spread of plaice from their nursery grounds off the Dutch and Danish coasts. (After Wimpenny.)

O.–T

4 to 6 years old they are 40 to 44 cm. long. By this time they are found in the western North Sea off north England and south Scotland. Their movements are shown in fig. 8–4. At 1 year old the plaice are only 3 inches long. Their diet varies seasonally, both in quantity and type of food. In winter they live on polychaete worms and in summer on bivalve molluscs, although in winter only 10 per cent of the fish feed at all.

Some interesting experiments have been made with marked fish, which give details of the growth rate and the percentage of the fish caught; this latter number is in some cases very large, as up to 70 per cent of the marked fish were recaught in one year. This is the minimum number, as some of the marks may never have been recovered. The main movements of the plaice are concerned with travelling to and fro from the spawning-ground; this accounts for the large catches made in the Flemish Bight in January, while in July the main catching area is farther north, although still concentrated in the southern North Sea. Similar movements take place around the other spawning-grounds.

Other interesting experiments have shown the relation between growth rate and food supply. The main nursery-ground for young plaice is off Holland, where there are so many fish competing for food that the growth rate tends to be slow. Some marked fish have been taken to the Dogger Bank, which is not a normal plaice nursery, but where the food supply is very rich. The growth of these fish has been compared with similar-sized ones which were marked and left in the original nursery. The transported plaice had grown about 13 to 14 cm. during the year after their move, while the fish remaining behind had only grown about 4 cm. This seems to offer one practical method whereby the wealth of the sea may be increased for the benefit of commercial fishing and human food supply.

Plaice are one of the prolific breeds of fish and it has been estimated that the southern North Sea stock contains about 246 million mature plaice (Wimpenny, 1953). The whole of the North Sea fishing-grounds probably contain about 2,000 million plaice at or near catchable size, although the figures can only be approximately correct. Plaice are also not limited to the North Sea, but are fairly widely distributed around the north Atlantic, although the southern North Sea probably contains the major concentration of numbers. They live on a sandy bottom, extending to a depth of 40 or even 100 fathoms, in an area stretching from the western Mediterranean as far as the extreme north of Norway and into the Murman coast of north Finland. Plaice are also widely distributed around Iceland, where their main spawning-ground is situated on the west coast. These widely distributed plaice probably belong to different races, which can be differentiated by certain physical characteristics, such as the number of vertebrae, although these variations may be more closely related to their different environments than to separate races.

Other creatures also adapted to life on the bottom by flattening of the body include such fish as skates and rays. In these fish the flattening is in the opposite direction, and their bodies are more symmetrical as a result. Their eggs are laid in cases and when young they feed on small crustacea, but later their diet is mainly fish, mostly herrings, which they hunt by smell. They are found to the west of Britain, in the water of the North Atlantic Drift, which provides conditions suited to their requirements.

Of the round demersal fish, the cod, haddock and hake are of particular importance commercially. The cod may be taken as an example of this group of fish, because of its great commercial significance and its wide distribution. Cod are found around nearly all the coasts of the north Atlantic Ocean, penetrating right into the arctic waters to the north of Norway. Southwards they extend to Cape Hatteras on the west of the Atlantic and to the Bay of Biscay on the east. They are particularly concentrated in the Barents and White Seas in the north, on the Faroe Plateau, round Iceland, off western Norway, in the Baltic and North Seas, and around the western coasts of Britain. On the western side of the Atlantic cod are particularly prolific on the Grand Banks off Newfoundland and around the coasts of Greenland and the eastern coasts of America. Somewhat similar fish, also called cod, are found in the north Pacific, around Japan and off North America. They are cold-water fish, who require a temperature lower than $10°C$, and can live in temperatures of $0°C$, while a temperature between 1 and $5°C$ is probably the optimum value.

The cod inhabiting this wide range of coasts belong to many species. The cod move around a lot in these northern waters, as indicated by tagging experiments; the fish round Newfoundland move to Iceland, while the latter may link up with the stock around North Norway, but the North Sea cod seem to be a distinct stock. They are limited in their distribution by the fact that they live near the bottom, and therefore are restricted to the shallower water. Their depth limit seems to be about 200 fathoms, but they must be able to cross deeper water to account for the results of the tagging experiments, although they are rarely caught in depths exceeding 200 fathoms.

As with other fish, in their earliest phases of life, the cod are classed with the plankton, as they are incapable of independent movement. The eggs and larvae are drifted from the spawning-grounds by the currents to the nursery-ground. Thus the Barents Sea cod spawn near the Lofoten Islands in March and April; they then drift in the West Spitzbergen Current to their nursery feeding-grounds in the Spitzbergen

Shelf, while others move with the North Cape current to the south-eastern part of the Barents Sea. They are very dependent on these currents to carry them to the nursery-grounds at the right time, when the plankton is rich. If the currents differ from normal the brood may fail, which is not uncommon, owing to the variability of the currents.

The North Sea cod are an important group of these fish. The spawning period is from February to April on the banks in the North Sea, particularly on a small area off Flamborough Head, the Great Fisher Bank, the Forties, and Ling Bank, as shown in fig. 8–5. A large female cod may spawn up to 4 million eggs at one spawning, which float with the plankton. The small fry when hatched spend $2\frac{1}{2}$ months in the plankton, living on the small copepods, and drifting with the currents, which do not take them out of the North Sea. When they are $\frac{3}{4}$ in. long they leave the plankton and take to the bottom. They stay on the bottom

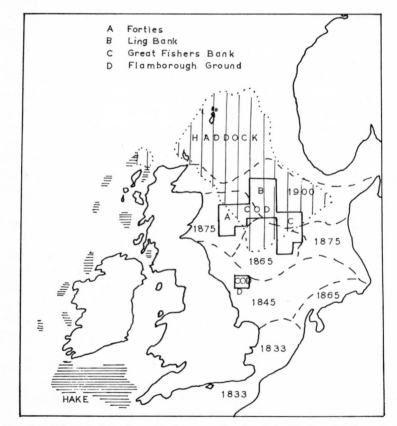

Fig. 8–5. Map to show the spawning grounds of cod, haddock and hake around Britain. The dates indicate the spread of trawling in the North Sea. (Modified from Hardy and Graham.)

in rough ground and are very difficult to catch, so that it is not easy to trace their subsequent development.

In $1\frac{1}{2}$ to 2 years the cod are 12 to 14 in. long, but they do not breed until they are about 5 years old when they are 27 in. long approximately. Their age can be ascertained by studying their scales, which show annual growth rings. Adult cod feed on other fish, particularly herrings, mackerel, small haddock and sand-eels. They differ in their food from their near relative the haddock, which enables the two species to live together on the same ground. The haddock live mainly on invertebrates, such as custracea, molluscs and brittle stars, and they also feed on herring spawn when this is available. Cod are caught over wide areas in the North Sea, the heaviest catches coming from off Denmark in winter, while in summer the greatest catches are made on the western side, off northern England; throughout the year the northern part of the sea is more prolific than the Flemish Bight at the southern end.

The haddock is another important fish in this group; it is very abundant in the northern North Sea, extending up into the Faroes, Iceland and Barents Sea areas, and is also prolific on the western side of the Atlantic, in the coastal waters from Cape Cod to Cabot Strait, and on the southern part of the Grand Banks off Newfoundland. Like the cod, the haddock spawns from February to April. It is smaller and matures earlier; when it is only 2 years old it is mature, but is only 10 in. long. Female haddock lay about 30,000 eggs at this stage, while a 6-year-old fish, about 16 in. long, will produce 280,000 eggs. The fish in the northern North Sea grow rather less fast than those in the south; at 5 years old the northern ones are about $12\frac{1}{2}$ in. long against $15\frac{1}{2}$ in. characteristic of those from the south; this is due to the extra warmth of the shallower sea bed in the southern part of the sea.

Haddock spawn mainly in the North Sea between Scotland and south Norway, and in small areas to the west of north-west Scotland, as shown in fig. 8–5. Hake, on the other hand, spawn along the edge of the western sea-board of Britain, between the coast and the 100-fathom line. These fish have a rather more southerly habitat than the cod and haddock. As the haddock get older they tend to spawn farther north, in the broad area already indicated. The exact location probably depends to some extent on the distance that the Atlantic water penetrates in any particular season.

Like the cod, they remain in the plankton for their early life, staying rather longer, till they are 2 in. long; during this time the circulation keeps them within the North Sea. The success of the brood depends very much on their survival in the plankton stage. There is a very great fluctuation in the success of the different broods; for example, very poor broods survived in 1922, 1937, and 1946. Work by Rae (1957) has suggested that the fate of the haddock brood can be correlated with the extension of Atlantic water down the west coast of the North Sea. This can itself be found by studying the distribution of particular plankton species which live in this water. The movement of the Atlantic water can in turn be related to the wind pattern over the area; the distance which this water penetrates off the east coast of Britain in late autumn depends on the strength and direction of the wind. This is an interesting example of the complex interrelationships of the different factors which play their part in the life of marine organisms, and in turn reflects on the success of the fishing industry, which is dependent for its success on so many variables.

4. *THE PELAGIC FISH*

In contrast to the demersal fish, who spend most of their life near the bottom of the sea, the pelagic fish swim, for part of the time at least, near the surface. One of the most numerous types, which is of great importance commercially, is the herring family, *Clupea*. The family also includes the sprat, pilchard, sardines and other near relatives. One important characteristic of this group of fish is their habit of swimming in shoals, which renders their capture much more easy and rewarding. The herring itself is the most important of the family; it is interesting, as it feeds entirely on zooplankton, being particularly fond of the copepod *Calanus*. Its movements and distribution are closely associated with its favourite food. Although members of the *Clupea* family are widely distributed around the world, the herring itself, *Clupea harengus*, is on the whole a northern fish; it extends from latitude 30°N to the Arctic. It is found on both sides of the Atlantic; on the west it is found in the St. Lawrence estuary and off the coasts of Labrador and Greenland; it is found around Iceland and in the open sea between Iceland and Norway, extending north of Novaya Zemlya and Spitzbergen. It lives all along the coast of Norway from the White Sea southwards and all around Britain and on the coast of Brittany as far as 47°N.

Some of the areas of most intensive fishing for herring are found in the North Sea and off the Norwegian coast, while a separate stock inhabits the Baltic. Another branch of the herring family, *Clupea pallasi*, belongs to the Pacific, being found on both Asiatic and American coasts. The herring around the North Sea can be differentiated by their characteristics into three stocks, the Baltic herrings, the Norwegian herrings, and the North Sea herrings, although there is some inter-mixing between the different areas. The different stocks of herrings move and decline from time to time. The Baltic herring were particularly prolific during the Middle Ages, when from the thirteenth to the fifteenth century they formed the basis of the richness of the Hanseatic League, who fished for the herring in the Baltic. It has been suggested by Pettersson that their presence in the Baltic during this period was due to particular tidal forces. There is a 1,800-year cycle which produces particularly strong tides in the Baltic at this interval, and it is suggested that the tidal conditions were responsible for the movement of the herring into the Baltic. Between 1416 and 1425 the herring disappeared from the Baltic and the decline and ruin of the Hanseatic League followed, while the North Sea fishery for herring by the Dutch increased in importance. It is likely that two different stocks of herring were involved, rather than that the Baltic herring moved to the North Sea. Another sudden change in the habitat of herring is indicated by the sudden disappearance of herring off Plymouth (Hodgson, 1957). This disappearance has been mentioned by Cushing, who shows how significant and prolonged can be the chain of events following a change of environmental conditions. He suggests that the decline of herring in the English Channel since 1930 is due to a change in the water in the Channel. The water characterized by *Sagitta elegans*, the Atlantic water, was replaced by *S. setosa* water. This caused a reduction in the number of small jellyfish, which preyed on the pilchard larvae. These latter, therefore, increased in numbers, leading to a decrease of phosphate in the water, and consequent decline in the herring numbers.

The herrings which occupy the Norwegian coastal waters are considerably larger than those in the southern North Sea; the former live to about 20 years and the latter only about 11 years. The age of a herring may be determined by counting the rings on its scales, these show annual growth rings, rather like those of a tree, as they grow quickly in summer when they feed well and slowly in winter when food is scarce. The herrings of the North Sea and those of the Norwegian coast can also be differentiated by the character of their scale rings.

The herrings of north-west Europe can be divided into groups according to their period of spawning. There are those that spawn in the spring; another group spawn in late summer and autumn, while a third group spawns in winter. The positions and periods of spawning are shown in fig. 8–6. The position of spawning influences the place of fishing; thus the fish congregate in large spawning-shoals off Shetland and north-east Scotland in summer, off Yorkshire in early autumn and East Anglia in October and November, while they used to be caught off Plymouth in December and January. This implies a very complex life history of the different groups of herrings. The North Sea herrings are divided into two groups, one of which spawns in the spring and the others in autumn and winter. The latter group itself seems to be composite according to Cushing; one part seems to move round the North Sea with the main current drift, feeding in the north and moving south to spawn near the Dogger Bank, then migrating back to the north-east as spent fish. The second group feeds in the summer off the east coast farther south, moving south in the autumn to make the most important herring fishery almost anywhere in the world off the East Anglian coast, and finally spawning at the eastern end of the English Channel in winter. They then drift northwards via the Dogger Bank to their feeding-grounds.

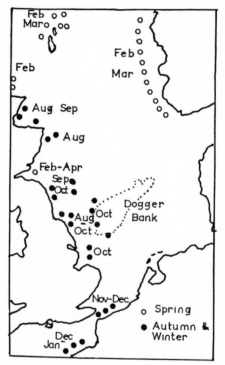

FIG. 8–6. Herring spawning grounds in the North Sea. (After Hodgson.)

The eggs of the spawning herrings are laid on the sea bed, the fish congregating in large shoals to spawn; these shoals may be 9 miles long and 2 to 3 wide. Each square mile probably contains about 500 million herrings, and each female herring lays about 10,000 eggs. This vast number of eggs attracts bottom-living predators, such as haddock and cod. They are mainly deposited on the western side of the North Sea in autumn and winter, with spring spawning taking place in the north around Shetland and off south-west Norway.

When the tiny herrings hatch they drift upwards to join the plankton for a time, feeding first on the minute phytoplankton and then changing to a diet almost exclusively of *Pseudocalanus*. If this particular species is in short supply there may be a heavy mortality among this particular brood of young herrings. At this stage they are very vulnerable to a large number of predators. As they grow they move up the estuaries, where they may be caught as whitebait. They live in this form for about 6 months and at this stage can eat almost the same diet as the adults. Thereafter they disperse for a number of years over the North Sea, only joining into shoals when they are sexually mature at 3 to 5 years old. Their nursery-ground for this intervening period seems to be situated to the east and south-east of the Dogger Bank.

A herring shoal usually contains a considerable variety of age groups. By studying these, interesting evidence has been deduced about the life of the fish. Lea found that in some particular year the fish spawned were extremely successful, and that a particular year-class could be followed for a considerable number of years, during which they made a significant proportion of the whole stock. Working with Norwegian herrings over the period from 1904 to 1921, the results showed that the fish spawned in 1904 survived as a successful group right through till 1922, when they would be 18 years old. This is illustrated in fig. 8-7. In 1910, when they were 6 years old, they formed about 80 per cent of the shoal; 1917 was another successful year. The early period of their life is shown by these observations to be vital to the success of the brood.

The herring itself feeds on the small organisms of the plankton, but it is itself the prey of other larger fishes and other creatures. Haddock eat its spawn, and its vulnerability at the planktonic stage has already been mentioned. The adult herring is preyed upon by killer-whales and other whales, porpoises, sea-gulls, and particularly cod. It is attacked by the cod when it goes down to the lower levels, which brings out an important aspect of the diurnal behaviour of the fish.

Although herrings are usually caught in the upper layers of water, they are known to spend part of each day on the bottom or in deeper water. Like the zooplankton, the herrings seem to follow the light; they are driven down by it during the day and rise up at night to the surface. The Norwegian herrings have been observed to descend to 75 fathoms during the day; they do not go to the bottom when the water is deeper than this. This is presumably the depth to which the light penetrates, from which they are moving. In the North Sea the situation is different, as the depth to which the light penetrates is below the bottom, the fish must, therefore, spread out on the bottom.

Another characteristic of the herring is its shoaling instinct, which normally keeps the fish in well-defined groups, a tendency which starts when the fish are small whitebait; it seems that each herring is trying to get into the safest place, which is the centre of a large shoal. This habit is of considerable importance when the methods of fishing for herring are considered. The shoals are compact and rounded, but they vary with the life cycle of the fish; when feeding they spread out somewhat, but while spawning they are very compact. Where the bottom is shallow they spread out on it during the day, rise up as dense shoal at dusk, in what is called the 'swim', and spread out on the surface during the night.

The other members of the herring family are widely distributed over the world, and include the sardines, pilchards, sprats, anchovies and others. These fish account for important fisheries in many areas, such as California, Japan, South America, Australia, and New Zealand, as well as western and southern Europe and South Africa. These fisheries are

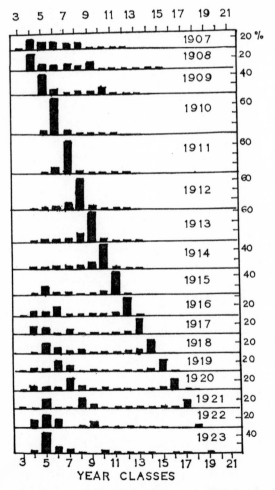

FIG. 8–7. Age groups of Norwegian herrings during the period 1907 to 1923. (After Graham.)

associated in many areas with the zones of coastal upwelling, which provide the fish with their necessary supply of plankton, in the nutrient rich waters.

The mackerel is next in importance as a commercial pelagic fish around Britain. Like the herring, it swims in shoals and lives on plankton, feeding mainly in spring and summer. The main mackerel shoals are found off south-west England, and are fished from Newlyn in Cornwall. Towards the end of October the fish leave the surface and sink in densely packed groups to hollows on the sea floor, till in December they spread out more widely over the bottom, feeding now on the benthos. Then towards the end of January or early February they move in shoals again towards the surface and slowly migrate towards their spawning-areas, which they reach about April. These areas are situated to the south of Ireland mainly, the fish spawning over the edge of the continental shelf; the spawning takes place between April and June, after which the fish disperse towards the coasts, feeding on plankton as they go.

The pelagic fish are also numerous in the tropical and subtropical waters; these fish include the tunny, bonitoes and sharks. The basking sharks are one of the largest of these fish, which exceptionally are found as far north as Norway. They may be 30 ft. long, but they feed entirely on plankton. They are only near the surface when feeding on plankton, which they filter through their gills. In winter they lose their gills and spend their time on the bottom till the new ones have formed in time for them to benefit from the spring flowering of plankton. The tunny are important members of the pelagic community and are found in both the Pacific and Atlantic, where they live to the west of Spain and Portugal and in the Mediterranean. They are large fish up to nearly 9 feet long and adapted for strong swimming; a tunny harpooned off Norway was later found near Tunis, which indicates the extent of their movements.

Although many of the pelagic fish travel considerable distances, the most interesting of the long distance movements recorded is that of the eels. It is well known that the common European eel lives much of its life in freshwater rivers, around the coast of Europe, arriving as a young elver, 2 to 3 inches long, and eventually going to sea again years later as a mature eel, ready to spawn, but never to return. The eels are about 5 to 7 years old when they leave the rivers to move 2,000 miles across the ocean to spawn in the Sargasso Sea area.

The eggs float in very deep water, and as the young gradually emerge as larvae they are swept along by the currents of the North Atlantic Drift, with the plankton of which they form part, until they eventually reach the coast from which their parents set out. It has not yet been found out how the mature eels navigate to the one small area in the

Sargasso Sea in which they were themselves born so many years before, nor is it known how the young elvers find their way back to the coastal waters and rivers. It has, however, been shown that the young elvers do, in fact, move out from their spawning-ground; isopleths, linking points where the average size of the elvers is the same, show that they increase gradually in size as they move away from their small spawning-area in the Sargasso Sea, in latitude 25 to 30°N and around 60°W.

5. *THE MARINE MAMMALS—WHALES AND WHALING*

The marine mammals belong to the order *Cetacea*; they are warm-blooded and feed their young on milk as do other mammals, yet the whales in particular spend their whole life in the sea and are perfectly adapted to this environment. Seals, on the other hand, still come to land to breed. Whales include the largest animals ever known; they are larger than land animals ever could be, as their great weight can be supported in the water. The largest whale measured reached about 100 ft. in length, while a whale 89 ft. long weighed 120 tons. The advantage a whale derives from its great size is its ability to swim faster; it can develop a greater muscular power, owing to its large volume, while its relatively smaller surface area creates less friction. It is the reverse of the argument used to account for the small size of the phytoplankton. Whales have been recorded as travelling at 20 knots for a short time.

Another reason why whales cannot be very small is that, being warm-blooded, they would lose too much heat if their volume were small. Since volume decreases more, relative to surface area, with diminishing size. The smallest marine mammal is a dolphin, which is still a few feet in length. There are a wide variety of different types of whales, each with its own feeding habits. A method of telling their age has been discovered by studying their ears, which has shown that whales can live at least up to 50 years of age. They can be broadly divided into whalebone whales and toothed whales.

The former have enormous mouths, in which there is an elaborate filtering device, as they are filter feeders. Water is taken in and forced through the filters by the tongue, which is then thought to scoop the trapped planktonic animals into the gullet. The large whales eat the larger animals of the zooplankton, particularly the shrimp-like krill, *Euphausiacea*. Thus the food chain of these largest creatures is remarkably short. The whalebone whales belong to two main families, the first of which is now rather rare due to overcatching in the past; these are the right whales and the rorquals.

The right whales were so called because they were the correct ones for catching, but too many have been caught, and the Atlantic right whale, *Balaena glacialis*, is now very rare, having first been hunted by the Basques in the tenth or eleventh centuries and also by the Norwegians. This was mentioned in a report made to King Alfred about a voyage to the White Sea in about 890. At one time it was thought that this whale and the more northern one the Greenland right whale, *B. mysticetus*, were extinct, but a few have been seen subsequently. The whales were caught for their baleen plates of whalebone, which were up to 9 ft. long; a single whale might produce $1\frac{1}{2}$ tons of whalebone at a price of £2,000 per ton, as well as about 30 tons of oil, so it is not surprising that they were fished nearly to extinction in the seventeenth and eighteenth centuries. The last northern whaling ship sailed in 1868.

The right whales had been hunted up to this time because they were more sluggish than the rorquals, which could not be hunted with the equipment available at the time; the development of the explosive harpoon in 1865, however, allowed these more powerful and often larger whales to be hunted, from the period when the northern fishing declined. The rorquals of the north suffered the same fate as the right whales before them, and hunting then moved to the recently discovered wealth of rorquals in the Antarctic seas, which were exploited from the beginning of the twentieth century.

The first southern whaling station was set up in South Georgia in 1904 (Brown, 1955). The whale catching in this area rapidly spread and became very extensive, there being eight whaling stations by 1911, while by 1953–4 there were 227 catchers, working from 17 stations, who together caught 34,869 whales, providing 2,285,720 barrels of oil. From the commercial point of view, the most important whales are now the rorquals and the humpback, and to a lesser degree the toothed or sperm whale.

The whalebone whales include the blue whale, *Balaenoptera musculus*, which is the largest, reaching 100 ft.; 1,987 of these were caught in 1955–6. The fin whale, *B. physalus*, is about 85 ft. long, and 31,496 of these were caught in the same season, amounting to 54·2 per cent of the total catch, as against only 3·4 per cent for the first species. Then the smaller sei whale, *B. borealis*, 50 ft. long, of which 2,076 or 3·5 per cent were caught, and finally the humpback, *Megaptera novae-angliae*, also 50 feet. long, of which 3,880 or 6·6 per cent were caught. The sperm whale is 60 ft. long, and 18,590 of these were caught, amounting to 31·9 per cent of the total whales caught. During the first part of this century the great toll on the whales was reaching such proportions that steps were taken to stop it; a tax was levied on the industry, some of which was used to collect scientific data on the whales, which led to the *Discovery* expeditions between 1925 and 1939.

The humpback whales live mainly in the Southern Hemisphere, and it is only there that they are caught. There seems to be five different stocks of these whales, which live more or less independently. In winter they travel to tropical coastal waters, where they are liable to be hunted, and return to the Antarctic for the southern summer. These whales are rather slower, smaller and fatter than the others, so they are more easily caught. They are taken in regulated numbers in winter in Australian and south-west Pacific waters, and also in summer farther south. The true rorquals are all world-wide in distribution and also travel towards the Equator in the winter, where they breed. In the southern population of whales there seems to be about one blue whale to every five fin whales, and it has been estimated that between 1933 and 1939 there were about 250,000 fin whales in the southern population. A limit on the number of these whales which can be caught was imposed by International Agreement in 1937 (Brown, 1955). This has reduced the limit to 15,000 units, where one blue whale is one unit and equals two fin whales and two and a half humpback whales. This means that the post-war catch is limited to about two-thirds of the pre-war amount, although as two fin whales equal one blue whale the total numbers may be the same. Blue whales are protected until late in the summer season, which is halting their decline. It is extremely difficult to get precise information concerning the state of the fin-whale stock, but many biologists consider that the stocks are still declining.

The four species of rorqual may move along the western coast of Britain to breed in the warmer seas, but there does not seem to be much evidence of the interchange between the northern and southern stocks, as the northern ones have never been recovered, despite the great activity in the south over a long period.

The blue whales feed entirely on krill, but the fin and humpback whale may also take some herring in their diet and other shoaling fish. The whales in the south follow very closely the areas in which the krill is abundant; the nutrient-rich waters to the south of the Antarctic convergence supports a very rich planktonic life, which helps to account for the large number of whales frequenting this zone. The sei whales have a finer seive than the others and often live on *Calanus*.

Blue whale calves are born about every two years, usually one at a time, but occasionally twins are born. They are about 23 ft. long at birth, which usually takes place in May. They remain with their mother till they are weaned about 6 months later, when they are about 52 ft. long and have reached the areas where the krill is plentiful. At a year old the calf is 62 ft. long and by the time it is two it becomes a mature adult of about 75 ft. length, although it may grow a further 25 ft.

The sperm whale, *Physeter catodon*, has a large blunt head with a narrow underslung mouth, in which there are many teeth. The sperm consists of liquid wax, which fills its broad head. It is thought to be a store of fatty emulsion, which can absorb the nitrogen released as the whale dives and surfaces rapidly to and from considerable depths. They must go to great depths, as they have been found entangled in submarine cables at a depth of 620 fathoms (3,720 ft.). They go considerably deeper than the rorquals. They do not suffer from overcatching to the extent of the rorquals, as their oil is less valuable. These sperm whales live in the warmer waters, and only the males, which are twice as big as the females, go to colder latitudes. They are polygamous and can be relatively easily controlled by limiting the size caught, which ensures that only males are taken. An important sperm-whale industry is developing in the north Pacific, and there is also a sperm-whale fishing industry in the Azores.

Large squids are the favourite food of the sperm whale, and occasionally very large ones are eaten, although the average size from the contents of 112 whales' stomachs was just over 3 ft., excluding their long arms, but one squid taken intact from the whale was altogether 34 ft. long (Clarke, 1955). This is, however, not their only food, which may include basking shark, and benthic animals, such as skate and crabs.

Interesting results have been obtained from the recovery of marked whales. Those recovered during 1957–8 season numbered sixty-eight, of which ten were marked 20 to 23 years before, all of these being fin whales. One blue whale had moved from 62°47′S, 60°E to 67°24′S, 127°25′W between 17 December 1955 and 22 February 1958; that is a total movement of 170 degrees of longitude, but it is not known whether the whale travelled eastwards or westwards. In contrast is the whale which was recovered 22 years later within 150 miles of the place where it was marked in 1936; this was a fin whale. The movement of humpback whales from the Antarctic area north of the Ross Sea, in 65°49′S, 170° 45′E, to east Australian waters has been confirmed by the recovery of a marked whale on 27 June 1958 at 28°38′S, 153°43′E, which was marked on 27 December 1957. These experiments are giving more precise information of the movement of the whales, and during the succeeding season, 1958–9, 102 marks were recovered. Some of these whales had been marked 24 years previously, and further evidence confirmed the movement of the humpback whales between the Antarctic and lower latitudes (Brown, 1958 and 1959).

The killer whales, *Orcinus orca*, are the most ferocious of the marine mammals; they prefer to feed on other warm-blooded animals, especially seals and porpoises. The males grow to 30 ft. in length, but the females to only 15 ft. Other members of the marine mammals are the seals, which still cling to a relic of their land life, in their breeding habits, as the young must be born on land. Seals are important in the ecology of the oceans, as their main diet consists of herring and other fish, in which they compete with man.

6. *SOME ASPECTS OF FISHING AND OVERFISHING*

Modern fishing methods, although they are much more advanced than those used by primitive peoples, can still be classed as hunting rather than husbandry. The seas are not farmed as is the land; the fish are caught in their natural state and man must compete with all the other predators. The method of fishing, which have been devised by different peoples for different situations throughout the ages, are very numerous, but they can be classified into a number of types. Firstly, fish may be snared; in other words, they catch themselves in a net or device into which they swim and cannot retreat and escape. Secondly they may be lured into capture by some bait, such as fly fishing, or the lobster-pot technique, and finally they may be hunted, with nets of various types, which are dragged through the water and collect the fish in their path.

The different methods are used to catch different fish according to their behaviour; successful fishing, therefore, depends on a sound knowledge of the behaviour of fish, and a successful skipper must be a good naturalist. A good example of the first method of catching fish is that used for many generations to catch the herring; this is the drift-net technique. The drifters, which go out after the herring, depend for their success on the shoaling habits of the fish and on their diurnal movements through the water. The drift-net method is only suited to the pelagic type of fish, which swim near the surface for part of the day.

The nets consist of a single line of netting, which hangs vertically down in the water and is supported by floats. A large number of nets may be joined to form a continuous wall of netting up to 2 or even 3 miles long; they are made of a series of nets, each 50 ft. in depth and 50 yards in length, each boat having about eighty nets. The netting has a diagonal mesh, into which the fish swim and are held by their gills. As the term implies, the drifters merely lie in the water, waiting for the fish to come to them. They go out in the evening, and return in the morning, fishing during the night, and hauling the nets in the early hours of the morning. This timing coincides with the upward movement or 'swim' of the herring shoals towards the surface during the night. Once caught the herrings are hauled on to the ship and shaken out of the net by extending the diagonal pattern of the meshes. The skill of fishing depends on shooting the nets in the area and at the depth where the fish are. A good catch of herrings can amount to between 50 and 100 crans. This measure is a volume of fish, which on the average includes about 1,000 herrings, varying from 900 to 1,300 according to their size.

The movements of the herrings are dependent on the wind and tide; it has been found that a strong onshore wind scatters the fish offshore, while a strong south-westerly wind, which is offshore on the east coast of England, concentrates them close to the shore and results in heavy catches. This is due to the development of an undercurrent in the opposite direction to the surface drift resulting from the wind. The East Anglian fishing is also influenced by the full moon, which is related to the period of spring tide. The full moon which is accompanied by the heaviest catches must take place in the middle of the season; that is during the second week of October, which caused two peaks of equal magnitude in the fishery (Hodgson 1957).

Fishing by this method has been going on for a very long time. There is evidence to suggest that the Yarmouth herring fishery started about A.D. 495, after the arrival of the Saxons. The herring fishing was important by Domesday, when the port of Dunwich, now lost beneath the sea by erosion, paid 60,000 herrings annually to the king. The richness of the Hanseatic League has already been mentioned in connexion with the Baltic herring fishery, until the fish deserted this area. After this, from the fifteenth to the eighteenth centuries, Holland was the leading herring-fishing nation, and became very wealthy on the proceeds of the fishery. It is said that Amsterdam is founded on herring-bones. The industry caused disputes between the Dutch and English, the latter demanding tribute for fishing in English waters; this led to the 1652–4 war, which started the naval supremacy of Britain and led to the decline of that of Holland. It was, however, not until the early nineteenth century that the British herring fishery became really important.

This development started first in Scotland. More than a thousand sailing herring drifters worked in Scottish waters all the summer and then moved south, with the herring, towards autumn to the Yorkshire coastal waters, and then finally the climax of the herring season took place off East Anglia, based on Yarmouth and Lowestoft, in October and November, the boats following the herring on their spawning migration to the southern North Sea, so that they were caught in good full conditions, just before spawning. The sailing drifters have now given place to steam drifters, and their numbers have declined rapidly during the twentieth century. The peak of the herring fishing was reached in 1913, when England and Scotland together produced 11,762,748 cwt. of herring, valued at £4,412,838, out of a total European catch of 22,018,130 cwt. Most of these herrings were exported salted. There was a very rapid decline in the fishing in the 1930s, when the markets disappeared. Of the 1,000 boats of 1913 which frequented the East Anglian fishing ports, only 106 remained in 1959, while the whole season's catch has been reduced to about 50,000 crans, the amount caught in one day in the past. The fishing there has recently shown a marked recovery, however.

For success in catching herrings one must be able to locate the shoals; various methods can be used, such as sampling the water to ascertain whether it contains *Calanus* in the plankton. A more recent technique is the use of echo-sounders. This instrument, which is normally used to obtain the depth of water, by the reflection of a sound wave from the bottom, also reflects from a tightly packed shoal of fish, giving information of their position and depth. It gives the skipper the ability to see the shoals and indicates where successful shoots of the nets may be made. All the modern drifters, which are now usually diesel driven, are fitted with echo-sounding devices. They have their limitations, however; they can show where the fish are if an echo is received, but there may be many fish present which they do not detect. In any case the fish can only be caught by the drift nets when they rise to the surface in the swim at night. The fish can only be registered by the echo when they are off the bottom, on their way up.

One of the problems of catching herring is their continual movement to and from the spawning-grounds and in search of food. At times they move to avoid water which is distasteful to them on account of some noxious plankton. There is evidence to suggest that shoals of herring can move up to 10 miles in 24 hours, when they are not spawning. Such movements make it difficult to track them, and the secret of successful drifting is to know enough about the behaviour of the fish to anticipate where they will rise for the swim.

The method of fishing with a line depends on attracting the fish to bait, fixed to a hook on the line. As a method of catching fish it was used before the much more efficient trawling became widespread, as it could be done from small boats with few men. The fish caught by this method are the demersal fish. In the fifteenth century boats were already going as far afield as Iceland to fish for cod with lines, while in the eighteenth century line fishing for cod was going on around the Dogger Bank, and it still is carried on off western Scotland, where the larger cod and halibut are caught by line, in areas where the bottom is too rough for trawling. Cod are also caught by line from Portuguese boats and many others on the rich Newfoundland Banks.

Some of the line-fishing boats from Aberdeen use lines up to 15 miles long, with a hook every 3 fathoms (18 ft.); the bait used is usually herring, which may have to be caught before fishing can start. The tunny are fished by American boats, using lines and live bait, in the Pacific; they may travel great distances across the ocean in search of the large and active fish.

Much of modern fishing is done with nets, in which the fish are pursued and trapped. There are two major types of net, the seine net and the trawl. The former is of very ancient origin, having been used in prehistoric times. The principle of the seine net is to surround the fish by netting, in which they are enclosed. This method of fishing is being increasingly used now by Dutch and Danish fishermen in the central North Sea.

The modern seiner starts operations by putting down a marker buoy and steaming about 100 yards, letting out a cable, then an abrupt turn is made to the right for about 60 yards, the net being lowered across the flow of tide, one end of which is fastened to the cable, the other end attached to another cable, which is lowered as the boat again turns abruptly towards the starting-point. By the time the buoy is regained the boat has completed a triangular course. The ends of the two cables are then hauled in, drawing the net towards the ship and gradually closing it and trapping all the fish that were in the triangle on the bottom. The gear is relatively light and the boats can be smaller, but the method can only be used in fairly shallow water. Some seiners now work from Grimsby and Lowestoft, and in the Moray Firth in Scotland. This method of fishing seems to take the maximum number of bottom fish, such as plaice, with the minimum amount of power and effort.

In some types of seine fishing, for example the purse seine, two boats are used and the net is drawn together by the two boats; this type of fishing can catch surface shoaling varieties, such as herring. Large catches, up to 1,000 crans, can be caught in one haul by this method if the shoal is dense. The South African pilchard fishery also uses the purse-seining method to make large catches. This type of seine net differs from the first in that it takes fish near the surface rather than from the bottom.

Trawling is now one of the most important methods of fishing; it is fairly new, because it depends on power to pull the trawl net along the bottom to catch the bottom-living fish. The trawl came into general use about 200 years ago, but it has only become an important fishing method and the basis of the industry in the last hundred years. However, as early as 1377 the Commons complained to King Edward III about a fishing device called the 'wondyrchoun', which seems to have been the forerunner of the beam trawl. This instrument was said to be destroying the fisheries by catching too many fish, and it seems to have been banned, as no more was heard of it, or this method of fishing, for another 200 years. If this ancient instrument could endanger the fisheries, it is not surprising that the modern trawls do so, and there is still a difference of opinion on this point amongst the fishery authorities (see letters to *The Times* in June 1961). The trawl was banned in the sixteenth and seventeenth centuries; this was done partly to encourage the herring drifters, who were setting up in opposition to the Dutch. However, trawling still went on despite the bans, and the great destruction caused by this method of fishing was commented on by King Charles I in 1635.

As a method of taking bottom fish, for which purpose it is designed, there is no doubt that the trawl is by far the most efficient technique. The larger the trawl the larger is its catch, if other things are equal; the decreasing number of fish is now being compensated for by larger and more efficient trawls, thus maintaining the amount of fish caught per hour's fishing. One of the main types of trawl is the beam trawl. The beam is a rigid bar, which keeps the top of the net above the sea floor and covers the bottom in front of the lower part of the net, which drags along the sea bottom. The flat fish are disturbed by the approaching net, but cannot escape upwards because of the net over them, held up by the beam; this is particularly true of the round demersal fish, such as cod, which tend to escape by swimming upwards.

The more modern otter trawl is similar in principle to the beam trawl, in that a net bag is drawn across the sea floor. The mouth of the net is kept open by otter boards on the towing lines, while the headline, or upper part of the net, is kept off the bottom by floats. This method requires two towing ropes, one attached to either end of the net, and more accurate towing is required to keep the net in the correct position. The otter trawl is more efficient for catching all fish except the flat fish.

One of the great advances in trawling came with the advent of steam; this affected the efficiency of the trawler much more than that of the seiner or drifter, which do not depend on power for the actual fishing process. With steam it was possible to fish more distant waters with increasing effect, which became more valuable as methods of keeping the fish fresh in ice were developed.

At first, as the modern methods were introduced, the catches increased, but so did the expenses as more distant grounds were sought, owing to declining catches on the familiar territory. The Grimsby trawlers first went to Iceland in 1891. In the nineteenth century the expansion of the cod fishing by trawler was taking place largely within the North Sea. In 1833 only the Flemish Bight was trawled by British ships as far north as Yarmouth and central Holland. By 1845 the fishing had extended northwards, particularly along the coasts as far as Edinburgh and nearly to southern Denmark. By 1865 the extension had largely taken place in the central part of the sea, but by 1875 the fishing had extended north along the coast as far as Aberdeen and central Denmark, while by the beginning of the twentieth century the whole North Sea was trawled by British boats; this expansion is shown in fig. 8–5.

The Barents Sea was first fished from Hull in 1905. The modern tendency is for the North Sea to be fished largely by seine nets, while the trawls are used in the more distant waters of the Arctic. The use of the distant fishing-grounds has meant the development of larger trawlers and trawls, which are so expensive that they can only be run by a company. The span of the otter trawl is 80 ft., compared with 30 ft. of the older beam trawl; it is, therefore, a more efficient catching device, but requires more power to tow it. Mid-water trawls are also being developed, which can catch herrings and other pelagic fish; these are sometimes pulled by two boats.

The total catch of fish is spread very unevenly over the oceans. These are divided into a number of different zones and the catch in these may be compared, as shown in fig. 8–8. The most important area is that of

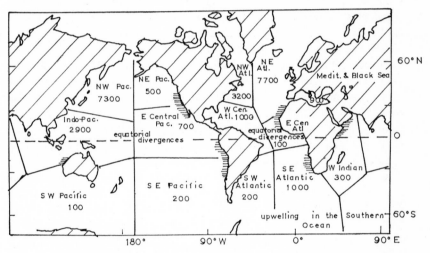

Fig. 8–8. Map to show the catch of fish in the different fishing zones in thousands of tons. The shading indicates zones of coastal upwelling. (After Lee in Lake (ed. Steers).)

the north-east Atlantic and North Sea, where 7,700,000 tons were caught in 1958; the north-west Atlantic is also important, producing 3,200,000 tons, while the north-west Pacific produces 7,300,000 tons. The north-east Pacific on the other hand produces only 500,000 tons. The Indo-Pacific region produces 2,900,000 tons and the west central Atlantic and south-eastern Atlantic both produce 1,000,000 tons, while the east central Pacific produces 700,000 tons. In 1959 the total world catch of fish amounted to 35,300,000 tons, of which nearly one-third came from the North Atlantic and adjacent seas. The distribution is such that of the total 21,000,000 were produced in the Northern Hemisphere, nearly one-tenth of this coming from the North Sea. Six million tons of fish were produced from tropical waters and only 1,400,000 tons from the

Southern Hemisphere. Fishing in Peru is increasing very rapidly; the catch was 3,531,000 tons in 1960, putting Peru third in the world (Cole, 1962). Of the total 5,300,000 tons are caught in fresh water, largely in Asia. From the point of view of commercial fishing, therefore, the Northern Hemisphere, which has the least area of sea, produces far the most fish; it is in this area that overfishing may be expected to become a serious problem.

The decline of the East Anglian herring fishery is an example of the problems of the modern fishing industry. This decline is partly due to economic factors, such as lack of markets, partly due to biological factors, but is also seriously affected by overfishing problems. The decline of the herring stock has been noted since 1951, when the forecast for the autumn fishery was incorrect due to lack of young recruits in the stock. This decline in the stock may be due to excess catching, which is going on to the east of the Dogger Bank by Danish trawlers, which are catching many of the immature herrings in this area (Hodgson, 1957). There are, however, arguments which could also indicate that this is not the entire cause of the decline, because it is the older fish which are also decreasing in numbers. It could possibly be that the herrings of the North Sea are declining in numbers as did those in the Baltic before them; this decline in the Baltic could have been due to changes in salinity. Nevertheless it seems clear that the vast capture of immature herring which is now going on cannot have any but adverse effects on the stocks in the North Sea.

Overfishing is definitely a problem in some of the most heavily fished parts of the world, such as the continental shelves around Europe. The North Sea in particular, being so close to densely populated countries with a long tradition of fishing, is liable to exploitation as new methods make fishing much more efficient. One of the problems concerning overfishing is that it is an international problem and demands international agreement, which is difficult to obtain. Limited success has been obtained in restricting the size of mesh, which will help to conserve the stock. The only aspect of fishing which is under reasonably efficient control at the moment seems to be the whaling industry.

Some of the most interesting evidence for overfishing has come as a result of the forced reduction in activity in this field during the two world wars. The four and a half years of the First World War produced a remarkable change in the fish caught; at the beginning of the war many small fish were caught, but by the end of it there were plenty of large fish. As fishing continued throughout the 1920s, however, the size of fish again declined considerably. The Second World War repeated the experiment, with even more striking results, as shown in fig. 8–9. The amount of fish caught doubled in 1946 the figure for 1938.

The problems of overfishing are extremely complex; however, the essential points can be shown simply in the expression (Hardy, 1959) $S_2 = S_1 + (A + G) - (C + M)$. S_1 is the weight of catchable stock at the beginning of the year, S_2 is the weight at the end of the year, A is the weight of young stock coming during the year, G is the extra growth of the stock S_1 and A, C is the weight of fish caught and M is the natural mortality. S_2 will be greater or smaller than S_1 according to whether $A + G$ is more than or less than $C + M$. The fluctuation of A will be

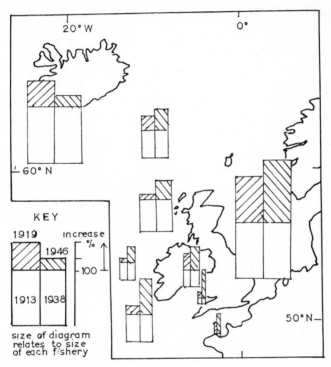

Fig. 8–9. The relative size of the fish catches before and after two world wars in the waters around the north-east Atlantic. (After Graham.)

great from year to year, as it has been shown that some broods are much more successful than others in their early life. G varies mainly with the availability of food and also with temperature. The growth of plaice on the Dogger Bank and their normal nursery-ground off Holland illustrates this point clearly. If C, the catching rate, decreases, $C + M$ will be smaller, and G will be greater as more fish survive; S_2 will be greater than S_1. If, on the other hand, C increases and G remains the same, S_2 will be less than S_1. The growth rate may not, however, remain the same; if C increases very much, there will be more food left and G may increase as well; if C decreases markedly this might have the opposite effect on G. Similarly a big increase in A would increase S_2, but it might decrease G, so there would be more fish, but they might not be so heavy.

If an unfished area in equilibrium is considered, the number S_2 and S_1 must be equal, and $A+G$ must equal M. If M is small, there must be little addition to the stock; this means that there are more likely to be a few large, old fish, as these use their food least efficiently to increase weight. Such a ground may well improve in quality as the younger fish have a chance to grow. Thus when the Barents Sea was first fished in 1907 the size of the plaice was much larger than those normally caught in the well-fished North Sea, and nearly all the fish were mature, while many of the North Sea fish were not. To exploit the fishing to the optimum extent S_2 should equal S_1, and the amount taken depends very much on the conditions of growth and recruiting to the stock.

That taking too many has an increasingly severe effect is easily demonstrated. Take, for example, 80 per cent fishing, starting with a stock of 1,000 at 1 year old. This year group will be only 200 strong at 2 years, and 40 at 3 years, dwindling to 2 at 5 years, and the amount caught will also have decreased to 6. With 50 per cent fishing, the original 1,000 will be fished out in 11 years, when the stock will be reduced to 1, but instead of a total of 1,000 caught in 6 years with 80 per cent removal, the same number would keep the fishery going for 11 years at 50 per cent. Although the catch in the first year is greater with the higher fishing rate of 80 per cent, after this the number of fish caught is higher with the 50 per cent rate, because the numbers remaining are higher. After 6 years, taking the weight increase into account, the 80 per cent fishing rate will have yielded 106,102 gm. as against 161,138 gm. for the 50 per cent rate. The lower fishing rate thus yields 50 per cent more fish.

As the extent of overfishing increases it means that more fishing effort is needed for reduced yields. Clearly there is an optimum amount of fish that should be caught to keep the stocks at their best conditions and yield. If the rate of catching cannot be controlled, and this requires international agreement, which is a slow and difficult process, something may be done by increasing the growth rate, or possibly the mortality due to predators other than man can be reduced. The experiment with the plaice shows how this might be achieved for one species of commercial fish. Another possibility, which is already used, is to increase the size of the mesh of the nets, to allow A, the new fish entering the fishery, to grow bigger before they are caught. This would for a time reduce the yield, but the effect is unlikely to be prolonged, as these fish become of catchable size in larger numbers than before. In fact, agreement on these lines was reached just before the second war.

7. THE TOTAL ORGANIC PRODUCTION OF THE SEA AND THE FOOD PYRAMID

All the production of the sea is derived ultimately from the phytoplankton. It is these minute plants which feed the zooplankton and other fish, and so through very complex food chains till the main commercial fish are reached. The relationship between the different species or the ecology of the seas is a vast subject, which cannot be dealt with, although some of the interrelationships have been mentioned. In considering the organic life of the ocean both the standing crop and annual production must be considered. The proportions of these will vary from species to species. Thus the phytoplankton, which increases with extreme rapidity, has a much larger annual production than the standing crop, while at the other extreme the large whales show just the reverse, as they only reproduce biennially, and then only one offspring at a time is born.

An interesting attempt to arrive at an estimate of the organic budget of the seas off southern California has been made by Emery (1960, p. 175). The annual production of phytoplankton is estimated at about 42 million tons dry weight, while 1·7 million tons of seaweed is produced, making a total plant production of about 44 million tons. This, however, only represents about 0·18 per cent efficiency of conversion of solar energy into plant tissue. The zooplankton then feeds on the phytoplankton; much of the material eaten turns again into chemical nutrients to re-enter the cycle. The annual production of zooplankton is estimated at about 3,400,000 tons, or 7·5 per cent of the phytoplankton production. The ratio between the standing crop and annual productivity is estimated at 1 to 35.

The commercial catch of fish over 5 years' average was 160,000 tons, plus 7,000 tons of fish caught for sport. This averages about 0·03 million tons dry weight. From tagging experiments with sardines, it seems that the fisheries are catching about 28 per cent of the total. Taking 5 per cent as the average catch for all fish, and a life span of about 6 years, the annual production of fish can be estimated as 0·1 million tons dry weight. This is only 3 per cent of the zooplankton production and 0·2 per cent of the total phytoplankton production. Taking the sea mammals, dolphins and porpoises, the annual production falls as low as 300 tons, a negligible amount in comparison with the fish. Considering the benthic invertebrates, a standing crop of 5·5 million tons wet weight is a reasonable estimate. The annual production of this group is fairly high, about twice the standing crop in shallow water, but less in deep water, giving a total of 7·4 million tons wet weight, or 1·5 million tons dry weight, as their water content is 80 per cent. This is about 3·4 per cent of the annual plant production. Of the total organic production about 7 per cent reaches the bottom, but only 0·6 per cent of the total production is permanently lost in the bottom.

This type of analysis, although at times the data on which it is based are by no means exact, does give some idea of the nature of the food pyramid in the oceans. There are a vast number of tiny plankton plants at the base, the rather larger planktonic animals are above them, and then with varying food chains, the benthic invertebrates, the fish and finally the marine mammals, with their very great size but relatively small numbers. Clearly it is more economical to catch and use animals or even plants which have a fairly short food chain. Thus the whales, and the herrings, both of which are plankton feeders, have a shorter food chain than the cod, which feeds on the herring and other fish, or the killer whales, which eat the seals, which themselves eat fish and so on down the chain to the phytoplankton, the basis of marine life. Much more nourishment for the growing human population could be obtained from the sea if there were some means by which the phytoplankton could be used directly, but this has not yet been achieved.

REFERENCES

Balls, R., *Fish capture*. Buckland lectures for 1959. Arnold, London, 1961.

Brown, S. G., 50 years of Antarctic whaling. *Naut. Mag.* **174**, 88–90. 1955.

Brown, S. G., Whale marks recovered during the Antarctic whaling season 1957–58. *Norsk. Hvalfangstid.* **10**, 503–7, 1958.

Brown, S. G., Whale marks recovered in the Antarctic seasons 1955–56, 1958–59 and in S. Africa 1958 and 1959. *Norsk. Hvalfangstid.* **12**, 609–12, 1959.

Carruthers, J. N., Some inter-relationships of oceanography and fisheries. *Archiv. für Met. Geophys. Bioklim.*, B **6**, 167–89, 1954.

Carruthers, J. N., Fish, fisheries and environmental factors. *Oceanus*. **4**, 14–20, 1956.

Clarke, R., A giant squid swallowed by a sperm whale. *Norsk. Hvalfangstid.* **44**, 589–93, 1955.

Cole, J. P., The growth of the Peruvian fishing industry. *Geog.* **47**, 186–7, 1962.

Cushing, D. H., and Burd, A. C., On the herring of the southern North Sea. *Fish. Invest. Lond. Ser.* II, 20, 1957. Also *New Scientist* **12**, 261, p. 410, Nov. 1961.

Emery, K. O., *The sea off southern California*, Wiley, 1960. (Life in the sea, pp. 139–79).

Graham, M., *Rational fishing of cod in the North Sea*. Buckland lecture. Arnold, London, 1948.

Graham, M. (ed.), *Sea fisheries: their investigation in the United Kingdom*. Arnold, London, 1956.

Hardy, A., *The open sea I. The world of plankton*. Collins, London, 1956.

Hardy, A., *The open sea II. Fish and fisheries*. Collins, London, 1959.

Hasle, G. R., A quantitative study of phytoplankton from the equatorial Pacific. *Deep-Sea Res.* **6**, 38–59, 1959.

Heezen, B. C., Whales caught in deep-sea cables. *Deep-Sea Res.* **4**, 105–15, 1957.

Hodgson, W. C., *The herring and its fishery*. Routledge and Kegan Paul, London, 1957.

Johnstone, J., Scott, A., and Chadwick, H. C., *The marine plankton*. Hodder and Stoughton, London, 1924.

Laughton, A. S., The sea floor. *Sci. Prog.* **47**, 230–49, 1959.

Laughton, A. S., Photography of the ocean floor. *Endeavour* **18**, 175–85, 1959.

Lee, A. J., chapter XVIII in P. Lake, *Physical Geography*, 4th Edition, edited by J. A. Steers. Cambridge U.P. 420–55, 1958.

Mackintosh, N. A., The natural history of whalebone whales. *Biol. Rev.* **21**, 60–74, 1946.

Menzel, D. W., and Ryther, J. H., The annual cycle of primary production in the Sargasso Sea off Bermuda. *Deep-Sea Res.* **6**, 351–67, 1960.

Rae, K. M., Continuous plankton records: a relationship between wind, plankton distribution and haddock brood strength. *Bull. Mar. Ecol.* **5**, 247–69, 1957.

Russell, F. S., The vertical distribution of marine macroplankton. i–xii. *Journ. Mar. Biol. Assoc. U.K.*, 13–19, 1927.

Wimpenny, R. S., *The plaice*. Buckland lectures for 1949. Arnold, London, 1953.

CHAPTER 9

THE GEOGRAPHICAL SIGNIFICANCE OF THE OCEANS

INTRODUCTION

IT will only be possible to state briefly one or two of the most important aspects of the interrelationship between the oceans and the land, as these are so diverse and complex. Nevertheless the oceans are vital to life on Earth. The essential part they play is due to the fact that all life, whether it be plant or animal, depends on water, and the oceans provide the inexhaustible supply.

1. *THE INTERACTION OF THE OCEANS AND ATMOSPHERE*

The air is the medium by which the water is transferred from the oceans to the land, thus their interaction is very important. The wind blowing over the water generates the waves, and these may eventually exert a very significant effect on the edge of the ocean, bringing into being all the diversity of coastal phenomena. The wind also plays an important part in the movement of the surface waters and in setting up the circulation of the ocean currents, whereby water of different characteristics is carried away from its place of origin, to modify the shore against which it may eventually flow. In this way the distribution of warmth received on the Earth is spread more evenly over the surface. The wind also plays its part in inducing zones of upwelling, which have been mentioned in connexion with the very rich fishing areas which result from the bringing of nutrient-rich waters to the surface by this process.

There are many features in common between the surface circulation of the oceanic waters and the atmosphere above them. There is also another most important interplay between the oceans and the air, which can be seen by studying the hydrological cycle and the part it plays in the life on Earth. The wind in blowing over the ocean takes up water vapour from the surface into the air by evaporation. It can then be distributed over the land surface by the wind and the processes that lead to precipitation. The ocean, therefore, plays a vital part in the character of the Earth's climate. It is one of the fundamental facts of climatology that the oceanic and continental climates differ very greatly, and through their influence on the climate the oceans play an important indirect part in many aspects of geography. However, it is very difficult to separate cause and effect in the interrelationship between the atmosphere and the oceans; each affects the other in a very complex way. The ocean currents and the general circulation of the oceans depend to a great extent on the wind and on the heating, cooling and evaporation, which in their turn depend on the energy of the Sun. On the other hand, by their transfer of heat to higher latitudes, the currents supply energy which helps to keep the atmospheric circulation going. The relationship between the atmosphere and oceans is in a state of dynamic equilibrium, whereby a steady state of movement is more or less achieved.

The essential difference between the oceans and the land, from the point of view of climate, is the ability of the oceans to store heat to a much greater degree than the land. The processes of mixing allow the heat to spread through a greater thickness of water, where it is stored to be given off when the air temperature falls; from this follows the effect of the oceans in reducing the extremes of the continental climates. Such effects will be most marked in the zones where the winds carry warmer air from the sea on to the land; that is, on the western coasts in the temperate west wind belt, where the warmer water from lower latitudes can penetrate farther north than normal. Thus the contrast arises between the east and west coast continental climate.

In considering the effect of the oceans on the weather, the amount of energy given off by evaporation is strongly localized; it is greatest where the water is relatively warmer than the air, which is mainly off the east coasts of the continents in the temperate regions in winter, for example where the warm waters of the Gulf Stream give abnormally high sea temperatures. These regions of excess energy loss from the sea can be correlated with the zones of most active frontal development, while it is the ocean currents which account for the position of these energy loss maxima. The presence and character of the water beneath an air mass can also change the character of the latter very fundamentally. Polar air moving south to lower latitudes will receive water vapour over the oceans, while tropical air, moving in the opposite direction in the Northern Hemisphere, will be cooled and may well lose water vapour by condensation and precipitation.

Of even greater significance is the water vapour which is carried from the oceans into the air and then transferred to the land. This supplies the capital on which the hydrological cycle operates, bringing water to the land as rain, snow and other forms of precipitation. It can then go through the cycle by a more or less direct route according to its subsequent movements. Some may be withheld from the ocean for a considerable time as snow, then ice, where it may be kept out of circulation for prolonged periods. Other water may return directly to the ocean via the rivers, while some may pass slowly through the Earth, before continuing the cycle on the surface, via the springs or wells. Much of the water is used by plants, animals or man on its way through the cycle, but eventually it will return to the ocean. One effect of the hydrological cycle has been indicated by Thornthwaite (Deacon *et al.*, 1955). He relates Munk's estimate of a reduction of $5 \cdot 1^{19}$ gm. of water from the ocean, in March, when its volume is this amount less than in October, to an increase of water on land in the form of groundwater, snow and other factors after the northern winter period. This demonstrates the dominant part played by the greater amount of land in the Northern Hemisphere. Defant (1961) gives the following analysis of the water budget of the Earth:

	Precipitation		Evaporation		Inflow+ and Outflow−	
	10^3 cu.km./yr.	cm./yr.	10^3 cu.km./yr.	cm./yr.	10^3 cu.km./yr.	cm./yr.
Oceans	324	90	361	100	+37	+10
Continents	99	67	62	42	−37	−25
Whole Earth	423	83	423	83	—	—

The effect of climate is such that the temperature and circulation of the oceans are affected by the external change of radiation as much as the temperature on land; but often these changes can be recorded in the sea more completely than they can on land, where all deposits are liable to subsequent erosion. In favourable sites in the oceans the changes of climate can be read with considerable accuracy from the character of the deep-sea sediments, as discussed in chapter 7. The oceans, therefore, also provide a means of studying the changes of climate which they help to bring about.

2. THE CHANGING SEA-LEVEL

The amount of water in the ocean varies with a large number of different factors, and the changes of sea-level which result can have a marked effect on the land adjacent to the coast. One of the most important causes of the fluctuations of sea-level during the last million years has been the waxing and waning of the ice caps, which have at different times locked up large quantities of water on the land. There have been significant falls of sea-level as a result, amounting to 100 m. (328 ft.) at the maximum, while at the present time sea-level is tending to rise. Some of the factors which cause changes in sea-level were mentioned in chapter 1; others may be stated, such as the amount held as water vapour in the atmosphere, although this is unlikely to cause large variations of sea-level.

Differences in water temperature and salinity are also important factors. If the mean temperature to a depth of 600 ft. increases from 50 to 51°F the water column will expand 1 in., and if the salinity is decreased from 35 to 34·9‰, the level would be raised by ¾ in. This causes the level of the north Atlantic temperate region to be about 10 in. higher in summer and autumn than in spring. Variations in evaporation and precipitation throughout the seasons also cause a variation in sea-level; thus in the northern winter there is in general about 1 in. lowering of water-level due to greater precipitation on land, partly in the form of snow. The Pacific is 8 in. higher than the mean level of the Atlantic over the whole year, the difference being greatest in October, which is the wet season. This is due to the lower salinity and less dense water of the Gulf of Panama, compared with the Caribbean Sea, in the region where this difference can most readily be assessed. There is also a rise of sea-level up the west coast of the United States from southern California to the State of Washington of about 1 ft. (Deacon, 1960c).

Regular variations of sea-level with about a four-day period have been recorded at Canton Island in the Pacific; these have an amplitude (half range) of 3 cm. and can be related to atmospheric waves in the easterly wind zone. The variations of the sea-level can be correlated with the north-south wind component, related to these atmospheric waves. This illustrates the capacity of the atmosphere to affect the level of the sea directly, which also applies to the development of surges, discussed in chapter 5.

Sea-level is rising at present, whatever the precise cause; whether it is the result of melting ice or warming water or other factors is not known. However, as long as large amounts of ice are locked up on land it is unlikely that sea-level will become stable. The ice will melt sooner or later, unless there is another glacial advance, so that sea-level will eventually rise by about 300 ft. Such a change will have profound effects on land, but it may be preceded by a fall of sea-level if another glacial advance should take place, on the scale of the Pleistocene advances. Such a falling sea-level would cause rejuvenation of the streams, while a rising one would tend to produce aggradation in the lower reaches of a river valley. Either change has a very important influence on the geomorphology of an area, quite apart from its effect on the people living in the region, which will be profound.

3. COASTAL CHANGE AS INFLUENCED BY MARINE FORCES

As well as affecting the rivers and settlements of the coastal zone, a change in sea-level will have an important influence on the processes at work on the coastline, where the marine forces have most direct access to the land. This is another sphere in which the ocean can exert a strong influence on the land, even if sea-level does not change, although some processes will be more effective with a changing sea-level. According to the circumstances the sea can either build out the land or cause erosion and its retreat inland, either slowly and imperceptibly or disastrously.

The disastrous action of the sea takes place under abnormal conditions, such as the action of earthquake-generated tsunami waves, or the development of a storm surge, through unusual meteorological conditions, whereby the normal sea-level is considerably raised, and storm waves are also likely to be generated. Such conditions have been discussed in dealing with the storm surges of the North Sea in chapter 5. The result of such periodic surges may well be serious and lead to considerable flooding where the coast behind the sea defences is below the high tide level. Such effects are very localized and occasional in their occurrence, but they may cause long-term change on the coast affected.

The more usual coastal erosion, which is often facilitated by a rising-sea-level, can be explained frequently by less abnormal conditions. The rare storms, however, produce waves which are notably destructive in their effect, except on shingle, where they build up ridges, which may survive for many centuries, out of the reach of normal waves. Rocky coasts, with their wave-cut platforms, are also most effectively attacked by storm waves; thus the permanent loss to cliffs is usually due to the destructive action of storm waves, acting in an area where other conditions are conducive to erosion. An important factor in this respect is the alignment of the coast in relation to the direction from which the most effective waves come. These waves will be particularly effective on a coast along which they can move material freely; that is one which is smooth in outline and which they approach at an angle, although here wave refraction must be considered as well. Where more material than the waves bring into the area is moved alongshore, there is very nearly always coast erosion. This is particularly liable to occur where the source of supply of beach material is cut off by a headland or break-water or some other feature.

Flamborough Head and the Holderness coast, which is noted for its serious erosion, illustrate this situation clearly. The headland acts as a very large groyne, preventing the movement south, in the direction of the main drift, of beach material, so that the deficit on the beach must be made good by erosion of the cliffs, which are easily eroded because they are entirely of glacial drift. Similar difficulties, but due to the building of a break-water, at Santa Barbara in California, have resulted from the cutting off of longshore movement of sand, with erosion downdrift of the obstruction. This erosion extended 10 miles down the coast in a few years after the completion of the break-water in 1929. From observations made during operations to restore this situation, it was estimated that the waves moved alongshore 279,650 cu. yards/year of sand. Such action by the waves can be very expensive to restore; some-times this is achieved by moving the sand artificially to the downdrift beaches from the area of accumulation updrift of the structure.

On the other hand, the sea can sometimes work in the other direction, bringing more sediment to an area than it removes and thus building out the coast. This implies that the waves operate in a positive sense, being constructive and moving sand on to the shore from offshore or along-shore. The long swells, due to very distant storms, are the most effective in this process, and where these can act effectively wide beaches will be built up. These may build out rapidly seawards, with the help of the wind in building dunes. Such regions may well be situated in an area into which material drifts from alongshore.

Dungeness, for example, is formed in a situation in which material could reach it from the south-west up the Channel and also from the southern North Sea. Accretion is often associated with the building of offshore barriers, particularly on sandy coasts, and sand covers the majority of the beaches of the world. The long swells bring much sand from offshore, specially where the offshore slope is gentle, so that the waves may feel the bottom a long way out, and therefore bring in material over a wide stretch, which is deposited in front of their break-point to build up the barrier beach. That this is dependent on construc-tive waves is evident from the fact that they may not be attached to the shore at either end, thus meriting the term 'barrier island', which is applied to the more complex forms.

These barriers are said to be found round the length of one-third of the world's coastline; they are therefore important coastal features. In some areas, such as Guiana, South America, and parts of the coast of the Gulf of Mexico, where rivers bring much mud to the sea, this may be deposited between the barrier ridges to form a Chenier plain. In other areas the barriers are raised above sea-level by the action of wind and vegetation to form coastal dunes, while the ebbing and flowing tide, coming and going into the lagoon behind the barrier, will also, with the aid of suitable vegetation, help to deposit silt and so build up a salt marsh, which can eventually be reclaimed from the sea to form fertile agricultural land. Thus the waves and tides are for ever either taking or giving back land, according to the many factors which influence their action on the edge of the ocean.

4. THE OCEANS IN EXPLORATION AND TRANSPORT

The broad horizons of the sea have always lured the more curious and adventurous members of the human race to seek what lay beyond. From the very earliest days of history, and prehistory before it, men have

o.–x

set out to seek the lands beyond the sea. The ancient Egyptians began marine exploration, but their lack of suitable shipbuilding material rather limited their vessels and voyages. The Minoans sailed right round Africa in 600 B.C., according to some accounts. Many of these earlier voyages were largely coastal explorations, and although the Phoenicians had sailed to Britain earlier, Pytheas first explored England from the sea in 310 B.C. In this way explorers spread out from the more restricted waters of the Mediterranean into the stormier, greater expanse of the open Atlantic Ocean, although they still kept fairly close to the coasts.

The early boats were difficult to control in rough weather and navigational equipment was virtually lacking, and familiar coastal landmarks provided the best means of location. However, such problems did not prevent some rather later and more seaworthy boats from setting out boldly across the oceans. The earliest Atlantic crossings were probably made by the Irish sailors, in their light but seaworthy skin boats, using the various stepping-stones, provided by islands, on their journeys. This took them to the North Atlantic via the Faeroes, and via Iceland and Greenland to North America, where they preceded the hardy Viking sailors in discovering America. Both of these early explorers reached there long before Columbus sailed westwards to reach the Bahama Islands in 1492. The Irish and Norse voyages took place before the eleventh century, and nearly all knowledge of them was forgotten by the fifteenth century.

In the early days of oceanic exploration the ships were often at the mercy of the winds and waves, and the set of the currents exerted a powerful influence on the ease and speed of a journey by sea, which could not be too long in those days, when suitable provisions could not be taken in and kept fresh on board. Some of the earliest winds and currents to be recognized and used by the early navigators were those of the monsoon, which greatly facilitated the journey from North Africa to India, if the voyage was timed to make use of the changing monsoon winds and currents. It was also not long before the Spaniards and other sailors in the north Atlantic began to be aware of, and to take advantage of, the circulation of the north Atlantic Ocean. Already by 1519, not long after Columbus had reopened the route to America, the navigators were going to America by a more southerly route. This enabled them to make use of the North Equatorial Current, and the favourable trade wind, to carry them westwards, while on the return they sailed through the Straits of Florida, where the Florida Current would help them on their way; they then followed the fast-flowing Gulf Stream to the latitude of Cape Hatteras, before turning eastwards towards Europe, helped by the North Atlantic Drift and westerly winds.

The importance of the currents to ships in the days of sail is clear, and the many voyages across the Atlantic in the sixteenth and seventeenth centuries provided a fair impression of the nature of the ocean currents in this part of the ocean. The counter-current landwards of the Gulf Stream was first recorded in 1590, while the sudden change of temperature across the Gulf Stream was noted in 1606. A chart showing the Gulf Stream was published in 1665; but at this time a knowledge of the ocean current pattern was far in advance of a reasonable explanation of them (Stommel, 1958).

Some of the most remarkable ocean voyages of discovery were those of Cook in the southern ocean, during 1772–1775, when he discovered New Zealand and charted parts of the Australian coast. He set a limit to the conjectural southern continent, which made it much smaller than previous guesses had suggested. He made use of the west to east drift in these southern latitudes, as did most of his successors. One of his major achievements was the conquest of scurvy, the disease which had for long been a menace to prolonged oceanic discovery. He put oceanic exploration on a much more scientific basis and produced very accurate charts of all his discoveries, assisted by the greatly improved navigational aids available by this time.

Other early voyages, for which the direct evidence is very limited, but for which the circumstantial evidence is strong, are the journeys made by the Polynesian peoples, largely in the south and west Pacific. These people had the advantage of travelling in very stable balsa-wood rafts, which were virtually unsinkable, and although some of these voyages may have been unintentional, the sailors being swept out to sea, they were nevertheless extensive. That such long passages were possible, even in a raft with limited steering capacity, has been shown by the voyage undertaken by Thor Heyerdal from Peru to the Polynesian Islands of the south Pacific. In journeys of this type it is essential to make use of the ocean current, and in this region the steadiness of the South Equatorial Current carried the raft at a steady speed westwards to cover 4,300 miles in 101 days at sea, an average of $42\frac{1}{2}$ miles/day. The Peru Current carried the raft from the coast into the South Equatorial Current. The oceans, therefore, are no barrier even to primitive craft, provided that they are seaworthy and the currents are sufficiently constant to carry them steadily across the ocean.

Now, in the days of steam, diesel power and stabilizers, ships are much more free of their oceanic environment; the oceans, however, still provide the most convenient highway between distant parts of the Earth for bulky goods and people who are not in a hurry. Under modern conditions, however, the competition of air transport is reducing the essential part played by the oceans for many centuries in the trade and communications between distant lands.

5. THE STRATEGIC ROLE OF THE OCEANS

The part played by the oceans in strategy and warfare throughout the years has varied considerably. In the early days of the history of Britain most of the invaders came by sea. The Romans and Normans landed on the south coast, while the Danes and Norsemen came from the north, also landing from the sea, for their raids and later settlement. The original Celtic peoples, who also came in originally across the sea, were driven more and more to the western highlands, by the later comers. However, the earliest inhabitants of Britain could have reached this country by land, as during the Palaeolithic and Mesolithic periods the Straits of Dover were at times, at least, dry land, owing to the lowering of sea-level towards the end of the Pleistocene in the last glaciation.

The sea was no barrier to the invaders for several reasons; their boats were small and they could sail up the rivers, while the defending population was sparsely scattered over the country and could not readily congregate together to repel the invader; they also had no navy to defend their shores. Another point was the difficulty of communicating, despite an elaborate system of signal towers set up as early as Roman times; these were often located on prominent headlands, such as Scarborough. Organization of this type declined after the Romans departed and so left the country relatively defenceless against the later Norman and northern invaders. These were, however, the last invasions which have succeeded in landing on the British Isles.

Although the great Spanish Armada set out to invade and conquer the country, the sea provided an effective barrier; partly this was due to the strength of the British Navy and the defences set up against the invader and partly owing to the action of the sea itself. Stormy conditions probably played almost as great a part in dispersing the invaders and wrecking most of their ships on the inhospitable shores of western Britain as did Drake and his ships.

The effectiveness of even a narrow sea barrier was clearly felt during the Napoleonic war and the 1939–45 war. As Bryant (1944) has pointed out, the strategy of Britain is determined to a considerable degree by her geographical position as an island. Sea power can give freedom of movement over three quarters of the surface of the Earth, which is as effective in the days of sail as of the aeroplane. Waterborne supply lines are more economical than land lines, and a distant base may be more easily supplied by a long sea line than a shorter land line. Often at the beginning of a war Britain faced a territorially expanded adversary, such as Napoleon or Hitler. In such circumstances she can choose the area to attack by sea, where the enemy's land communications are most strained, provided she has the mastery of the sea; this makes the best use of a small force, for example Wavell's campaign in the winter of 1940 and Moore at Corunna in the Napoleonic wars. Such an assault at a distant point is possible for the power which controls the sea, and this may be an easier way to attack an enemy than trying from much nearer.

It might appear easier to cross 20 miles of sea, but in some circumstances as attack across 2,000 miles may be more effective. It is much more difficult to maintain and use effectively a long land line than a long sea line of communications. Air power has extended and supported sea power and enabled Britain to resist invasion in 1940, and by 1944 had given such control of the sea that the adversary, who was widely deployed, could not resist attack on all fronts. Sea power defeated the invasion threat of Napoleon, who was waiting to cross the Channel in 1803 and 1804; Nelson's victory at Trafalgar in 1805 put an end to his plans, because of the supremacy of Britain on the sea.

During two world wars, however, being an island brought its problems, as well as its safeguards. It proved impossible to invade the British Isles, but the attempts to prevent ships reaching the country to bring essential supplies from overseas nearly proved effective at some stages of both world wars. Only the efficient and powerful British Navy, built up to protect far-flung dominions, could prevent the starving of the people of Britain.

The necessity to mount an elaborate invasion by sea during the Second World War in order to re-enter Europe provided a very good reason for examining the forces at work in the ocean, as they could make such an important contribution to the success or otherwise of such a complex undertaking. One of the problems brought to light as a result of the preliminary study of the invasion areas was the lack of knowledge of the effects of waves on the character of the beaches on which the landings were to be made. In the Mediterranean, for example, it was found that there were submarine bars beneath the sea, on which the landing craft might run aground, leaving a trough of deeper water between them and the shore. In some of the landings in Italy, on the first day these bars were successfully cleared, but changing wave conditions increased the height of the bars overnight, so that on the following day the landing craft grounded on them. A great deal has since been learnt about the influence of the waves on these features, but the basic research that was done in planning for these landings will be of permanent value. Similarly the beaches selected for the landings in Normandy provided problems which have stimulated research into the character of such beaches and the effects of the waves on the ridges which are typically found on them.

Other basic research work, which was found to be essential for the successful prosecution of the landings, was a study of the behaviour of waves; information on their generation, subsequent movement and shallow water modification were all needed to produce reasonably reliable forecasts of the wave pattern. The complexity of the planning required for these invasions shows that even a narrow belt of sea is a very strong defence under the conditions of warfare of the last two great wars. It is much more difficult to anticipate the part the ocean would play in any future conflict, but it is sure to be important. The part played by the sea in strategy has changed markedly, from being an easy route for invaders to being a strong line of defence against them. In the modern days of complex life the ocean is now a vital link between the island fortresses and their overseas sources of supply, such as it was not in the days of self-sufficient communities.

6. *THE OCEANS AS A SOURCE OF FOOD*

One of the major problems confronting the world is the continued increase of population, in relation to the resources available to produce food for the growing numbers. There are varying estimates concerning the relationship between these two factors. It is uncertain how soon, if at all, a shortage of land-derived food will be really serious, given more efficient means of distribution than prevail at the moment, when some parts of the world population are seriously underfed while others enjoy a superfluity of food.

In comparison with farming on land, the resources of the sea for food are very inefficiently used. It has already been noted in chapter 8 that the procuring of food from the sea has not yet advanced beyond the stage of hunting. In the sea even the basic knowledge on which marine husbandry could be based is not yet available. The problems of the marine environment make research into the ecology of the sea a slow and difficult process, but until this is better known it will be difficult to determine what can best be done to husband its resources. The difficulty of implementing these findings, in an uncontrollable environment such as the sea, will be immense, particularly as they must depend on international co-operation.

The food production of the oceans becomes involved with political and commercial factors, which determine the size and character of the so-called territorial waters. Some countries, such as Iceland, depend mainly on their fishing industry for their trade balance and exports; it is, therefore, natural that they should wish to protect their main fishing-grounds, breeding and nursery areas from overfishing by other fleets, by extending their territorial waters and excluding other fishing boats. It is equally reasonable that trawlers from Britain and other

European countries should wish to fish in the waters that they know, especially when the fish near at hand are being heavily overfished by boats of many nations, as seems to be happening in the North Sea. Thus quite apart from the difficulty of reaping a controlled harvest from the sea, due to lack of knowledge of the ecology of the sea, there are the human problems of political and commercial rival claims and factors.

From what has been said about the amount of fish caught in the different parts of the world it will be apparent that the resources are used in a very irregular fashion at present. One of the problems is to relate the major fishing areas with those in which the natural production of fish is greatest, and to relate the supply to the demand. It is known that the primary production of life in the oceans is not uniformly distributed, owing to the limiting factors of light, nutrient supplies and other conditions, but how closely the pattern of primary production agrees with that of fishing is more difficult to determine. The bulk of the fish are caught in the Northern Hemisphere, mainly in such specially favoured shallow seas as the North Sea and Newfoundland Banks area and other wide shelf zones. In these areas the nutrient supplies are very rich and hence the fish grow abundantly; the rate of fishing, however, exceeds natural replacement in some areas, resulting in the problems of overfishing, already commented upon.

The high southern latitudes are very rich in nutrient supplies, but fishing in this region is very limited due to a number of factors, both economical and physical; it is far from the main centres of population, which means that until modern refrigeration was available fishing could not be undertaken, and even with this amenity the long voyages to and from the fishing-grounds would seriously reduce the profits. Physical difficulties include the lack of suitable shallow shelves around land masses, which provide the best fishing-grounds in the Northern Hemisphere, where the shelves are exceptionally wide owing to the glaciation of the area, and they are also near the market.

In the far southern latitudes, however, there are the large whales, which provide some of the best value in marine food, as their food chain is very short; they represent a relatively large proportion of the primary production. Their products, the oil in particular, can be treated on the spot by large factory ships or land whaling stations. The products can then be transported to the centres of population without loss of food value to supplement the much-needed fat and protein supply for the world's nourishment. The supply of this food is not unlimited, and it has been shown recently how carefully the stocks must be controlled by international agreement if this source of supply is to be maintained.

The other major area of possible fish production which could be extended in the future is in the equatorial and tropical areas. Some of the physical problems of these zones have already been mentioned; the difficulty of the stratification of the water, preventing the renewal of nutrient supply from below and thus limiting primary production, is one of these, except in those areas specially favoured by upwelling or divergence of currents. There may, therefore, be a physical limit to the exploitation of these waters, where the production tends to be lower than in high latitudes. Growth rates in these warmer seas might partially compensate for the relatively smaller supply of nutrients, although many factors, which are as yet insufficiently understood, must be considered.

It is probably true that the oceans are not so efficient at converting energy of light into organic matter as the land, and certainly the use of fish is much less economic of organic matter than the use of plant food on land. As yet there is no means whereby the plant production of the sea can be harvested directly for human consumption, but this is without doubt the major source of food in the oceans. There may come a time when the population of the Earth is such that the maximum nourishment must be obtained from the sea, and if this were to happen, then some means of using the phytoplankton would have to be found.

7. INTERNATIONAL CO-OPERATION IN THE OCEANS

That there is still much to learn about the oceans will be very apparent from the foregoing account. It is in this wide expanse which belongs to all nations, outside the relatively small but important areas of territorial waters, that international co-operation must be sought. Many countries possess their own national research organization, such as the National Institute of Oceanography in Britain, and the Woods Hole Oceanographic Institute and the Scripps Institute in the United States, but some of the most valuable work has been done when these organizations co-operate, as in the deep-current work in the Atlantic. The fruits of international co-operation will soon become evident as the results of the work now being undertaken in the Indian Ocean become available. This work was initiated by the Special Committee on Oceanic Research set up by the International Council of Scientific Unions in 1957 (Deacon, 1960b); it aims to study all aspects of oceanography in this ocean, both physical and biological, which may lead eventually to a better use of the resources of the ocean for the benefit of the large underfed population of some of the surrounding lands.

The United Nations Organization takes an active interest in the great variety of oceanographic work, emphasizing the importance of exploring the oceans to become better informed concerning the basic problems on which a more efficient use of the oceans for peaceful purposes depends.

They may have to provide more food, as well as remaining important routes for transport; they may even become dumping-grounds for atomic and other waste. In order to achieve a better knowledge of the oceans and their problems many international organizations have been set up and these receive the support of U.N.E.S.C.O. Such bodies as the U.N. Food and Agricultural Organization take an interest in fishery problems, while the International Atomic Energy Agency is concerned with oceanic disposal problems, and the World Meteorological Organization is well aware of the importance of the oceans to meteorology. U.N.O. itself is also concerned in the problems of fishing rights, territorial waters and the rights of exploration on the sea bed for the resources on and beneath it, such as the drilling for oil offshore.

The oldest international organization interested in the oceans was founded in Stockholm in 1899; it was the International Council for the Exploration of the Sea. This organization has been largely concerned with fishery research. Another important international body was founded in 1919, the International Association of Physical Oceanography, which is a member of the International Union of Geodesy and Geophysics. This deals mainly with physical oceanography to balance the effort put into the two major branches of the subject. There are also other committees dealing with the various branches of the subject. This shows that a very lively scientific effort is being made to solve the problems, so important in many fields of life, of such a wide and varied subject.

CONCLUSION

The subject of oceanography is so wide that it has not been possible to do more than indicate some of the very interesting fields which are now being actively explored. A few of the ways in which the oceans influence and play their part in human life on Earth have been briefly mentioned, but the interaction of the oceans and the land are so intricately interwoven that it is impossible to unravel all the threads. However, it is hoped that enough has been said to show how vital are the oceans to life on Earth and how wide are the topics and interests of the oceans in themselves. They play a part on the Earth which is much greater than the attention normally given to them would suggest, and exert an influence either direct or indirect over the whole surface of the globe, of which they cover over two-thirds. Within them are still hidden many secrets, but elaborate and detailed research work is gradually revealing the unknown and fascinating processes operating in the oceans, on their surface, at their edge, where they meet the land, and on their floor.

REFERENCES

Bryant, A., *Years of victory*. Collins, London, pp. viii to xx, 1944.

Deacon, G. E. R., chapter 5 of *The world around us*, ed. G. Sutton. *The sea and its problems*. English Univ. Press, 77–97, 1960.

Deacon, G. E. R., International co-operation in marine science. *Sci. Prog.* **48**, 667–72, 1960a.

Deacon, G. E. R., The Indian Ocean Expedition. *Nature* **187**, 561–62, 1960b.

Deacon, G. E. R., Sverdrup, H. U., Stommel, H., and Thornthwaite, C. W., Discussions on the relationships between meteorology and oceanography. *Journ. Mar. Res.* **14**, 499–515, 1955.

Heyerdal, T., The voyage of the raft Kon-tiki. *Geog. Journ.* **115**, 20–41, 1950.

Privett, D. W., and Francis, J. R. D., The movement of sailing ships as a climatological tool. *Mariner's Mirror* **45**, 292–300, 1959.

Proudman, J., *Dynamical oceanography*. Methuen, London, 1953.

GLOSSARY

Adiabatic changes in temperature of ocean water take place without transfer of heat. Such changes generally are due to variation in pressure brought about by changes in depth; these changes are less important in the ocean than in the atmosphere, due to the relatively low compressibility of water.

Amphidromic refers to the type of tide in which the high water rotates anti-clockwise in the Northern Hemisphere round a point of zero range, the amphidromic point. It is caused by the midiyfing effect of the rotation of the Earth on a standing oscillation.

Anaerobic conditions are those in which oxygen is excluded, and as a result normal life, which depends on the presence of oxygen, is not possible. Some bacteria can, however, live in these conditions.

Anamolistic tidal cycle is that which depends on the varying distance of the Moon from the Earth. This cycle has a period of $27\frac{1}{2}$ days.

Andesite. An intermediate volcanic rock, Plagioclase feldspar exceeds orthoclase feldspar and hornblend or augite occur. The name is derived from the Andes. where it occurs commonly.

Apogee. The position in which the Moon is farthest from the Earth.

Aragonite. A form of calcium carbonate, which is the same mineralogically as calcite, but has a rhombic form. It is often deposited from strongly saline waters and is not stable, the mineral altering eventually to calcite.

Barrier island. A wave-built deposit of sand mainly, raised above sea-level by constructive wave action and separated from the shore by a lagoon. Its height may be increased by dune formation.

Benthos. Life on the sea floor.

Bouguer anomaly. A method of stating the isostatic anomaly, derived from gravity observations. It allows for height above sea-level and the visible excess or deficit of mass. It is called after Bouguer, who first noticed that the Andes did not disturb gravity as much as their mass would suggest.

Boundary current. A fast-flowing current concentrated near the edge of an ocean, usually fairly close to the western shore.

Chenier Plain. Sandy offshore barriers which have become linked to the coast by deposition of clay in the lagoons between them and the shore. This coastal feature is well developed on the coast of South America, between the Amazon and the Orinoco rivers.

Clapotis. A standing wave in which there is no horizontal motion of the crests. It results from the interference caused by the reflection of a wave train from a barrier which it approaches with its crest parallel to the barrier.

Coriolis force arises through relative motion on a rotating body, such as the Earth. It is proportional to the relative velocity and the sine of the latitude, acting to the right of the direction of movement in the Northern Hemisphere and to the left in the Southern Hemisphere.

Cran. A measure of herrings, amounting to between 900 and 1,300 according to their size, the average number being about 1,000 herrings.

Decibar. A unit of pressure. One decibar is one-tenth of a bar i.e. nearly 'one atmosphere', which is 10^6 dyn./cm.^{2} The pressure in decibars increases almost as the geometrical depth increases in m. Thus the pressure is 100 decibars at a depth of 99·24 m. and 1,000 decibars at 984·41 m., the difference being about 1 per cent.

Declination is the angular distance of the Sun or Moon north or south of the Equator, measured along the meridian. The declination of the Moon varies between 28°35′N. and S. and of Sun between 23°27′N. and S.

Demersal. Living near the sea floor.

Diastrophism refers to all processes of earth movement and rock deformation, many of which result in changes of relative position, both vertical and horizontal.

Diorite. A rock which is chemically similar to Andesite (see above), but which has cooled slowly to a coarsely crystalline state, and is, therefore, called a Plutonic rock.

Erosion surface is an area which has been flattened by subaerial or marine erosion to form an area of relatively low relief at an elevation close to the base-level (sea-level) existing at the time of its formation. Relics of such surfaces may now be found far above sea-level, owing to the falling base-level.

Eustatism. The fluctuations of sea-level due to the changing capacity of the ocean basins or the volume of ocean water. *Glacio-eustatism* causes variations of sea-level related to the changing volume of glacier ice; *sedimento-eustatism* is related to the rise of sea-level due to the filling of the ocean basins with sediment; and *tectono-eustatism* is due to changes in the capacity of the ocean basins resulting from earth movements, such as basin formation, which, by increasing the capacity of the ocean receptacles, lowers sea-level.

Fetch. The distance over which the generating wind blows in a constant direction during wave generation. In the open ocean it is limited by the meteorological situation.

Firn. Granular snow which is in an intermediate state between newly fallen crystalline flakes of snow and glacier ice. Its density is about 0·5 to 0·6, increasing as it becomes more and more compressed beneath newly fallen snow above.

Flux. The amount of water crossing a given area in a given time.

Foraminifera. A type of planktonic organism; most species have a shell of carbonate of lime, often globe- or flask-shaped. They are called foraminifera from the Latin word 'foramen', meaning a hole, because thread-like processes protrude through holes in their shells or through the open mouth of their shells.

Frustule. The pair of silica valves of the diatoms which fit together as pill-boxes in some species; in others the silica cell walls glide back and forth over each other.

Geostrophic. The current or wind which results from the effect of the Coriolis force on the pressure gradient force, resulting in movement parallel to the isobars and proportional to their spacing, itself related to the pressure gradient force. Hence from the spacing of the isobars the velocity can be determined.

Geosyncline. An elongated trough in which sediments accumulate to considerable thickness (up to 40,000 ft.) where they are available from neighbouring land masses by erosion. Such geosynclinal areas, for example the southern North Sea, have a tendency to prolonged subsidence.

Glauconite. A complex silicate mineral containing iron, grains of which produce green colouring. It has been suggested that the grains are the internal casts of foraminifera, but this interpretation is doubtful. It only occurs in marine formations.

Graded bedding. Beds whose grain size of particles decreases systematically upwards; the finer material overlies the coarser, owing to the more rapid settling out of coarse material from a mixture of grain sizes.

Gradient wind. When the isobars are not straight the curvature causes the centrifugal force to deflect a moving particle. The gradient wind is the geostrophic wind adjusted to the curvature of the isobars and can be obtained from the spacing of the isobars. In most instances it is not substantially different from the geostrophic wind, and is approximately equal to the wind at 2,000 ft. altitude.

Guyot. A flat-topped submarine mountain, rising at least 1 km. above the surrounding ocean floor.

Gyre. A closed circulatory system.

Harmonic analysis. The process of splitting a complex curve into its harmonic or sine curve constituents, which will differ in period and amplitude.

Hydraulic tidal stream. A tidal stream due to the differences in level caused by different tidal range or time of high water at either end of a strait.

Hydrocarbon in the ocean is derived mainly from phytoplankton, being an organic compound of carbon. It represents a minor proportion of the organic matter in ocean sediment, partly because it is susceptible to solution and other chemical processes; oxidation is the most important factor. Petrol is largely made of hydrocarbons.

Hydrographic data are the observations of temperature and salinity, in particular, from which ocean movements can be computed.

Isohaline. A line joining points of equal salinity.

Isopleth. A line joining points of equal quantity of any factor.

Isopycnal. A line joining points of equal density.

Isostasy. The equilibrium of density and mass in the Earth, whereby visible excess of mass is compensated by deficiency of density and vice versa. Isostatic equilibrium is nearly obtained over the Earth's surface. Isostatic recovery is the process by which isostatic balance is restored; for example, the rise of the land following deglaciation.

Isotherm. A line joining points of equal temperature.

Juvenile water. Water which enters the hydrological cycle for the first time, coming directly from magma inside the Earth.

Kelvin wave. A tidal system in which the tidal range is increased on the right-hand side of a narrow channel and decreased on the left-hand side in the Northern Hemisphere, if a progressive wave is travelling in the direction the observer is facing.

Krill. The Norwegian name for the principal food of the whalebone whales, the planktonic creatures, *Euphausiacea.*

Lutite. Material of grain size less than 4 microns. This term may be used instead of clay, to avoid mineralogical implications.

Mass transport is the transfer of water in the direction of wave propagation in deep water. It is due to the open-circular orbits of the water particles. In shallow water the direction of mass transport varies with depth, being forward on the surface and sometimes on the bottom, but seaward at intermediate depths.

Microseism. Minute earth tremors caused by wave trains of the same period but different amplitude, moving in opposite directions, interfering with each other. The period of the microseism is half that of the waves causing it.

Mohorovičić discontinuity is the level at which primary seismic waves suddenly increase to a speed of about 8·1 km./sec .This boundary is usually taken to indicate the upper limit of the mantle, separating it from the crust above, although it has also been suggested that it may only indicate a change of state and not of material.

Meridional flow is that which moves in a north–south flow, along the meridians.

Nekton. Freely swimming organisms.

Neritic. Shallow water marine environment.

Normal. At right-angles to, or perpendicular to.

Orogeny. An epoch of mountain building, usually associated with the formation of a fold mountain range; for example, the Caledonian orogeny which built mountains in north-west Britain and Scandinavia from a geosynclinal environment, during the Palaeozoic era.

Orthogonal. A line at right-angles to wave crests. The energy theoretically remains almost constant between two orthogonals as they are traced from deep water towards the shore. They can, therefore, be used to indicate zones of convergence and divergence of energy of wave action on the shore.

Pelagic. Pertaining to the open sea, when used in connexion with sediment type; it also refers to fish which do not spend their whole life on the bottom, although they may remain fairly near the shore, such as herrings or sardines.

Peneplain. The penultimate stage of the cycle of erosion, which is reached when an area has been reduced to very low relief by subaerial erosion.

Peridotite. An ultrabasic rock of which the mantle is thought to be composed. It is made up almost entirely of ferro-magnesian minerals, with olivine predominating.

Perigee. The position in which the Moon is nearest to the Earth.

Pyroclastic. Solid material ejected from a volcano, ranging from large volcanic bombs to fine volcanic ash and dust.

Quarter-diurnal tide. A shallow water type of tide, which has four high waters and four low waters during one day. It originates as a result of the distortion of the normal tidal curve in shallow water.

Rayleigh wave. A type of surface seismic wave in which the oscillation is partly in the direction of propagation and partly vertical. The waves are controlled by the elasticity of the crust and occur in a uniform solid.

Resonance occurs when the natural period of oscillation of a water body, which depends on its length and depth, approximates to the period of one of the tide-producing forces.

Rotational and irrotational motion. An ideal non-viscous liquid must have irrotational motion, as there is no internal friction between particles to make the individual particles spin. Water has a low viscosity, but nevertheless motion in it is probably irrotational. One wave theory, however, demands rotational motion.

Serpentinization is the process by which water is added to olivine, a major constituent of the ultrabasic rocks of the mantle, to form seprentine, which is a hydrated silicate of magnesia. Peridotite may alter to serpentine with a 14 per cent addition of water, causing a large increase in volume. This process operates at temperatures below 500°C; above this temperature the process can reverse, leading to deserpentinization.

Sorting co-efficient. The degree of sorting of sediment is expressed frequently in terms of Trask's co-efficient. This is given by $S_0 = \sqrt{Q_1/Q_3}$, where S_0 is the sorting co-efficient, Q_1 and Q_3 are lower and upper quartiles respectively, that is the diameters of the 25th and 75th percentiles on a cumulative frequency curve. The closer S_0 is to unity the better sorted the sample is.

Spectrum. A spectrum of waves consists of the combination of a large number of wave trains of different periods and amplitudes, moving in the same or different directions. This gives the complex pattern of waves normally to be found in the ocean.

Standing-crop refers to the total quantity of any species living at any one time, which may be compared with the quantity produced by reproduction.

Stereographic projection. A zenithal perspective projection, which has the property of preserving shape correctly (orthomorphic) and on which angles are correctly represented; this makes it of value for the analysis of tidal forces.

Synodic. Tides in which the fortnightly cycle of spring and neap tides are dominant.

Tectogen. The down-buckled root of a geosynclinal trough.

Thermocline. The layer of water in which there is a rapid decrease of temperature with increasing depth in the ocean. It is usually found at the base of the surface water masses.

Thermohaline. The processes which depend on the variations of temperature and salinity, and thus on the density, which is dependent on these properties.

Tillite. An ancient consolidated till or boulder clay, deposited directly from a glacier or an ice-sheet. It is an unsorted deposit, often containing striated stones set in a clay matrix.

Tsunami. Long waves generated in the ocean by a submarine earthquake. It is a Japanese term, meaning literally 'harbour waves'.

Trochoid. The curve traced out by a point within a circle, which is rolled along a straight line.

Ultrabasic rocks consist mainly of the dense minerals olivine, augite and other ferro-magnesian minerals. They contain very little or no plagioclase feldspar. This type of rock is thought to form the Earth's mantle. See Peridotite.

Urstromthal is a large channel cut by a substantial melt-water stream, flowing along the edge of an ice-sheet.

Vorticity. The vorticity of each water particle is twice its angular momentum. The vorticity of a vertical column of water is called positive if an anticlockwise spin is imparted to the water and negative if the spin imparted is clockwise. On a rotating Earth the vorticity is made up of the vorticity of the rotating Earth and the relative vorticity of the water moving relative to the Earth. The relative vorticity is given by $\dfrac{(\delta u}{(\delta x} - \dfrac{\delta v)}{\delta y)}$, where u is the horizontal component of velocity in the y direction, and v is the horizontal component of velocity in the x direction, x is the horizontal component, usually eastwards, and y is the horizontal component, usually northwards. The absolute vorticity is the relative vorticity plus the Coriolis parameter, while the potential vorticity is the absolute vorticity divided by the depth, in a homogenous layer of water. Vorticity tendencies may be induced by wind stress, friction or the Coriolis force.

Wind-stress curl is the vorticity component of the wind stress. It is a three-dimensional vorticity vector. $Curl_z$ refers to the vertical vorticity component.

Zonal flow is the movement in an east-west direction.

Geological time scale		(in millions of years) started
Quaternary	{ Holocene	
	Pleistocene	I
	Pliocene	II
	Miocene	25
Tertiary	{ Oligocene	40
	Eocene	60
	Paleocene	70 ∓ 2
	Cretaceous	135 ∓ 5
Mesozoic	{ Jurassic	180 ∓ 5
	Triassic	225 ∓ 5
	Permian	270 ∓ 5
	Carboniferous	350 ∓ 10
Palaeozoic	{ Devonian	400 ∓ 10
	Silurian	440 ∓ 10
	Ordovician	500 ∓ 15
	Cambrian	600 ∓ 20
	Pre-Cambrian	

after A. Holmes, 1960.

INDEX